Electromagnetism

Book 2

Electromagnetic fields

Edited by Stuart Freake

SMT359 Course Team

Course Team Chair
Stuart Freake

Academic Editors
John Bolton, Nicholas Braithwaite,
Stuart Freake, Tom Smith

Authors
John Bolton, Nicholas Braithwaite,
Stuart Freake, Bob Lambourne,
Tom Smith, Mike Thorpe

Consultants
Derek Capper, Andrew Coates,
Andrew Conway, Alan Durrant,
Allister Forrest, David Grimes,
Ian Halliday, Craig McFarlane,
Robin Preston, Gillian Stansfield,
Steve Swithenby, Stan Zochowski

Course Manager
Michael Watkins

Course Team Assistant
Tracey Woodcraft

LTS, Project Manager
Rafael Hidalgo

Editors
Peter Twomey, Alison Cadle,
Rebecca Graham

TeX Specialist
Jonathan Fine

Graphic Design Advisors
Mandy Anton, Sarah Hofton

Graphic Artists
Roger Courthold (Lead artist),
Steve Best, Sarah Hack

Picture Researchers/Copyrights
Lydia Eaton, Martin Keeling

Software Designers
Fiona Thomson, Will Rawes

Video Producers
Owen Horn, Martin Chiverton

External Assessor
Don Davis (University College, London)

The editor wishes to thank the following for their contributions to this book: Chapter 2, Gillian Stansfield; Chapter 3, Stan Zochowski; Chapter 4, Robin Preston, Mike Thorpe; Chapter 5, David Grimes, Steve Swithenby; Chapter 6, Andrew Conway; Chapter 7, Allister Forrest, Derek Capper; Chapter 8, Craig McFarlane; Chapter 9, Stan Zochowski; Chapter 10, Derek Capper, Bob Lambourne; Chapter 11, Mike Thorpe.

This publication forms part of an Open University course SMT359 Electromagnetism. The complete list of texts which make up this course can be found at the back. Details of this and other Open University courses can be obtained from the Student Registration and Enquiry Service, The Open University, PO Box 197, Milton Keynes, MK7 6BJ, United Kingdom: tel. +44 (0)870 333 4340, email general-enquiries@open.ac.uk

Alternatively, you may visit the Open University website at http://www.open.ac.uk where you can learn more about the wide range of courses and packs offered at all levels by The Open University.

To purchase a selection of Open University course materials visit http://www.ouw.co.uk or contact Open University Worldwide, Michael Young Building, Walton Hall, Milton Keynes MK7 6AA, United Kingdom for a brochure. tel. +44 (0)1908 858785; fax +44 (0)1908 858787; email ouwenq@open.ac.uk

The Open University, Walton Hall, Milton Keynes MK7 6AA

First published 2006. Copyright © 2006. The Open University

Edited and designed by The Open University.

Typeset at The Open University.

Printed in the United Kingdom by Latimer Trend and Company Ltd, Plymouth.

ISBN 0 7492 6986 3

1.1

ELECTROMAGNETIC FIELDS

Introduction

This book is the second in a series of three books that aim to develop an understanding of important concepts and applications of electromagnetism. The first book, *An introduction to Maxwell's equations*, starts from basic concepts of charge, current, and electric and magnetic fields, and shows how the relationships between these quantities are encapsulated in Maxwell's equations, a set of four equations that is one of the foundations of physics and of modern technology. The end-point of the first book is a demonstration that Maxwell's equations lead to the prediction of electromagnetic waves, and the third book, *Electromagnetic waves*, focuses on the properties of these waves, how they are generated and how they travel through, and interact with, different media. This second book, *Electromagnetic fields*, develops a range of additional concepts and topics in electromagnetism, many of which will be developed further in Book 3.

We assume that by now you have a sound knowledge and understanding of many aspects of electromagnetism. In particular, our starting point is Maxwell's equations in empty space, which relate electric and magnetic fields, $\mathbf{E}$ and $\mathbf{B}$, to the electric charge density ρ and current density $\mathbf{J}$ that produce them. Each of the four equations can be written in a differential version, using the vector operators div and curl, and in an integral version, using volume, surface and line integrals.

- ● Can you recall the two versions of each of Maxwell's four equations? Try to jot down as many of them as you can remember.
- ○ You can check your recall by referring to the list of Maxwell's equations inside the front cover of this book.

Though you will normally be able to refer to lists of equations when doing assignments, Maxwell's equations play such a central role in physics that you will find it helpful if you can commit them to memory. Some physics students and teachers have them emblazoned on their clothing, either as a memory aid, or to convey the importance of the equations to non-physicists (Figure 1).

Figure 1 The editors of the three books in this series wearing their Maxwell's equations T-shirts.

Two other important equations that underpin electromagnetism are also displayed inside the front cover — the equation of continuity, which relates current density and charge density, and the Lorentz force law, which specifies the electromagnetic force on a charged particle in electric and magnetic fields.

In Chapter 1, we shall briefly review these six important equations, and provide exercises that will allow you to check your understanding of them. All six equations were introduced in Book 1 of this series, and if you have difficulties with the exercises you may wish to refer back to that book to revise your understanding of basic concepts.

It is assumed that at this stage of your studies you are equipped with the mathematical skills that are necessary for understanding and expressing concepts and relationships in electromagnetism. You should be able to handle with confidence vectors in Cartesian, cylindrical and spherical coordinate systems, use the differential vector operators div, grad and curl, and use integral calculus to evaluate line, surface and volume integrals. If you do not feel confident in your ability to use vector calculus, then you are recommended to have a quick look at the *Mathematical Toolkit* in Book 1. You will have many opportunities to practise your mathematical skills as you study this book.

After reviewing the vital foundations of electromagnetism in Chapter 1, the content of this book develops in the following way.

Figure 2 The magnetic material within the coil of this electromagnet enhances the magnetic field by a factor of over 1000, enabling it to lift several tonnes of ferromagnetic metal.

- The versions of Maxwell's equations referred to above are valid for any distributions of charge and current. However, they are practically impossible to apply to real materials containing huge numbers of atoms consisting of many charged particles. So in Chapters 2 and 3 we derive alternative versions of Maxwell's equations that can be used when materials are present, for example, between the plates of capacitors or in an electromagnet (Figure 2).

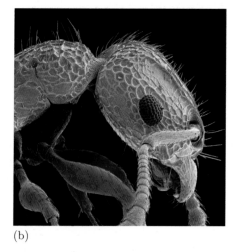

Figure 3 (a) A scanning electron microscope. (b) Electron micrograph of part of an ant. The head is on the right, with one of the compound eyes (dark brown) at its centre, the mouth parts at the bottom and one of the sensory antennae attached on the right.

(a)

(b)

- In Chapter 4 we introduce a range of methods for solving electrostatics problems, and in Chapter 5 we discuss a range of methods for determining the magnetic fields produced by currents. Determining the fields produced by specified distributions of charge and current is of immense practical importance. For example, the design of the scanning electron microscope shown in Figure 3a requires an understanding of how the electric field in the electron gun used to accelerate the electrons depends on the shape of the electrodes. Designing the coils for the magnetic lenses used to focus the electron beam requires the ability to compute the fields produced by current-carrying coils with complex shapes.

- In Chapter 6 we explore a variety of applications of the Lorentz force law to charged particles in electric and magnetic fields. These range from particle accelerators and electron microscopes, to the motion of charged particles in the Earth's ionosphere, the Sun's photosphere (Figure 4) and distant galaxies.

Figure 4 The structure seen in this ultraviolet image of the outer region of the Sun is due to the channelling by the Sun's magnetic field of hot ionized gases at temperatures of millions of degrees.

- Chapter 7 is concerned with motion of charged particles in conducting materials — electric currents. An electric current flows in a conductor in response to electric and/or magnetic fields, and the magnitude of the current depends on the electrical resistance and inductance of the conductor. Measurements of potential differences associated with current flow provide information about the underlying material, and this is the basis of techniques used in archaeology to detect buried structures and in medicine to produce images of the inside of the body. Inductance and induced emfs are the basis of much of the technology associated with generation, transmission and measurement of electrical power.

- In Chapter 8 we discuss the energy stored in charged capacitors and in current-carrying coils. This can be quantified either in terms of the circuit parameters — the charge and voltage on the capacitor and the current through the coil — or in terms of the electric field produced by the capacitor and the magnetic field produced by the coil. Capacitors are used for energy storage in applications ranging from camera-flash units and cardiac defibrillators to electric vehicles and emergency power for computer systems.

- Chapter 9 discusses the electromagnetic properties of superconductors. Currents can flow through these materials without resistance or energy dissipation, and magnetic fields are excluded from their interiors. Superconductors have many applications, from high-field magnets for levitating trains and for magnetic resonance imaging (MRI) scanners (Figure 5), to microscopic devices for measurement of tiny magnetic fields. We shall be mainly concerned with the ways in which these materials respond differently from normal materials to electromagnetic fields.

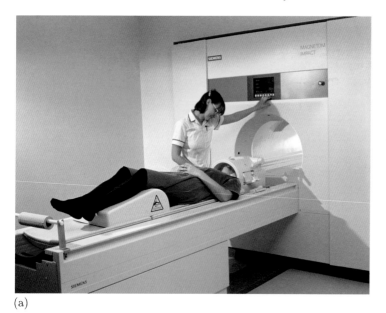

(a)

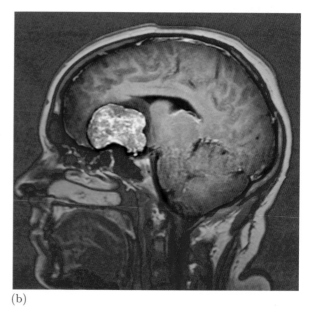

(b)

Figure 5 (a) Magnetic resonance imaging scanner. The patient is positioned in the illuminated cylindrical aperture of the machine, which is surrounded by a superconducting solenoid, which generates a 1 T magnetic field. (b) MRI image of a slice through the brain of a patient who has a large (benign) tumour, shown in yellow.

- Electromagnetism was a crucial ingredient in Einstein's development of the theory of relativity, and in Chapter 10 we shall show that Maxwell's equations are perfectly compatible with the axioms of relativity. The effects of relativity are most pronounced in high-energy particle accelerators (Figure 6), where the electric and magnetic fields appear very different from the viewpoint of a scientist who is operating the machine and the viewpoint of a high-energy particle travelling through the accelerator at a speed very close to that of light.

- Finally, Chapter 11 reviews major concepts developed in this book, and gives you opportunities to revise and consolidate your understanding of them.

Figure 6 Site of the Large Hadron Collider at CERN near Geneva, with the location of the 27 km circumference tunnel that contains the beam line indicated. The particles in the beam take only about $100\,\mu$s to travel around the ring at a speed that approaches the speed of light, $3 \times 10^8\,\mathrm{m\,s^{-1}}$.

Chapter 1   Foundations of electromagnetism

In this chapter we review six equations that are the basis of electromagnetism. Our purpose here is not to derive or justify these equations — you can refer to Book 1 if you want a reminder of these derivations. We shall simply review the meaning of the equations and provide exercises that allow you to check your understanding of them. The goal is to ensure that you have a solid foundation before we introduce new concepts in subsequent chapters.

1.1   Charge is conserved — the equation of continuity

The law of conservation of electric charge is very well established by experiment. This law does not mean that charge cannot be created or destroyed, but it does mean that when charge creation or destruction occurs, the *net* charge is unaltered. This fundamental conservation law applies both on the scale of the Universe — the total charge in the Universe is constant — and on the scale of an individual experiment or process.

Charge conservation can be expressed in both differential and integral versions:

Equation of continuity

$$\operatorname{div} \mathbf{J} = -\frac{\partial \rho}{\partial t}, \tag{1.1}$$

$$\int_S \mathbf{J} \cdot \mathrm{d}\mathbf{S} = -\frac{\mathrm{d}}{\mathrm{d}t} \int_V \rho \, \mathrm{d}V, \tag{1.2}$$

where $\mathbf{J}$ is the current density, ρ is the charge density, and S is a closed surface bounding a volume V.

Exercise 1.1   (a) Write a sentence that summarizes the meaning of the integral version of the equation of continuity.

(b) Starting from the integral version of the equation of continuity, derive the differential version of this equation.

Exercise 1.2   Could the function $\mathbf{J} = J_0[xy\mathbf{e}_x + 2yz\mathbf{e}_y + (x - yz - z^2)\mathbf{e}_z]$ represent a *steady* current flow? ∎

In Exercise 1.1 you demonstrated that the two versions of the equation of continuity are equivalent. However, there is an important difference between them. The differential version relates the divergence of the current density *at a point in space and an instant of time* to the rate of change of charge density *at that same point and time* — it is a *local* relationship. In contrast, the integral equation relates the rate of change of charge within a volume to the total current that is flowing out through the surface bounding that volume. It is true for any volume we care to specify, however large or small, so the integral version of the equation of continuity is certainly not a local relationship between values of different variables at a single point in space and time. The same distinction applies to the two versions of each of Maxwell's equations: the differential versions express local relationships between fields, charge densities and current densities at a point in space-time, whereas the integral versions are non-local relationships that involve integrals over volumes or surfaces or lines that can be as large or small as we choose.

1.2   Gauss's law

Gauss's law relates the electric field $\mathbf{E}$ to the charge density ρ, and can be expressed in both differential and integral versions:

Gauss's law

$$\text{div}\,\mathbf{E} = \frac{\rho}{\varepsilon_0}, \tag{1.3}$$

$$\int_S \mathbf{E} \cdot d\mathbf{S} = \frac{1}{\varepsilon_0} \int_V \rho\, dV, \tag{1.4}$$

where the constant ε_0 ($= 8.85 \times 10^{-12}\,\text{C}^2\,\text{N}^{-1}\,\text{m}^{-2}$) is the permittivity of free space. Gauss's law in the electrostatic case is a direct consequence of the fact that the law for the field of a point charge (Coulomb's law) is an inverse square law. But as Maxwell realized, Gauss's law is true for moving as well as stationary charges.

The integral version of Gauss's law is useful for calculating electric fields in situations where the charge distribution and the electric field have high symmetry. In such situations, it is usually advantageous to make use of a coordinate system that allows the symmetry to be expressed in a straightforward way.

Exercise 1.3   Derive the integral version of Gauss's law from the differential version. Which version expresses a local relationship between electric field and charge density?

Exercise 1.4   The charge density $\rho(r)$ in a certain region has the form $\rho(r) = br^2$, where b is a constant, for $0 < r \leq R$, and $\rho(r) = 0$ for $r > R$. Derive expressions for the electric field produced by this charge density.   ∎

1.3   **Magnetic monopoles do not exist**

Magnetic fields are produced by electric currents — electric charges in motion — and can always be represented by continuous field lines (Figure 1.1). Though many physicists have searched long and hard, they have not yet detected a magnetic monopole, which would be the magnetic analogue of an electric charge. A consequence of the non-existence of magnetic monopoles is that lines representing the magnetic field $\mathbf{B}$ are *always* continuous, so the equivalent of Gauss's law for magnetic fields is

No-monopole law

$$\text{div}\,\mathbf{B} = 0, \tag{1.5}$$

$$\int_S \mathbf{B} \cdot d\mathbf{S} = 0. \tag{1.6}$$

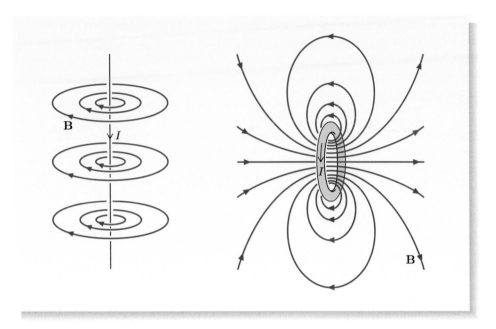

Figure 1.1 Magnetic field lines are continuous — they always form closed loops. For the current loop, the field lines that are cut off at the right of the figure circle around to reconnect with the same field lines at the left of the figure.

Exercise 1.5 Which of the following expressions could represent a possible magnetic field?

(a) In spherical coordinates, $\mathbf{B}(r, \theta, \phi) = (k/r)\mathbf{e}_r$.

(b) In Cartesian coordinates, $\mathbf{B}(x, y, z) = k(y\mathbf{e}_x + x\mathbf{e}_y)$.

(c) In cylindrical coordinates, $\mathbf{B}(r, \phi, z) = k(1 - r/R)\mathbf{e}_\phi$ for $r \leq R$.

(In each case, k is a constant.) ∎

1.4 Faraday's law

The third of Maxwell's equations relates a time-dependent magnetic field to the electric field that it produces. It is generally called Faraday's law, since Faraday was the first to investigate systematically the electromagnetic induction phenomena that are important consequences of this law. The differential and integral versions of this law are:

Faraday's law

$$\operatorname{curl}\mathbf{E} = -\frac{\partial \mathbf{B}}{\partial t}, \tag{1.7}$$

$$\oint_C \mathbf{E} \cdot \mathrm{d}\mathbf{l} = -\frac{\mathrm{d}}{\mathrm{d}t}\int_S \mathbf{B} \cdot \mathrm{d}\mathbf{S}. \tag{1.8}$$

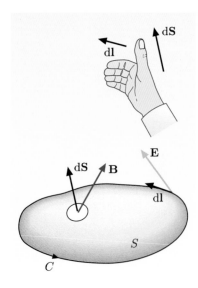

Figure 1.2   The right-hand grip rule for the senses of the elements of path length and surface area in Faraday's law.

The relationship between the line and surface integrals is illustrated in Figure 1.2. If the fingers of your right hand bend in the direction in which the line integral is taken, then your outstretched right thumb indicates the direction of the surface element $\mathrm{d}\mathbf{S}$.

The integral version allows us to calculate the induced emf in an electrical circuit when the magnetic field is changing, but it is important to note that Equations 1.7 and 1.8 are true whether there are circuits present or not. They provide relationships between a changing magnetic field and the associated electric field in a vacuum, or in an insulating material, as well as in the conducting circuits with which Faraday is associated.

Exercise 1.6   Derive the integral version of Faraday's law from the differential version.

Exercise 1.7   Changing the current in a long solenoid produces a time-dependent magnetic field in the solenoid. Use the differential version of Faraday's law to derive an expression for the electric field within the solenoid.

Exercise 1.8   Faraday's law indicates that $\operatorname{curl}\mathbf{E} = -\partial\mathbf{B}/\partial t$, but you should also be familiar with the relationship $\operatorname{curl}\mathbf{E} = 0$. Explain why there is no inconsistency between these two equations.   ∎

1.5   The Ampère–Maxwell law

This is the most complex of Maxwell's equations, since it relates magnetic field $\mathbf{B}$ to both current density $\mathbf{J}$ and the rate of change of electric field $\partial\mathbf{E}/\partial t$.

Ampère–Maxwell law

$$\operatorname{curl}\mathbf{B} = \mu_0\mathbf{J} + \varepsilon_0\mu_0\frac{\partial\mathbf{E}}{\partial t}, \tag{1.9}$$

$$\oint_C \mathbf{B}\cdot\mathrm{d}\mathbf{l} = \mu_0\int_S\left(\mathbf{J} + \varepsilon_0\frac{\partial\mathbf{E}}{\partial t}\right)\cdot\mathrm{d}\mathbf{S}, \tag{1.10}$$

where the constant μ_0 ($= 4\pi\times 10^{-7}\,\mathrm{N\,A^{-2}}$) is the permeability of free space. Note that when the fields do not depend on time, these equations reduce to Ampère's law, which relates a magnetostatic field $\mathbf{B}$ to the current density $\mathbf{J}$ that produces it:

$$\operatorname{curl}\mathbf{B} = \mu_0\mathbf{J}, \tag{1.11}$$

$$\oint_C \mathbf{B}\cdot\mathrm{d}\mathbf{l} = \mu_0\int_S\mathbf{J}\cdot\mathrm{d}\mathbf{S}. \tag{1.12}$$

As usual, the relationship between the directions of the line integral and the surface integral is given by a right-hand rule.

The integral version of Ampère's law can be used to calculate the magnetic fields produced by currents, but in practice this method is useful only in situations with high symmetry. These include long straight-line currents, current densities with cylindrical symmetry, and currents in long solenoids and toroidal coils. In all of these situations, it is possible to deduce from the symmetry that the field is constant along a specified path, so the line integral is straightforward to calculate.

Exercise 1.9   The toroidal solenoid shown in Figure 1.3 has 100 turns, each with a square cross-section with side length 5.0×10^{-2} m. The internal radius of the toroid is 0.20 m, and the external radius is 0.25 m. Derive an expression for the field within the solenoid, and use this to determine the field 0.24 m from the central axis when a current of 3.0 A is passed through the solenoid. ■

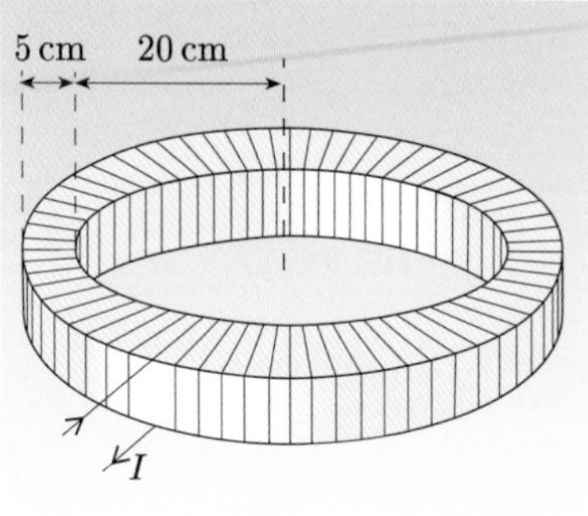

The equations for Ampère's law omit the time-dependent field that appears in the more general equations for the Ampère–Maxwell law, so they are only strictly true for constant currents and constant magnetic fields. However, in practice, Ampère's law can be used to calculate the magnetic fields produced by currents even when there are quite rapid variations of the currents and fields. It is only when we are dealing with electromagnetic waves and radiation that the contribution from the $\varepsilon_0 \mu_0 \partial \mathbf{E}/\partial t$ term becomes significant, and the magnetostatic approximation represented by Ampère's law becomes inappropriate.

The $\varepsilon_0 \mu_0 \partial \mathbf{E}/\partial t$ term was introduced by Maxwell, and is generally referred to as the Maxwell term. Some authors refer to $\varepsilon_0 \partial \mathbf{E}/\partial t$ as the displacement current density, but although $\varepsilon_0 \partial \mathbf{E}/\partial t$ has the same unit and dimensions as current density $\mathbf{J}$, it is clearly not a real current, since it can be present in a vacuum where there are no charged particles.

Figure 1.3   Toroidal coil with square cross-section.

1.6 The Lorentz force law

The electromagnetic force $\mathbf{F}$ acting on a particle with charge q travelling with velocity $\mathbf{v}$ is given by

Lorentz force law

$$\mathbf{F} = q(\mathbf{E} + \mathbf{v} \times \mathbf{B}). \tag{1.13}$$

This law encapsulates definitions of the electric field $\mathbf{E}$ and the magnetic field $\mathbf{B}$. The first term on the right-hand side ($q\mathbf{E}$) is the electric force on charge q. The electric field at a point is the force acting on a unit charge that is *at rest* (i.e. $\mathbf{v} = \mathbf{0}$) at that point:

$$\mathbf{E} = \mathbf{F}/q.$$

The second term, $q(\mathbf{v} \times \mathbf{B})$, is the magnetic force, and this is the additional force that is experienced by a *moving* charge:

$$\mathbf{F} = q\mathbf{v} \times \mathbf{B}.$$

Exercise 1.10   Derive an expression for the force on a proton at a point where $\mathbf{E} = E\mathbf{e}_x$ and $\mathbf{B} = B\mathbf{e}_y$ if the proton's velocity is $\mathbf{v} = v\mathbf{e}_z$. ■

1.7   The generality of Maxwell's equations

Maxwell's four equations in the form presented in this chapter are universally valid. If you specify the charge density $\rho(\mathbf{r}, t)$ and the current density $\mathbf{J}(\mathbf{r}, t)$, then the electric field $\mathbf{E}(\mathbf{r}, t)$ and the magnetic field $\mathbf{B}(\mathbf{r}, t)$ are uniquely determined. The fields are functions of position and time, and they depend on the spatial and temporal variation of the charge density and current density. This is true however simple or complex the distribution of charges and currents. In particular, it is true for charges and currents that originate at the atomic level, within atoms themselves.

Of course, it is impractical to contemplate solving Maxwell's equations with the spatial and temporal dependence of all of the charges on the electrons and the protons in each atom and all of the currents associated with the motion of the electrons around the atomic nuclei. The electric and magnetic fields fluctuate wildly in magnitude and direction on the scale of the radius of a typical atom, 10^{-10} m, and they also fluctuate with time due to the motion of the atoms. If we were investigating the inner workings of atoms, or the interactions between neighbouring atoms or molecules, then it might be necessary to take account of these microscopic variations of the fields. However, we are normally concerned only with fields on a much larger scale. We can then consider charge and current densities that are averages over volumes that contain millions of atoms, and the related fields will be averages over similar volumes. These fields are generally referred to as **macroscopic fields**. The actual atomic scale field variations are replaced by fields averaged over the volume, and the charge density and the current density are replaced by average values for the volume.

The versions of Maxwell's equations that we have discussed in this chapter apply equally well to fields, charge densities and current densities that vary on the atomic scale and to macroscopic fields, macroscopic charge densities and macroscopic current densities where all of the quantities are averaged over volumes containing millions of atoms. This is a consequence of the linearity of Maxwell's equations, which means that they apply to these macroscopic fields which are averages (which are linear combinations) of the microscopic fields. You should assume that all of the fields that we refer to in this book are macroscopic fields, except in situations where the effects of fields on individual atoms and molecules are being considered.

The macroscopic fields will depend on the materials that are present. Electric and magnetic fields cause changes to the charge density and current density in the materials, and these changes in turn will affect the fields. In the next two chapters you will see how the seemingly intractable problem posed by these interactions can be overcome by introducing two additional fields, $\mathbf{D}$ and $\mathbf{H}$, that are related to the free charges and free currents, and do not depend on the charge and current that are bound to individual atoms.

If you are unsure about your understanding of any of the equations, laws and concepts that have been briefly reviewed in this introductory chapter, you should refer to the relevant chapters in Book 1 or another electromagnetism textbook. You might also find it helpful to look at relevant simulations on the course DVDs.

Chapter 2   Electric fields in materials

Conducting and insulating materials respond in very different ways to static electric fields. A conducting material, such as a metal, contains one or more electrons per atom that are free to move throughout the material in response to an applied electric field — these are the *conduction* electrons that transport electric currents, and we shall refer to their charge as **free charge**. When an isolated piece of conducting material is placed in an electric field $\mathbf{E}$, the conduction electrons move in the opposite direction to the field (Figure 2.1a). Negative charge accumulates on the surface at one side of the conductor, and there is a depletion of electrons from the surface on the opposite side, creating a net positive charge there. The separation of charge continues until the surface charge creates an electric field, $-\mathbf{E}$, within the conductor that exactly cancels the applied field $\mathbf{E}$ (Figure 2.1b). There is then no net electric field within the conductor, and so no electrical forces to cause further net motion of the free charges. The electrostatic potential V is the same at all points in the conductor. Since $\mathbf{E} = \mathbf{0}$, Gauss's law ($\mathrm{div}\,\mathbf{E} = \rho/\varepsilon_0$) tells us that the net charge density is zero throughout the bulk of a conducting material. The distribution of charge over the surface of the conductor, its potential and the electric field around it depend only on the applied field and the shape and size of the conductor, and they are independent of whether the conducting material is gold or lead.

Contrast this with what happens when an electric field is applied to an insulating material, often referred to as a **dielectric material**, or a dielectric for short. In a dielectric, the electrons are all bound to atoms — they are unable to move freely through the material — and we shall refer to the charge associated with these electrons as **bound charge**. An applied electric field causes a small displacement of the negatively-charged electrons relative to the positively-charged nuclei, but not the large-scale migration that occurs in a conductor.

You might think that a small displacement of the electrons — and we shall show later that the typical displacement is a very small fraction of the diameter of an atom — would have little effect on fields inside and outside the dielectric material, but this is not the case, because of the very large number of atoms involved. Consider the following thought experiment. The plates of an air-filled capacitor are charged with equal and opposite charges, $+Q$ and $-Q$, and then disconnected from the power supply. A slab of polythene (a dielectric) is then inserted to fill the gap between the plates, and the potential difference ΔV between the positive and negative plates is seen to decrease by a factor of about two. This indicates that the electric field between the plates has decreased by the same factor — remember, $\mathbf{E} = -\,\mathrm{grad}\,V$. Also, since capacitance is defined as $C = Q/\Delta V$, the halving of the potential difference indicates that the polythene doubles the value of the capacitance. This effect of dielectrics is of great importance in the electronics industry, since more capacitance can be fabricated within a given volume if the plates of a capacitor are separated by a solid dielectric than if they were separated by air. Figure 2.2 shows part of a memory chip, in which each memory element stores one bit of data as charge on a tiny capacitor that has a silicon oxide / silicon nitride dielectric. Chip designers are always seeking to increase the amount of memory per unit volume of chip, and among other things they need to optimize the dielectric layer in the capacitors.

The challenge that we face in describing the fields in and around a dielectric

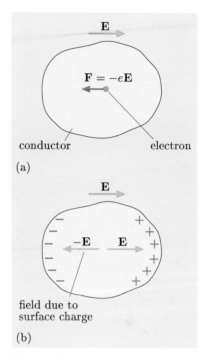

Figure 2.1   (a) When a field $\mathbf{E}$ is applied to a conductor, free electrons experience a force $\mathbf{F} = -e\mathbf{E}$. (b) Electrons accumulate on the left surface of the conductor and are depleted from the right, and equilibrium is reached when the applied field $\mathbf{E}$ is exactly cancelled at each point in the conductor by a field $-\mathbf{E}$ due to the surface charges.

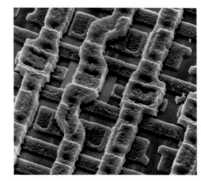

Figure 2.2   Part of the surface of a 256 Mb computer memory chip.

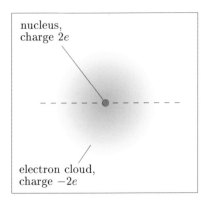

Figure 2.3   The nucleus of the most common isotope of helium contains two protons (each with charge e) and two neutrons (uncharged). The two electrons (each with charge $-e$) can be visualized as a 'cloud' of negative charge around the nucleus.

material is that the response of the bound charges to electric fields depends on the atomic structure of the atoms and on the ways that the atoms are bonded together in molecules and solids. Unlike conductors, there is not a unique distribution of electric charge for all dielectrics with a particular geometry in a given field. In addition, the distribution of bound charge in the dielectric depends on the field within the dielectric, and the field is itself partly determined by the displaced charges, so the problem appears somewhat circular.

In this chapter we have a number of goals. First we shall give a qualitative explanation of what happens within a dielectric when a field is applied. This will be a microscopic explanation — a description of what happens at the atomic level. However, our main concern is to describe the macroscopic fields in and around dielectric materials, and in Section 2.3 we shall show how polarization of atoms and molecules leads to macroscopic distributions of charge on the surface and throughout the volume of materials. We shall introduce a new field, the electric displacement **D**, which is directly related to the free charge and which simplifies solution of many problems, and shall show how both **D** and **E** change at interfaces between different materials. Finally, we shall indicate what happens when the electric fields are not static but vary with time.

2.1   The microscopic picture

The response of a material to an electric field depends on its microscopic components — atoms, molecules, ions. It also depends on whether the material is in the gaseous, liquid or solid state, since this determines the number density of the components and the extent to which they interact with each other.

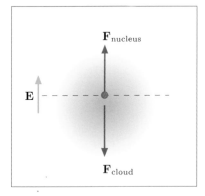

Figure 2.4   In an applied electric field **E**, the positively-charged nucleus and the negatively-charged electron cloud are pulled in opposite directions by the forces $\mathbf{F}_{\text{nucleus}}$ and $\mathbf{F}_{\text{cloud}}$. These forces are balanced by the attractive forces between the nucleus and the electron cloud.

2.1.1   Induced dipoles

Let us start by considering a single isolated atom of helium (Figure 2.3). This has a charge $+2e$ on its nucleus, and we can visualize its two electrons as a negatively-charged cloud, with charge $-2e$, centred on the nucleus. Suppose that we now apply an electric field **E** in the region of the atom (Figure 2.4). The nucleus and the electron cloud are pulled in opposite directions by the electric forces $\mathbf{F}_{\text{nucleus}} = 2e\mathbf{E}$ and $\mathbf{F}_{\text{cloud}} = -2e\mathbf{E}$. However, the greater the distance between the nucleus and the centre of the electron cloud, the greater are the forces that are trying to pull them back together. Equilibrium is established when the force $\mathbf{F}_{\text{cloud}}$ on the electron cloud due to the external field is balanced by the force attracting it to the nucleus, and in this equilibrium state the centre of the electron cloud is displaced by a small distance from the nucleus. The atom is said to be *polarized*.

Point charges $+q$ and $-q$ separated by a displacement **d** constitute an **electric dipole**, and the dipole is said to have an **electric dipole moment p** given by

$$\mathbf{p} = q\mathbf{d}. \tag{2.1}$$

Note that **d** is the displacement from the negative charge to the positive charge, so **p** points from the negative charge to the positive. The SI unit for dipole moment is the coulomb metre, C m.

The electric field **E** produced by a dipole has the form shown in Figure 2.5a. This field pattern is simply the superposition of the radial fields associated with each of the charges, shown in Figure 2.5b.

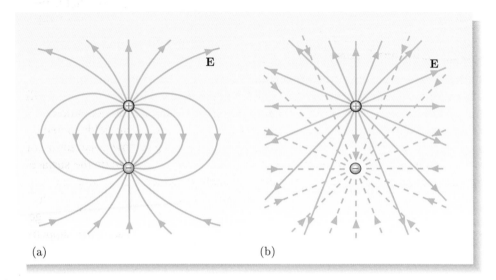

(a)   (b)

Figure 2.5   (a) The electric field of an electric dipole. (b) The fields of the positive charge (solid lines) and negative charge (broken lines). The vector sum of these fields is the dipolar field in (a).

Electron clouds in atoms are not point charges, so the polarized atom in Figure 2.4 is not an ideal dipole. This means that close to the polarized atom, the field will be more complex than that shown in Figure 2.5. However, at distances large compared with the diameter of the electron cloud, the field will have the dipolar form produced by a positive point charge at the nucleus and a negative point charge at the centre of the electron cloud. The important point is that the atom in Figure 2.4 has an **induced electric dipole moment** — it has been induced by application of an electric field. The induced moment points in the direction of the applied field, because that is the direction of the displacement of the positive charge relative to the negative charge.

● How does the magnitude p of the induced dipole moment depend qualitatively on the magnitude E of the applied field?

○ Increasing the electric field will increase the forces tending to separate the electrons and the nucleus, so will increase the equilibrium distance d between the centre of the electron cloud and the nucleus. Since $p = qd$, increasing the field will increase the induced dipole moment.

● In a field with magnitude $E = 10^4 \, \text{V m}^{-1}$, the measured magnitude of the induced dipole moment of an isolated helium atom is $2.3 \times 10^{-37} \, \text{C m}$. What is the separation d between the centre of the electron cloud and the nucleus?

○ Since $p = qd$, the separation is $d = p/q$, so

$$d = \frac{2.3 \times 10^{-37} \, \text{C m}}{2 \times 1.60 \times 10^{-19} \, \text{C}} = 7.2 \times 10^{-19} \, \text{m}.$$

The diameter of a helium atom is 3.6×10^{-10} m, so the displacement of the electron cloud relative to the nucleus of the helium atom is only a very small fraction of the atomic diameter.

For simplicity, we introduced the idea of induced dipoles by considering an *isolated* helium atom. This model is a good description for what happens in gaseous helium, where the atoms are widely spaced and the field at each atom is just the applied field. In liquid helium, where the atoms are much closer together, the local field in the region of a particular atom will be the sum of the applied field and the fields due to nearby induced dipoles in the liquid. However, in terms of this local field, we can describe the induced polarization of the atoms in the liquid in the same way that we did for the gas.

Many materials contain molecules that are made from several types of atom, chemically bonded together. In such cases the electron clouds will have more complex shapes, and will spread over a number of nuclei. However, the basic idea of induced polarization still applies: electron clouds and nuclei are pulled in opposite directions by the applied electric field, and the two distributions of charge reach equilibrium when the restoring force attracting them to each other balances the force due to the applied field. Thus *all* materials have an induced polarization in an applied electric field. This induced polarization is proportional to the magnitude of the field, and in the next exercise you can confirm this proportionality for a very simple model of an atom.

Exercise 2.1   Suppose that the electron charge distribution of an atom, with atomic number Z, can be modelled by a uniform charge density within a sphere of radius R, and that this spherical distribution is not distorted by an applied field.

(a) Derive an expression for the electric field at a distance r ($< R$) from the centre of the electron charge distribution.

(b) Hence determine the equilibrium displacement of the nucleus from the centre of the electron cloud in an applied field of magnitude E_{applied}, and confirm that the dipole moment is proportional to the applied field for this model atom.

Exercise 2.2   An electrostatic field is applied to a block of copper. Will a copper atom in the middle of the block have an induced dipole moment?   ■

2.1.2   Permanent dipoles

Many molecules have a **permanent electric dipole moment**, which is present even when there is no applied electric field. This is because the centre of the positive charge distribution of the nuclei does not coincide with the centre of the negative charge distribution in the electron cloud. Hydrogen chloride is an example of a simple molecule that has a permanent dipole moment. In isolated hydrogen and chlorine atoms, the electron clouds are centred on the nuclei, but when a hydrogen chloride molecule is formed, the chemical bonding leads to a net shift of the electron cloud from the hydrogen atom to the chlorine atom. This leaves the hydrogen end of the molecule with a deficit of negative charge, and the chlorine end has an excess of negative charge. The result is a permanent electric dipole moment that has been measured to be 3.7×10^{-30} C m directed from the negative chlorine end of the molecule towards the positive hydrogen end. This is equivalent to displacing one electron by a distance of 2×10^{-11} m, which is much smaller than the separation of the hydrogen and chlorine atoms in the molecule (about 2×10^{-10} m), but much larger than the induced displacement calculated earlier for a helium atom (about 10^{-18} m).

Molecules that have a high degree of symmetry do not have a permanent dipole moment, because the centres of their positive and negative charge distributions coincide. Thus the nitrogen, carbon dioxide and ethane molecules shown in Figure 2.6a do not have permanent dipole moments, and the only polarization in these materials arises from induced dipoles. Contrast these molecules with the molecules of nitric oxide, water and ethanol shown in Figure 2.6b, all of which have lower symmetry. In nitric oxide, electrons from the nitrogen atom are displaced towards the oxygen atom when the chemical bond is formed, producing an electric dipole. In the water molecule, electrons from the hydrogen atoms are displaced towards the oxygen atom, and because the molecule is bent, this generates a permanent dipole moment in the direction indicated. In carbon dioxide there is a similar displacement of electrons between each oxygen atom and the carbon atom, but because the molecule is linear and symmetrical about the carbon atom, there is no permanent dipole moment. The asymmetry of the ethanol molecule also accounts for its large dipole moment, whereas the symmetrical ethane molecule has no permanent dipole moment.

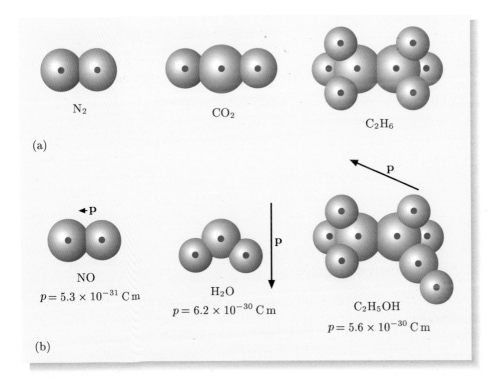

Figure 2.6   (a) Nitrogen (N_2), carbon dioxide (CO_2) and ethane (C_2H_6) molecules are all symmetric about their centres, so they do not have permanent dipole moments. (b) Nitric oxide (NO), water (H_2O) and ethanol (C_2H_5OH) molecules lack centres of symmetry, and have permanent dipole moments.

In the absence of an applied electric field, permanent dipoles in a liquid or a gas are randomly oriented. Collisions between molecules are continually changing their orientations, and there is no preferred direction for the dipoles. But what happens if an electric field is applied?

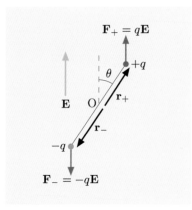

Figure 2.7   Equal but opposite forces, $\mathbf{F}_+$ and $\mathbf{F}_-$, exert a torque that attempts to align the dipole with the direction of the field $\mathbf{E}$.

Consider first a simple dipole oriented at an angle θ to an electric field, as shown in Figure 2.7. There is no net force on the dipole, but the equal and opposite forces on the two charges constitute a torque about the point O that tends to align the dipole with the field direction. The torque $\mathbf{\Gamma}$ is given by

$$\mathbf{\Gamma} = [\mathbf{r}_+ \times \mathbf{F}_+] + [\mathbf{r}_- \times \mathbf{F}_-] = [\mathbf{r}_+ \times q\mathbf{E}] + [\mathbf{r}_- \times (-q)\mathbf{E}] = (\mathbf{r}_+ - \mathbf{r}_-) \times q\mathbf{E}.$$

The dipole moment is given by $\mathbf{p} = q\mathbf{d} = q(\mathbf{r}_+ - \mathbf{r}_-)$, so the torque on the dipole in field $\mathbf{E}$ is simply

$$\mathbf{\Gamma} = \mathbf{p} \times \mathbf{E}. \tag{2.2}$$

This torque is zero when the dipole is aligned with the applied field.

Now you might think that since molecules in a liquid or a gas are free to rotate, each of the permanent dipoles would become aligned parallel to the applied field and stay there. However, because a molecule is constantly being buffeted by other molecules, its position and orientation are continually changing. The extent to which molecules become aligned with the field depends on the relative magnitudes of the energy exchanged in molecular collisions and the potential energy difference between states where a molecule is aligned parallel and antiparallel with the electric field.

It is straightforward to derive an expression for the dependence of the potential energy of a dipole on its orientation with respect to the field direction. From the definition of potential V, the energy U of a charge q at a point with potential V is simply $U = qV$. So the energy of the dipole is $U = q(V_+ - V_-)$, where V_+ and V_- are the potentials at the locations of the positive and negative charges of the dipole. (We are ignoring the contribution to the energy of the dipole from each charge experiencing the potential of the other charge, because this depends only on the separation of the charges and is independent of the dipole's orientation.) Now, in a uniform field $\mathbf{E}$, the potential difference $(V_+ - V_-)$ is

$$(V_+ - V_-) = -\mathbf{E} \cdot \mathbf{d},$$

so

$$U = q(V_+ - V_-) = -q\mathbf{E} \cdot \mathbf{d} = -\mathbf{p} \cdot \mathbf{E}.$$

● What is the potential energy difference between states in which the dipole moment of a water molecule is aligned perpendicular to and parallel to a field of magnitude $10^4 \, \text{V m}^{-1}$?

○ The energy difference is $-pE(\cos 90° - \cos 0°) = -pE(0 - 1) = pE$. Using the value $p = 6.2 \times 10^{-30} \, \text{C m}$ from Figure 2.6, the energy difference in a field of $10^4 \, \text{V m}^{-1}$ is $6.2 \times 10^{-26} \, \text{J}$.

Compare this energy difference with the typical thermal energy of a molecule at absolute temperature T, which is of order $k_B T$, where $k_B = 1.38 \times 10^{-23} \, \text{J K}^{-1}$ is Boltzmann's constant. At room temperature (20 °C), $T = 293 \, \text{K}$, and the typical thermal energy is $4 \times 10^{-21} \, \text{J}$. This is about five orders of magnitude larger than the potential energy difference calculated in the question above. This means that the disruptive effect of collisions between molecules prevents the dipoles becoming permanently aligned with the field. However, the amount of time the dipole moment of a molecule has a positive component in the direction of the field is slightly greater than the time it has a negative component in this direction, because a positive component corresponds to lower energy. The *average* dipole moment $\langle \mathbf{p} \rangle$ therefore lies in the direction of the field, but its magnitude is a tiny fraction of the magnitude of the permanent dipole moment of the molecule. It can be shown both theoretically and by experimental measurements that the magnitude of the average dipole moment is proportional to the magnitude of the field and inversely proportional to the absolute temperature T, that is,

$$|\langle \mathbf{p} \rangle| \propto E/T.$$

In the previous subsection we quoted a value for the induced dipole moment of a helium atom in a field of $10^4 \, \text{V m}^{-1}$ as $2.3 \times 10^{-37} \, \text{C m}$. This is some seven orders of magnitude smaller than the permanent dipole moment of a water (H_2O) molecule ($6.2 \times 10^{-30} \, \text{C m}$), and it is generally the case that induced dipoles are much weaker than permanent molecular dipoles. Of course, the randomizing effect of molecular collisions means that the average component of a permanent dipole moment in the direction of an applied field is many orders of magnitude smaller than the magnitude of the permanent dipole moment. But even so, permanent dipoles generally make a much larger contribution to the average dipole moment than is made by induced dipoles, and this means that the contribution of induced dipoles can generally be ignored when permanent dipoles are present.

2.2 Macroscopic polarization

The discussion of the effect of electric fields on dielectric materials so far has concentrated on single atoms or molecules. However, real materials, whether they be gases, liquids or solids, comprise large numbers of molecules, and we are therefore generally interested in the combined effect of many dipoles.

A useful way of characterizing the effect of the dipoles in a dielectric material is to introduce a quantity known as the **polarization P**, defined as the dipole moment per unit volume. If the **number density** — the number per unit volume — of dipoles in the material is n, and the average moment of each of the dipoles is $\langle \mathbf{p} \rangle$, then the polarization is defined by

$$\mathbf{P} = n \langle \mathbf{p} \rangle. \tag{2.3}$$

From this definition of polarization, it is clear that its SI unit is $\text{m}^{-3} \times \text{C m} = \text{C m}^{-2}$.

The polarization $\mathbf{P}$ is a macroscopic concept — the number density of dipoles and the average dipole moment are evaluated for a volume that is large enough to contain millions of dipoles but small enough that it does not average out any variations of interest in the situation being considered.

2.2.1 Electric susceptibility

The ease with which a material is polarized is quantified by its **electric susceptibility** χ_E, which is defined by

$$P = \chi_E \varepsilon_0 E. \tag{2.4}$$

Remember that the macroscopic field **E** is the average, over a volume containing millions of molecules, of the applied field and the field due to all of the polarized molecules.

The reason for including ε_0 in this equation is to make the susceptibility a pure number, with no unit.

● Verify that χ_E is a pure number.

○ The SI unit of polarization is $C\,m^{-2}$, as shown in the previous subsection. From the expression for the magnitude of the field due to a point charge, $E = q/4\pi\varepsilon_0 r^2$, it is clear that the unit of $\varepsilon_0 E$ is also $C\,m^{-2}$. Thus χ_E has no unit, so it must be a pure number.

Measurements have shown that many dielectric materials are linear, isotropic and homogeneous, often described as **LIH materials** for short.

- A dielectric material is a **linear material** if the susceptibility χ_E is independent of the magnitude of the field, so P is proportional to E.

- A dielectric material is an **isotropic material** if the susceptibility is independent of the direction of the applied field, so **P** is in the same direction as **E**.

- A dielectric material is a **homogeneous material** if the susceptibility is the same at all points in the material.

Most materials are linear as long as the field is not too large, because the average dipole moments due to both induced dipoles and alignment of permanent dipoles are proportional to the electric field. However, the susceptibility usually depends on temperature, and for gases it depends on pressure too.

Gases and liquids are generally isotropic, but many solids are not. The intermolecular forces responsible for the rigidity of solids restrict the rotation of molecules in solids, and counteract the tendency of any permanent dipoles to align with an applied field. Also, the strongly directional bonding between atoms and molecules in a crystalline solid means that inducing dipole moments is easier in some directions than it is in others. Consequently, in many solids the susceptibility depends on the direction of the field, and the polarization is not parallel to the applied field. These materials are described as *anisotropic*, and their susceptibility is not described by a single constant. Instead, the components of polarization are related to the electric field components by equations of the form

$$P_x = \varepsilon_0[\chi_{xx}E_x + \chi_{xy}E_y + \chi_{xz}E_z],$$

with similar expressions for P_y and P_z.

Gases and liquids generally have a homogeneous composition, though temperature variations can mean that the susceptibility varies with position. The composition and structure of solids may not be homogeneous, and this may mean that the susceptibility depends on position.

In this book we shall restrict our discussion to LIH dielectric materials. For such materials,

$$\mathbf{P} = \chi_E \varepsilon_0 \mathbf{E}, \tag{2.5}$$

and χ_E is independent of the magnitude of the field (linear material), independent of the direction of the field in the material (isotropic material), and independent of the position within the material (homogeneous material). The value of χ_E for each material is determined from experimental measurements. However, keep in mind that though Equation 2.5 is generally true for liquids and gases, and sometimes true for solids, it is *not* a law of physics, and is not derived from Maxwell's equations. There are many materials or conditions where there is a more complex relationship between **P** and **E**. Contrast this with Gauss's law, div $\mathbf{E} = \rho/\varepsilon_0$, which is a law of physics and therefore is valid in *all* situations.

Air at ambient temperature and pressure has an electric susceptibility χ_E of about 5×10^{-4}, whereas a non-polar solid like polythene has a susceptibility of about 1, and the polar H_2O molecules in pure water give it a susceptibility of about 80.

2.3 Polarization charges

In the presence of an electric field, the atoms and molecules within any material are polarized, and we want to know how this polarization modifies the electric field. In this section you will see that we can replace the microscopic charge distribution due to the polarization of the material by a macroscopic **polarization charge**, which comprises a volume charge density and a surface charge density. The field produced by these charge densities is equivalent to the field produced by all of the polarized atoms in the material.

2.3.1 Surface polarization charges

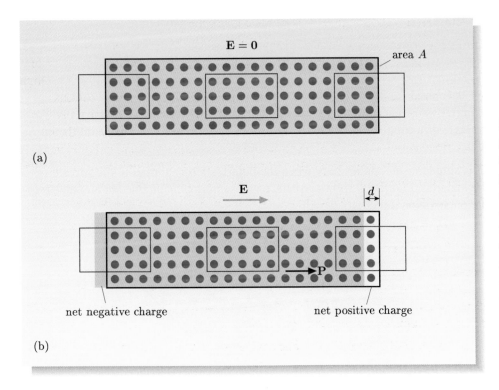

(a)

(b)

Figure 2.8 (a) With no applied field, the charge densities from the positively-charged nuclei (red dots) and negatively-charged electrons (blue cloud) produce a net macroscopic charge density of zero throughout the dielectric rod. (b) When a field **E** is applied, the electrons are displaced relative to the nuclei, so the ends of the rod become oppositely charged. (The displacement has been greatly exaggerated for clarity.)

We shall consider a rod of dielectric material, as shown in Figure 2.8a, which is made up of identical atoms that have no permanent dipole moments. In the absence of any applied electric field, the macroscopic charge densities due to the negatively-charged electrons and to the positively-charged nuclei are both uniform throughout the rod and have equal magnitudes. Therefore the net macroscopic charge density is zero throughout the material, and the net charge in each of the three boxes outlined in Figure 2.8a is zero. But what happens when an electric field is applied parallel to the rod?

In an electric field, the electron clouds surrounding each of the atoms are displaced a distance d, say, relative to the nuclei of the atoms, in the opposite direction to the applied field (see Figure 2.8b). Within the bulk of the material this shift of the negative charge distribution relative to the positive charge distribution has no effect on the net charge density — the same number of electrons enters the right side of the central box in Figure 2.8b as leaves through the left side, so the net charge within this box is still zero. However, the inflow of electrons to the box at the left end is not balanced by any outflow, so now there is a layer of negative charge at the left end of the rod. Similarly, the outflow of electrons from the box at the right end does not have a compensating inflow, so there is a layer of positive charge at the right end.

It is straightforward to calculate the surface charge density — the charge per unit area of surface. We shall assume that the atoms have atomic number Z and that the number density (the number per unit volume) of atoms is n, so the macroscopic volume charge density of the nuclei is $+Zen$ and that of the electrons is $-Zen$. If the electron clouds are displaced by distance d relative to their nuclei, then the magnitude of the charge on each end-face of the rod, of area A, will be $Zen \times d \times A$. Since the magnitude of the average dipole moment of each atom is $\langle p \rangle = Zed$, this surface charge is $n\langle p \rangle A$. The polarization of the rod is $P = n\langle p \rangle$ (Equation 2.3), so the surface charge is PA, and the surface charge density σ_b is

We write $\langle p \rangle$ as a shorthand for $|\langle \mathbf{p} \rangle|$.

$$\sigma_\mathrm{b} = \frac{PA}{A} = P.$$

We have used the subscript b here to denote that the charge is *bound* to the material, and we shall refer to this as the **bound surface charge density**. Unlike the case of a conducting material, we cannot easily remove charge from the dielectric material.

This simple result applies only when the polarization is normal to the surface of the material. Figure 2.9 shows a surface whose normal is inclined at an angle θ to the polarization direction.

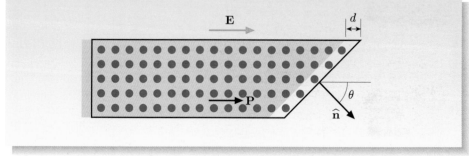

Figure 2.9   For a surface for which the unit vector normal to the surface, $\widehat{\mathbf{n}}$, is at angle θ to the field $\mathbf{E}$, the surface charge is $\sigma_\mathrm{b} = P\cos\theta = \mathbf{P} \cdot \widehat{\mathbf{n}}$.

The electrons' charge density is still shifted by distance d in the opposite direction to the field, so the charges on the ends of the rod are the same as in Figure 2.8b.

However, the area of the inclined face on the right in Figure 2.9 is $A/\cos\theta$, so the surface charge density is

$$\sigma_{\mathrm{b}} = \frac{PA}{A/\cos\theta} = P\cos\theta.$$

Using vector notation, the bound surface charge density for a dielectric is

$$\sigma_{\mathrm{b}} = \mathbf{P}\cdot\widehat{\mathbf{n}}, \tag{2.6}$$

where $\widehat{\mathbf{n}}$ is the outward-pointing unit vector normal to the surface. This shows that the effect of polarizing the atoms in a dielectric is to distribute bound charge with surface charge density $\sigma_{\mathrm{b}} = \mathbf{P}\cdot\widehat{\mathbf{n}}$ over the surfaces of the material. So the charge on a small element $\delta\mathbf{S}$ of the surface is $(\mathbf{P}\cdot\widehat{\mathbf{n}})\delta S = \mathbf{P}\cdot\delta\mathbf{S}$.

Exercise 2.3 The wax sphere shown in cross-section in Figure 2.10 has a uniform polarization $\mathbf{P}$. What is the surface charge density σ_{b} at the points A, B, C and D? ∎

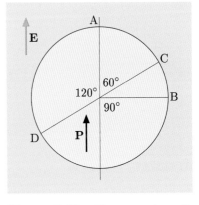

Figure 2.10 Cross-section of wax sphere for Exercise 2.3.

2.3.2 Volume polarization charges

A polarized dielectric will always have a distribution of bound charge on its surface given by the expression $\sigma_{\mathrm{b}} = \mathbf{P}\cdot\widehat{\mathbf{n}}$. If the polarization is uniform throughout the dielectric, then there is no net macroscopic charge distribution within the bulk of the material. However, in regions where the polarization is not uniform, there is a distribution of bound charge in the bulk of the material, and we shall now derive an expression for this volume charge density.

Consider a small volume V bounded by a surface S lying within a dielectric, as shown in Figure 2.11. When the material is unpolarized, there is no net charge density within this volume. However, when a field is applied, polarization of the atoms causes displacement of negative charge across the surface in the opposite direction to the polarization. For a small region δS on the surface, the charge crossing the surface from inside volume V to outside is the same as the charge that would appear on the surface of that region if the volume V were isolated from the rest of the material, and from Equation 2.6 this is simply $\mathbf{P}\cdot\widehat{\mathbf{n}}\,\delta S$.

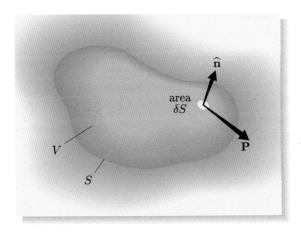

Figure 2.11 When this dielectric material is polarized by an electric field, the charge crossing area δS is $\mathbf{P}\cdot\widehat{\mathbf{n}}\,\delta S$.

The total charge that is displaced out of the volume shown in Figure 2.11 is therefore

$$\int_S \mathbf{P} \cdot \hat{\mathbf{n}} \, dS = \int_S \mathbf{P} \cdot d\mathbf{S}.$$

We can use the divergence theorem to convert the surface integral to a volume integral:

$$\int_S \mathbf{P} \cdot d\mathbf{S} = \int_V \operatorname{div} \mathbf{P} \, dV.$$

Now if a certain amount of charge has been displaced out of the volume V, then conservation of charge tells us that the charge within the volume must have decreased by the same amount. Since the unpolarized dielectric had no net charge within the volume, for the polarized dielectric we have

> bound charge in volume
> $= -$ charge displaced from volume due to polarization,

so

$$\int_V \rho_b \, dV = - \int_V \operatorname{div} \mathbf{P} \, dV,$$

where ρ_b is the density of bound charge in the volume of the dielectric.

Now this equation is true whatever volume we choose within a dielectric, no matter how small the volume, so the integrands on either side must be equal. Hence the **bound volume charge density** within a dielectric is

$$\rho_b = - \operatorname{div} \mathbf{P}. \tag{2.7}$$

For uniform polarization, $\operatorname{div} \mathbf{P} = 0$, so there is no bound charge within the material, but there will be bound charge on the surface.

Exercise 2.4   The dielectric cube in Figure 2.12 has polarization $\mathbf{P} = (a + bx)\mathbf{e}_x$, where a and b are constants.

(a) What is the bound volume charge density ρ_b within the block?

(b) What is the bound surface charge density σ_b on each of the faces of the block?

(c) Verify that the net charge on the block is zero.   ■

> You can reinforce your understanding of dielectrics by viewing the video sequence *Dielectrics* on the course DVD.

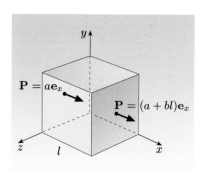

Figure 2.12   A block with non-uniform polarization $\mathbf{P} = (a + bx)\mathbf{e}_x$ (Exercise 2.4).

2.4   The electric displacement field $\mathbf{D}$

The electric field $\mathbf{E}$ is related to the charge density ρ by the differential version of Gauss's law:

$$\operatorname{div} \mathbf{E} = \rho/\varepsilon_0. \tag{Eqn 1.3}$$

This equation is *always* true. However, the charge density ρ includes all charge that is present, so it includes both the bound charge density ρ_b due to polarization of dielectric material and any additional charge density that may have been added to the material. We shall refer to this additional charge density as the *free* charge density ρ_f. We can therefore rewrite Gauss's law as

$$\mathrm{div}\,\mathbf{E} = (\rho_f + \rho_b)/\varepsilon_0. \tag{2.8}$$

(We shall restrict our attention to the inside of the material, so we can ignore surface charges.)

However, in general we do not know the bound charge density, and in this section you will see how this problem can be circumvented.

You saw in Subsection 2.3.2 that the bound charge density is related to the polarization $\mathbf{P}$ by the relationship

$$\rho_b = -\,\mathrm{div}\,\mathbf{P}. \tag{Eqn 2.7}$$

If we use this to substitute for ρ_b in Equation 2.8, we obtain

$$\mathrm{div}\,\mathbf{E} = (\rho_f - \mathrm{div}\,\mathbf{P})/\varepsilon_0.$$

Rearranging this equation leads to

$$\varepsilon_0\,\mathrm{div}\,\mathbf{E} + \mathrm{div}\,\mathbf{P} = \rho_f,$$

and because the divergence operator is linear, this can be written as

$$\mathrm{div}(\varepsilon_0\mathbf{E} + \mathbf{P}) = \rho_f. \tag{2.9}$$

It is customary to give the vector field that is subjected to the divergence operator in Equation 2.9 a special name and symbol. The **electric displacement** $\mathbf{D}$ is defined by

$$\mathbf{D} = \varepsilon_0\mathbf{E} + \mathbf{P}. \tag{2.10}$$

Thus in terms of the vector field $\mathbf{D}$, Gauss's law takes the following form.

Differential version of Gauss's law

$$\mathrm{div}\,\mathbf{D} = \rho_f. \tag{2.11}$$

There are two important points to note about this version of Gauss's law. First, Equation 2.11 explicitly involves only *free* charge; the effects of the bound charges associated with polarization of the material are all subsumed into the displacement field $\mathbf{D}$, and we do not need to have explicit knowledge of these bound charges to calculate $\mathbf{D}$. Second, since we have made no assumptions about the relationship between $\mathbf{P}$ and $\mathbf{E}$ when deriving Equation 2.11, this equation is *always* true, and is not restricted to LIH materials.

We can obtain an integral version of Gauss's law involving the electric displacement $\mathbf{D}$ by performing a volume integral of both sides of Equation 2.11. Thus

$$\int_V \mathrm{div}\,\mathbf{D}\,\mathrm{d}V = \int_V \rho_f\,\mathrm{d}V,$$

and using the divergence theorem to convert the left-hand side of the equation to a surface integral, we obtain

Integral version of Gauss's law

$$\int_S \mathbf{D} \cdot d\mathbf{S} = \int_V \rho_f \, dV = Q_f, \tag{2.12}$$

where Q_f is the total free charge in the volume V enclosed by the surface S. This version of Gauss's law is very useful for solving problems that have high symmetry, because the integrals involved are then generally straightforward.

The discussion so far has glossed over the surface charges. A true surface charge occupies a layer that has infinitesimal thickness, and this means that the derivatives in div $\mathbf{E}$ and div $\mathbf{D}$ are not well defined at places where there is surface charge. Thus the local relationship in Equation 2.11 cannot be used at charged surfaces. However, the integral version of Gauss's law (Equation 2.12) is not so restricted. The surface over which the integral of $\mathbf{D} \cdot d\mathbf{S}$ is evaluated can enclose both volume and surface charges, and Q_f represents the total free charge within the volume bounded by this surface.

The electric displacement $\mathbf{D}$ does not have a simple physical interpretation. The electric field $\mathbf{E}$ tells us the force that would act on a unit charge, and the polarization $\mathbf{P}$ tells us the dipole moment per unit volume, but an equivalent interpretation for the electric displacement $\mathbf{D}$ cannot be given. You may wonder then why we introduced this new vector field. Is it really necessary, or is it just an additional complication? The answer to both of these questions is 'no'. Given that the electric displacement is defined by $\mathbf{D} = \varepsilon_0 \mathbf{E} + \mathbf{P}$, it would be possible to simply substitute $\varepsilon_0 \mathbf{E} + \mathbf{P}$ in place of $\mathbf{D}$ wherever it appears in this book, so we could dispense with $\mathbf{D}$ altogether. However, that would make many equations look much more complicated. The simplification that results from the introduction of $\mathbf{D}$ and the identification of its divergence with the free charge density outweighs the inconvenience of familiarizing yourself with an additional field. The electric displacement is simply related to the *free* charges, and it can be evaluated without any need to know what distributions of bound charge these free charges have induced. The effects of polarization and bound charges are all incorporated into $\mathbf{D}$. But determining $\mathbf{D}$ does not mean that we can ignore $\mathbf{E}$. The electric forces on charged particles and the potential difference between two points are related to $\mathbf{E}$, so we need to know how $\mathbf{E}$ is related to $\mathbf{D}$.

2.4.1   Relative permittivity

The relationship between the macroscopic fields $\mathbf{D}$, $\mathbf{E}$ and $\mathbf{P}$ in Equation 2.10 is true for all materials. But to solve this equation for $\mathbf{E}$ we need to make an assumption about the relationship between $\mathbf{P}$ and $\mathbf{E}$. In Subsection 2.2.1 we said that for many materials experimental measurements have shown that the magnitude P of the polarization is proportional to the magnitude E of the electric field — the material is linear — and the polarization $\mathbf{P}$ is in the same direction as the electric field $\mathbf{E}$ — the material is isotropic. For such materials, $\mathbf{P} = \chi_E \varepsilon_0 \mathbf{E}$ (Equation 2.5). We can use this relationship to eliminate $\mathbf{P}$ from Equation 2.10:

$$\mathbf{D} = \varepsilon_0 \mathbf{E} + \mathbf{P} = \varepsilon_0 \mathbf{E} + \chi_E \varepsilon_0 \mathbf{E} = (1 + \chi_E) \varepsilon_0 \mathbf{E}.$$

Now it is customary to define a new quantity, the **relative permittivity** ε of a material, as

$$\varepsilon = 1 + \chi_E. \tag{2.13}$$

Thus for a linear, isotropic material,

$$\mathbf{D} = \varepsilon\varepsilon_0\mathbf{E}. \tag{2.14}$$

For a vacuum, the polarization is zero, so $\chi_E = 0$ and $\varepsilon = 1$, and $\mathbf{D} = \varepsilon_0\mathbf{E}$. Values of ε for various materials are shown in Table 2.1.

Table 2.1 Relative permittivities of various materials at $20\,°C$ and 1 atmosphere pressure (unless otherwise stated).

Material	Relative permittivity ε	Material	Relative permittivity ε
helium He	1.000 065	ethane C_2H_6	1.9
air (dry)	1.000 54	ethanol C_2H_5OH	25
nitrogen N_2	1.000 60	benzene C_6H_6	2.3
nitric oxide NO	1.000 55	polythene	2.3
carbon dioxide CO_2	1.000 92	polyvinyl chloride (pvc)	3.4
water vapour ($100\,°C$)	1.005 9	germanium Ge	16
water vapour ($20\,°C$)	1.000 22	silicon Si	12
liquid water H_2O	80	silica SiO_2	4.4
ice ($-30\,°C$)	99	glass	5–10

This is the end of our quest to determine the macroscopic field in a dielectric material: from Gauss's law and knowledge of the free charge density we can determine $\mathbf{D}$, and then we can use Equation 2.14 to determine $\mathbf{E}$, assuming the material is linear and isotropic.

Worked Example 2.1

A parallel plate capacitor has plates with area A and separation d, and is filled with an LIH dielectric with relative permittivity ε.

(a) If the charges on the plates are $+Q$ and $-Q$, what are the magnitudes and directions of the fields $\mathbf{D}$, $\mathbf{E}$ and $\mathbf{P}$ in the dielectric?

(b) Derive an expression for the capacitance in terms of d, A and ε.

Solution

(a) We assume that the gap between the plates is thin, so we can ignore the fringing fields near the edges, and that the charge is spread uniformly over the (inner) surfaces of the plates. The symmetry then tells us that the fields between the plates must be perpendicular to the plates.

We first use Gauss's law, in the integral version involving $\mathbf{D}$ (Equation 2.12). We choose as our Gaussian surface the cylindrical pillbox shown in cross-section in Figure 2.13.

Essential skill

Determining $\mathbf{D}$, $\mathbf{E}$ and $\mathbf{P}$ in a dielectric

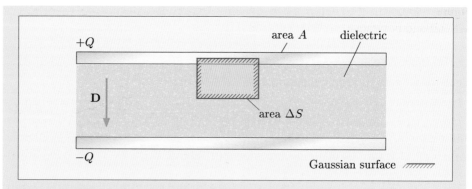

Figure 2.13   A Gaussian surface in the form of a cylindrical pillbox is used to determine the field **D** in the dielectric.

The charge enclosed by this surface is $(Q/A)\Delta S$. Within the conducting plate **D** is zero, and **D** is parallel to the curved cylindrical surface of the pillbox outside the plate. So the only contribution to $\int \mathbf{D} \cdot d\mathbf{S}$ comes from the field **D** that is perpendicular to the plane circular face with area ΔS in the dielectric. Thus $\int \mathbf{D} \cdot d\mathbf{S} = D \times \Delta S = (+Q/A) \times \Delta S$, so $D = (+Q/A)$. This result is independent of the height of the pillbox, so **D** is independent of the distance from the plates.

From the calculated constant value of **D** between the plates, we can determine the field **E** in the dielectric using Equation 2.14, $\mathbf{D} = \varepsilon\varepsilon_0\mathbf{E}$. This leads to $E = D/\varepsilon\varepsilon_0 = Q/A\varepsilon\varepsilon_0$.

The polarization can now be calculated using Equation 2.5, $\mathbf{P} = \chi_E\varepsilon_0\mathbf{E}$, and Equation 2.13, $\varepsilon = 1 + \chi_E$. Combining these equations leads to $\mathbf{P} = (\varepsilon - 1)\varepsilon_0\mathbf{E}$, so in the dielectric $P = ((\varepsilon - 1)/\varepsilon) \times (Q/A)$.

(b)   Capacitance is defined as $C = Q/\Delta V$, so we need to determine the potential difference ΔV between the positive and negative plates. Since $V = -\int \mathbf{E} \cdot d\mathbf{l}$, and the field **E** is uniform and perpendicular to the plates and in the opposite direction to $d\mathbf{l}$ for a path from the negative plate to the positive plate, the potential difference is

$$\Delta V = E \times d = \frac{Q}{\varepsilon\varepsilon_0 A} \times d = \frac{Qd}{\varepsilon\varepsilon_0 A}.$$

Thus

$$C = Q/\Delta V = \varepsilon\varepsilon_0 A/d. \tag{2.15}$$

The solution to this worked example shows that the capacitance is proportional to the relative permittivity of the material between the plates. Filling the gap with polythene ($\varepsilon = 2.3$) gives a capacitance 2.3 times greater than if the gap were filled with air ($\varepsilon = 1.00054$), as we indicated in the introduction to this chapter. Comparing the magnitudes of the fields when the capacitor is filled with polythene and with air, we see that

$$D_{\text{poly}}/D_{\text{air}} = 1, \quad E_{\text{poly}}/E_{\text{air}} = 1/2.3,$$
$$P_{\text{poly}}/P_{\text{air}} = (1.3/2.3) \times (1.00054/0.00054) \simeq 1000.$$

Figure 2.14 shows the fields $\mathbf{D}$, $\varepsilon_0\mathbf{E}$ and $\mathbf{P}$ between the plates of capacitors filled with air and polythene.

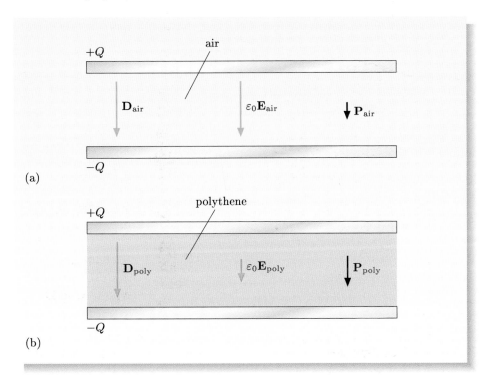

Figure 2.14 The fields $\mathbf{D}$, $\varepsilon_0\mathbf{E}$ and $\mathbf{P}$ in similar capacitors with the same charges on the plates but filled with (a) air ($\varepsilon_{\text{air}} = 1.000\,54$) and (b) polythene ($\varepsilon_{\text{poly}} = 2.3$). (Note that we show $\varepsilon_0\mathbf{E}$ because it has the same unit as $\mathbf{D}$ and $\mathbf{P}$.) The polarization field $\mathbf{P}$ is one thousand times smaller in the air than in the polythene, so we have magnified its length by $\times 500$, to make it visible. However, the sum $\varepsilon_0\mathbf{E} + \mathbf{P} = \mathbf{D}$ is the same in both air and polythene.

Exercise 2.5 Figure 2.15 shows a cross-section through a capacitor used to store 1 bit of information on a memory chip. The dielectric layer is made from aluminium oxide with relative permittivity 13 and thickness 17 nm, and the depth of the capacitor is $4.4\,\mu$m. If its capacitance is 30×10^{-15} F (30 fF), what is the circumference of the (approximately) tubular dielectric layer? (The thickness of the aluminium oxide dielectric layer is much less than the radius of the cylinder, so you should use the expression for the capacitance of a parallel plate capacitor.)

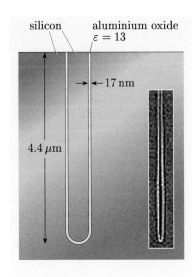

Figure 2.15 A schematic diagram (not to scale) of a section through a capacitor on a DRAM memory chip, with an electron micrograph of such a capacitor inset. The capacitor is made by etching a deep cylindrical pit in the silicon substrate, generally referred to as a 'trench', growing a very thin layer of aluminium oxide on the sides of the pit, and then filling the pit with silicon. The 'plates' of the capacitor are the silicon substrate and the silicon inside the pit.

Exercise 2.6   Figure 2.16a shows a cross-section of a coaxial cable, which consists of a central conducting wire, radius r_1, and an outer conducting cylinder, internal radius r_2, with the space between them filled by an LIH dielectric material that has relative permittivity ε. The charge per unit length on the inner wire is $+\lambda$, and that on the outer cylinder is $-\lambda$.

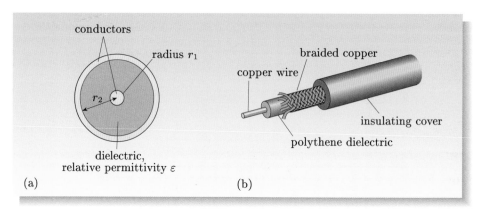

Figure 2.16   (a) Cross-section of a coaxial cable. (b) The various layers of a coaxial cable exposed to reveal its structure. This type of cable is used for connecting an aerial to a television.

(a) Derive expressions for the fields **D**, **E** and **P** as functions of r, the distance from the central axis of the cable.

(b) Derive an expression for the capacitance per unit length of the cable.   ■

2.5   Boundary conditions for the D and E fields

The polarization **P** will change discontinuously across the boundary between different dielectric materials, and in general the fields **D** and **E** will also change discontinuously at a boundary. In this section we shall use two of Maxwell's equations to derive the conditions that must be satisfied by the fields on either side of a boundary, the so-called **boundary conditions for D and E**.

The two equations that we shall use are the integral versions of Gauss's law and Faraday's law, namely $\int_S \mathbf{D} \cdot \mathrm{d}\mathbf{S} = \int_V \rho_f \, \mathrm{d}V$ (Equation 2.12) and $\oint_C \mathbf{E} \cdot \mathrm{d}\mathbf{l} = \int_S \partial \mathbf{B}/\partial t \cdot \mathrm{d}\mathbf{S}$ (Equation 1.8). We shall consider only static fields, so the right-hand side of the second equation is zero, and the equation simplifies to the electrostatic equation, $\oint_C \mathbf{E} \cdot \mathrm{d}\mathbf{l} = 0$.

Figure 2.17 shows the horizontal plane boundary between two dielectric materials with relative permittivities ε_1 and ε_2. We assume that the field **D** is uniform in each of the materials, but that the directions of **D** on either side of the boundary are different.

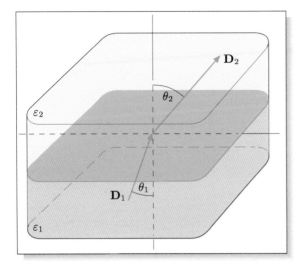

Figure 2.17 Uniform fields $\mathbf{D}_1$ and $\mathbf{D}_2$ on either side of a plane boundary between dielectric materials with relative permittivities ε_1 and ε_2.

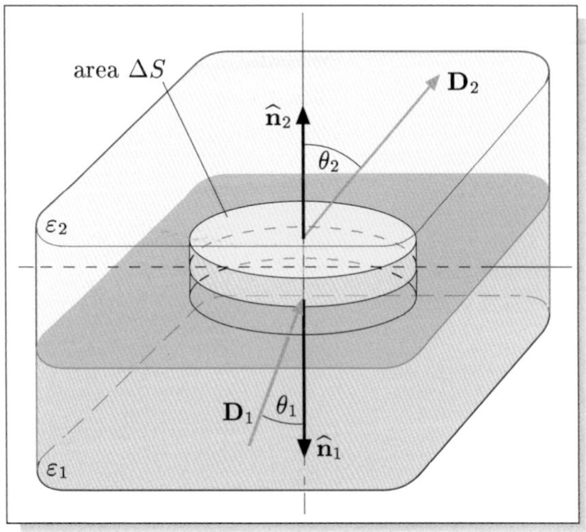

Figure 2.18 Pillbox-shaped Gaussian surface used to determine a boundary condition on the fields $\mathbf{D}_1$ and $\mathbf{D}_2$ either side of the boundary.

First we apply Gauss's law to the thin pillbox shown in Figure 2.18. The plane faces of the pillbox lie on either side of the boundary, and both faces are parallel to the boundary. We assume that there is no free charge on the boundary, so $\int_V \rho_f \, dV = 0$. Then in the limit where the thickness of the pillbox tends to zero, we can ignore any contribution to the flux of $\mathbf{D}$ from the edges of the pillbox, and obtain

$$\int_{\text{pillbox}} \mathbf{D} \cdot d\mathbf{S} = \mathbf{D}_1 \cdot \widehat{\mathbf{n}}_1 \, \Delta S + \mathbf{D}_2 \cdot \widehat{\mathbf{n}}_2 \, \Delta S = 0,$$

where $\widehat{\mathbf{n}}_1$ and $\widehat{\mathbf{n}}_2$ are outward-pointing unit normals to the plane faces of the pillbox in the two materials, and ΔS is the area of each plane face.

We can simplify this by using the fact that $-\widehat{\mathbf{n}}_1 = \widehat{\mathbf{n}}_2$:

$$-\mathbf{D}_1 \cdot \widehat{\mathbf{n}}_2 \, \Delta S + \mathbf{D}_2 \cdot \widehat{\mathbf{n}}_2 \, \Delta S = 0.$$

Writing this in terms of the components of $\mathbf{D}$ in the two materials in the $\widehat{\mathbf{n}}_2$ direction, perpendicular to the boundary, $D_{1\perp}$ and $D_{2\perp}$:

$$-D_{1\perp} \, \Delta S + D_{2\perp} \, \Delta S = 0.$$

Thus

Boundary condition for perpendicular field component

$$D_{1\perp} = D_{2\perp}. \tag{2.16}$$

The component of the $\mathbf{D}$ field perpendicular to the boundary remains the same across a boundary that carries no free charge.

Note that this result is true only when there is no free charge at the boundary. If there were a thin conducting film at the boundary carrying a free surface charge density σ_f, then the charge within the Gaussian surface in Figure 2.18 would be $\sigma_f \, \Delta S$. This would lead to the boundary condition

$$D_{2\perp} - D_{1\perp} = \sigma_f.$$

Now let us see what we can deduce about the **E** fields either side of the boundary by using the relationship $\oint_C \mathbf{E} \cdot \mathrm{d}\mathbf{l} = 0$. Consider the small rectangular path shown in Figure 2.19, which has its two longer elements, $\delta\mathbf{l}_1$ and $\delta\mathbf{l}_2$, parallel to the boundary between materials 1 and 2.

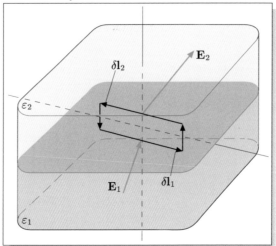

Figure 2.19   Rectangular path used to determine a boundary condition on the fields $\mathbf{E}_1$ and $\mathbf{E}_2$ either side of the boundary between materials with relative permittivities ε_1 and ε_2.

We can make the two shorter sides so small that their contribution to the line integral of the electric field around the loop is negligible, and then the line integral becomes

$$\oint \mathbf{E} \cdot \mathrm{d}\mathbf{l} = \mathbf{E}_1 \cdot \delta\mathbf{l}_1 + \mathbf{E}_2 \cdot \delta\mathbf{l}_2 = 0.$$

Since $\delta\mathbf{l}_2 = -\delta\mathbf{l}_1$, we can rewrite this as

$$(\mathbf{E}_1 - \mathbf{E}_2) \cdot \delta\mathbf{l}_1 = 0,$$

and this equation indicates that the components of $\mathbf{E}_1$ and $\mathbf{E}_2$ in the direction of $\delta\mathbf{l}_1$ must be equal. Now this result must be true whatever direction parallel to the surface we choose for $\delta\mathbf{l}_1$, and this means that the components of the electric field parallel to the boundary in materials 1 and 2, $E_{1\parallel}$ and $E_{2\parallel}$, must have the same magnitude and be in the same direction. Thus

Boundary condition for parallel field component

$$E_{1\parallel} = E_{2\parallel}. \tag{2.17}$$

The component of the **E** field parallel to the boundary remains the same across a boundary.

In deriving these boundary conditions for **D** and **E**, we assumed a planar boundary and uniform fields on either side of the boundary. However, whatever the shape of the boundary and whatever the form of the fields on either side of it, we can always make the pillbox in Figure 2.18, and the path in Figure 2.19, small enough that the boundary enclosed is essentially plane and the fields within them are uniform. Thus the results that we obtained are local relations that apply at any point on any boundary between any two dielectric materials.

Now Equations 2.16 and 2.17 do not completely specify the fields **D** and **E** on either side of the boundary, because they tell us nothing about the components $D_\parallel$ and $E_\perp$. To determine these components, we need to know the relationship between **D** and **E** in each of the materials. We shall assume that we are dealing with LIH materials, so $\mathbf{D} = \varepsilon\varepsilon_0\mathbf{E}$. This means that **D** and **E** are parallel in each of the dielectrics.

- ● Use the boundary condition on the perpendicular component of **D** at the interface between two LIH materials with dielectric constants ε_1 and ε_2 to deduce the relationship between the components of the electric field **E** perpendicular to the boundary in the two materials.

- ○ For an LIH material, $\mathbf{D}_1 = \varepsilon_1\varepsilon_0\mathbf{E}_1$, so $D_{1\perp} = \varepsilon_1\varepsilon_0 E_{1\perp}$. But we know that $D_{1\perp} = D_{2\perp}$ (Equation 2.16), so $\varepsilon_1\varepsilon_0 E_{1\perp} = \varepsilon_2\varepsilon_0 E_{2\perp}$, or $\varepsilon_1 E_{1\perp} = \varepsilon_2 E_{2\perp}$.

- ● Deduce the relationship between the components of the **D** field parallel to the boundary between two LIH materials.

- ○ For an LIH material, $\mathbf{D}_1 = \varepsilon_1\varepsilon_0\mathbf{E}_1$, so $E_{1\parallel} = D_{1\parallel}/\varepsilon_1\varepsilon_0$. We know that $E_{1\parallel} = E_{2\parallel}$ (Equation 2.17), so $D_{1\parallel}/\varepsilon_1 = D_{2\parallel}/\varepsilon_2$.

We therefore have two 'primary' boundary conditions, that were derived directly from Maxwell's equations and that are always valid:

$$D_{1\perp} = D_{2\perp} \quad \text{and} \quad E_{1\parallel} = E_{2\parallel}.$$

We also have two subsidiary equations, that apply only to materials for which $\mathbf{D} = \varepsilon\varepsilon_0\mathbf{E}$:

$$\frac{D_{1\parallel}}{\varepsilon_1} = \frac{D_{2\parallel}}{\varepsilon_2} \quad \text{and} \quad \varepsilon_1 E_{1\perp} = \varepsilon_2 E_{2\perp}.$$

Since the last two equations are valid only for LIH materials, and can easily be derived from the first two equations in situations where they are valid, we recommend that you commit to memory only the first two equations.

As you can see in Figure 2.17, the fields on one side of a boundary between materials with different dielectric constants generally are in a different direction to the fields on the other side. It is only in the special cases when the fields are parallel or perpendicular to the boundary that the fields are in the same direction in the two materials. So how are the directions of the fields on either side of a boundary related?

In Figure 2.18, the **D** field makes an angle of θ_1 with the normal to the boundary in material 1, and an angle of θ_2 to the normal in material 2. Continuity of the perpendicular component of **D** requires that

$$D_1 \cos\theta_1 = D_2 \cos\theta_2. \tag{2.18}$$

Similarly, continuity of the parallel component of **E** requires that

$$E_1 \sin \theta_1 = E_2 \sin \theta_2. \tag{2.19}$$

Now, assuming that we are dealing with LIH materials, we can use the relationship $\mathbf{D} = \varepsilon \varepsilon_0 \mathbf{E}$ to replace the D-components in Equation 2.18 by E-components:

$$\varepsilon_1 \varepsilon_0 E_1 \cos \theta_1 = \varepsilon_2 \varepsilon_0 E_2 \cos \theta_2. \tag{2.20}$$

Eliminating E_2/E_1 between Equations 2.19 and 2.20, we obtain

$$\frac{\sin \theta_1}{\sin \theta_2} = \frac{\varepsilon_1 \cos \theta_1}{\varepsilon_2 \cos \theta_2},$$

or, equivalently,

$$\frac{\tan \theta_1}{\tan \theta_2} = \frac{\varepsilon_1}{\varepsilon_2}. \tag{2.21}$$

This result indicates that the angle that the field makes to the normal to the boundary is greater in the material with the higher relative permittivity. Note, however, that there are two special cases that arise for any values of ε_1 and ε_2, namely when the fields on either side are perpendicular to the boundary (i.e. $\theta_1 = \theta_2 = 0°$), and when the fields on either side are parallel to the boundary (i.e. $\theta_1 = \theta_2 = 90°$).

Essential skill

Applying the boundary conditions for **D** and **E**

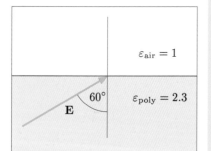

Figure 2.20   A uniform field **E** near the surface of a polythene slab.

Worked Example 2.2

Figure 2.20 shows a uniform **E** field, magnitude 0.15 V m^{-1}, near the surface of a large slab of polythene, relative permittivity 2.3. What is the **E** field in the air outside the surface? (Assume that $\varepsilon_{\text{air}} = 1.0$.)

Solution

To determine $\mathbf{E}_{\text{air}}$, we need to find $E_{\text{air}\parallel}$ and $E_{\text{air}\perp}$, and this requires the use of the boundary conditions for both parallel and perpendicular fields,

$$E_{\text{air}\parallel} = E_{\text{poly}\parallel} \quad \text{and} \quad D_{\text{air}\perp} = D_{\text{poly}\perp}.$$

We assume that polythene is an LIH material, so $\mathbf{D}_{\text{poly}} = \varepsilon_{\text{poly}}\varepsilon_0 \mathbf{E}_{\text{poly}}$. Also, we know that $\mathbf{D}_{\text{air}} = \varepsilon_0 \mathbf{E}_{\text{air}}$, since $\varepsilon_{\text{air}} = 1$. The second boundary condition can therefore be rewritten as

$$\varepsilon_0 E_{\text{air}\perp} = \varepsilon_{\text{poly}}\varepsilon_0 E_{\text{poly}\perp}.$$

Thus

$$\begin{aligned} E_{\text{air}\parallel} &= E_{\text{poly}\parallel} \\ &= E_{\text{poly}} \sin 60° \\ &= 0.15 \text{ V m}^{-1} \times 0.866 = 0.13 \text{ V m}^{-1} \end{aligned}$$

and

$$\begin{aligned} E_{\text{air}\perp} &= \varepsilon_{\text{poly}} E_{\text{poly}\perp} \\ &= \varepsilon_{\text{poly}} E_{\text{poly}} \cos 60° \\ &= 2.3 \times 0.15 \text{ V m}^{-1} \times 0.500 = 0.17 \text{ V m}^{-1}. \end{aligned}$$

These two components determine the field in the air outside the polythene surface.

Exercise 2.7   Figure 2.21 shows a slab of a material with relative permittivity $\varepsilon = 1.5$ embedded within a material with relative permittivity $\varepsilon = 2.5$. The field **D** in the top layer has magnitude $2.0 \times 10^{-10}\,\mathrm{C\,m^{-2}}$ and is perpendicular to the boundary. There are no free charges in either material, and both are linear, isotropic and homogeneous.

(a) What is the field **D** in the central layer and in the bottom layer?

(b) What are the fields **E** and **P** in the three layers?

(c) What are the densities of bound charge σ_b at the two boundaries?   ■

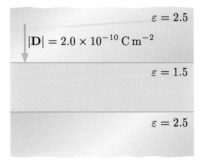

Figure 2.21   The boundary conditions for **E** and **D** should enable you to determine the fields **E**, **D** and **P** in the three regions and the densities of bound charge at the boundaries from the information in this figure (Exercise 2.7).

2.6   Time-dependent fields

So far in this chapter we have been concerned only with the response of dielectric materials to static electric fields. However, dielectrics are often used in situations where the field is varying rapidly: an obvious example is the dielectric in a capacitor used in an ac-circuit. So how does the polarization of a dielectric respond to changing electric fields?

Consider what happens at the microscopic level when a sinusoidally-varying electric field is applied to a dielectric. As the field changes, the electron clouds will readjust their displacements from the nuclei. Because the mass of an electron is very small, the electron clouds can respond very rapidly to the field changes, and the induced dipole moments at any instant are just what you would expect from the instantaneous value of the field. At low frequency, the polarization of any permanent dipoles are also what would be predicted from the instantaneous value of the electric field; the dipoles can be reoriented rapidly enough to track the applied field.

However, if we increase the frequency at which the field oscillates, eventually the permanent dipoles will be unable to readjust their orientation fast enough, and their contribution to the relative permittivity will drop. Increase the frequency still further and there will come a point when the inertia of the electrons becomes important — they cannot respond rapidly enough to keep up with the field changes. At sufficiently high frequencies, the material is not polarized at all, because the permanent dipoles cannot reorient themselves fast enough, and the electron clouds cannot be displaced fast enough, to respond to the rapid changes in the field.

The frequency dependence of the relative permittivity of pure water, shown in Figure 2.22, is a good illustration of this. At zero frequency — i.e. static fields — $\varepsilon_{\mathrm{water}} \simeq 80$, and the major contribution to this high permittivity comes from orientation of the large permanent dipole moments of the water molecules. As the frequency increases above about 10^{10} Hz, the relative permittivity falls because the drag on the water molecules due to their interactions with their neighbours prevents them from following the rapid changes of the field, and at optical frequencies (10^{14} Hz) the relative permittivity is only 1.8, which is a typical value for a non-polar liquid. For frequencies above about 10^{16} Hz, even the electron clouds cannot follow the field variations, and the relative permittivity drops to unity.

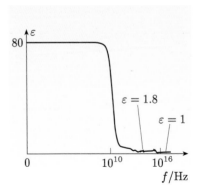

Figure 2.22   Frequency dependence of the relative permittivity of water at $20\,^\circ$C.

2.6.1 Modifying the Ampère–Maxwell equation

When a dielectric material is placed in a time-dependent electric field, the polarization of the material will vary with time. The bound charges in the material move in response to the changing electric field, and this motion constitutes an electric current, which we shall refer to as the **polarization current density** $\mathbf{J}_p$. This polarization current is a source of magnetic field, so it must be included as part of the current density term in the Ampère–Maxwell equation (Equation 1.9):

$$\operatorname{curl} \mathbf{B} = \mu_0 \left(\mathbf{J} + \varepsilon_0 \frac{\partial \mathbf{E}}{\partial t} \right) = \mu_0 \left(\mathbf{J}_f + \mathbf{J}_p + \varepsilon_0 \frac{\partial \mathbf{E}}{\partial t} \right),$$

where $\mathbf{J}_f$ is the normal free current density. The polarization current is related in a simple way to the rate of change of polarization, as we shall now show.

In the discussion of volume polarization charges in Subsection 2.3.2, you saw that the net charge Q that crosses an oriented area $\delta \mathbf{S}$ when a material develops polarization $\mathbf{P}$ is $Q = \mathbf{P} \cdot \delta \mathbf{S}$. If we simplify the situation by considering an area that is perpendicular to the polarization, then the charge crossing the area is $Q = P \, \delta S$. Now if the polarization changes by an amount dP in time dt, then the additional charge dQ transferred across the area is given by $dQ = dP \times \delta S$, and the current that flows across the area in the direction of $\mathbf{P}$ is

$$I = \frac{dQ}{dt} = \frac{dP}{dt} \delta S.$$

Recognizing that $\mathbf{J}_p$ has magnitude $I/\delta S$ and is in the direction of $\mathbf{P}$, we can write the polarization current density as

$$\mathbf{J}_p = \frac{\partial \mathbf{P}}{\partial t}.$$

We can use this expression, together with the definition of $\mathbf{D}$, to rewrite the Ampère–Maxwell law in the following form:

$$\operatorname{curl} \mathbf{B} = \mu_0 \left(\mathbf{J}_f + \frac{\partial \mathbf{P}}{\partial t} + \varepsilon_0 \frac{\partial \mathbf{E}}{\partial t} \right) = \mu_0 \left(\mathbf{J}_f + \frac{\partial \mathbf{D}}{\partial t} \right). \tag{2.22}$$

This is the form of the Ampère–Maxwell law that takes account of the dielectric properties of materials. It is not, however, the final version of this equation, because we have yet to include the effect of the magnetic properties of materials. That is the subject of the next chapter.

Exercise 2.8 A low-frequency potential difference, $V = V_0 \sin \omega t$, is applied to a parallel plate capacitor, with plate spacing d, which is filled with an LIH dielectric with relative permittivity ε. Derive an expression for $\operatorname{curl} \mathbf{B}$ in the dielectric. ∎

Summary of Chapter 2

Section 2.1 In the presence of media, Maxwell's equations need to take account of charges and currents due to atoms. Charges $+q$ and $-q$ separated by a displacement $\mathbf{d}$ form an electric dipole, which has dipole moment $\mathbf{p} = q\mathbf{d}$. Electric fields induce a dipole moment in each atom by displacing the electron cloud relative to the nucleus. Asymmetric molecules generally have permanent dipole moments, and an electric field exerts a torque on such molecules that tends to align them preferentially in the direction of the field. However, alignment with the field is disrupted by thermal motion, and is small if the electric potential energy of the dipole pE is small compared with k_BT.

Section 2.2   The polarization $\mathbf{P}$ is the electric dipole moment per unit volume: $\mathbf{P} = n\langle\mathbf{p}\rangle$, where n is the number density of dipoles and $\langle\mathbf{p}\rangle$ is the average dipole moment per molecule. The electric susceptibility χ_E is defined by $\mathbf{P} = \chi_E\varepsilon_0\mathbf{E}$. For linear, isotropic, homogeneous (LIH) materials, χ_E is independent of $\mathbf{E}$, polarization $\mathbf{P}$ is in the same direction as $\mathbf{E}$, and χ_E is independent of position. The value of χ_E depends on the material and on the temperature.

Section 2.3   The polarization of the molecules in a dielectric is equivalent to a volume charge density $\rho_b = -\operatorname{div}\mathbf{P}$, together with a surface charge density $\sigma_b = \mathbf{P}\cdot\hat{\mathbf{n}}$, where $\hat{\mathbf{n}}$ is an outward-pointing unit normal to the surface.

Section 2.4   The electric displacement, $\mathbf{D} = \varepsilon_0\mathbf{E} + \mathbf{P}$, is directly related to the free charge density ρ_f by the form of Gauss's law that is used for materials: $\operatorname{div}\mathbf{D} = \rho_f$. The integral version of this relationship is $\int_S \mathbf{D}\cdot d\mathbf{S} = \int_V \rho_f\,dV$. For an LIH material, $\mathbf{D} = \varepsilon\varepsilon_0\mathbf{E}$, where ε is the relative permittivity of the material.

Section 2.5   At the interface between dielectric materials 1 and 2, the fields $\mathbf{D}$ and $\mathbf{E}$ satisfy the boundary conditions $D_{1\perp} = D_{2\perp}$ and $E_{1\|} = E_{2\|}$.

Section 2.6   For time-dependent fields, the relative permittivity of materials decreases as the frequency of variation of the field increases, initially because the permanent dipoles cannot reorient fast enough, and then because of the inertia of the electron clouds. Inclusion of polarization effects in the Ampère–Maxwell equation leads to the form of the equation appropriate for dielectric materials: $\operatorname{curl}\mathbf{B} = \mu_0(\mathbf{J}_f + \partial\mathbf{D}/\partial t)$.

Achievements from Chapter 2

After studying this chapter you should be able to do the following.

2.1   Explain the meanings of the newly defined (emboldened) terms and symbols, and use them appropriately.

2.2   Describe the microscopic origins of polarization of dielectric materials.

2.3   Explain how the atomic and molecular dipoles in a dielectric can be represented by a surface charge density and a volume charge density, recall how these charge densities are related to the polarization, and calculate these charge densities when the polarization is specified.

2.4   Recall the relationships between $\mathbf{D}$, $\mathbf{E}$ and $\mathbf{P}$, and make use of these relationships to solve problems.

2.5   Derive, recall and apply the differential and integral versions of Gauss's law and the Ampère–Maxwell law that involve $\mathbf{D}$.

2.6   Derive and recall the boundary conditions on $\mathbf{D}$ and $\mathbf{E}$ at a boundary between two dielectric materials, and use these boundary conditions to solve problems.

Chapter 3   Magnetic fields in materials

You will be aware that iron has magnetic properties — it can both be attracted to a magnet and become a magnet in its own right. What may be less familiar is that *all* materials have magnetic properties. For example, when an aluminium bar is placed parallel to a magnetic field, it generates a magnetic field that has the same form as the field of a familiar bar magnet, but the field strength is so many orders of magnitude weaker that aluminium is generally regarded as non-magnetic.

There are many similarities between the effects of magnetic fields on materials and the effects of electric fields on dielectric materials that we discussed in the previous chapter. A magnetic field produces induced *magnetic* dipoles in all types of atom, and it also changes the orientation of any permanent *magnetic* dipoles that are associated with atoms or molecules. Alignment of these magnetic dipoles creates a macroscopic magnetization of the material, analogous to the polarization produced by an electric field. This magnetization is put to practical use in devices ranging from hard disks for data storage in computers to powerful electromagnets (Figure 3.1).

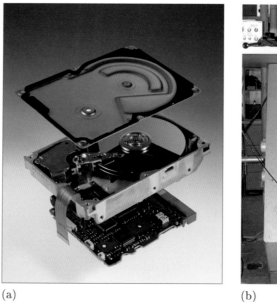

(a)   (b)

Figure 3.1   (a) Each bit of data stored on this hard disk corresponds to magnetization of an area smaller than $10^{-14}\,\text{m}^2$. (b) A 5 T electromagnet, which is used for research into the properties of materials.

As with the discussion of dielectric materials, we shall start with a qualitative discussion of the microscopic origin of magnetic effects. The combined effect of many atomic dipoles is a macroscopic magnetization of a material, and we shall show that this is equivalent to macroscopic currents in the volume and on the surface of the material. We shall define a new field, the magnetic intensity **H**, which is directly related to the free currents flowing through conductors and which simplifies solution of various problems. Boundary conditions for **B** and **H** at interfaces between different materials will be derived, and we shall conclude the chapter with a brief discussion of electromagnets.

3.1   The microscopic picture

Macroscopic objects contain many atoms or molecules, each with many associated electrons. We require quantum mechanics for a full explanation of the behaviour of these electrons, but for our purposes here we can think of each of them as moving in an orbit around a nucleus. The orbital motion of a charged electron creates a tiny current loop, and this in turn produces a magnetic field. The magnetic field pattern produced by a small current loop is very similar to the electric field pattern produced by an electric dipole except in the immediate vicinity of the sources (Figure 3.2), so the small current loops are called **magnetic dipoles**.

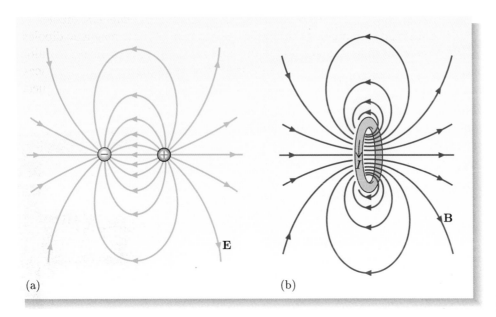

(a)   (b)

Figure 3.2   (a) The electric field produced by an electric (charge) dipole. (b) The magnetic field produced by a small current loop, a magnetic dipole.

The strength of the field produced by a magnetic dipole is proportional to both the current I in the loop and the area ΔS of the loop, so we define the **magnetic dipole moment m** by

$$\mathbf{m} = |I|\,\Delta\mathbf{S}, \tag{3.1}$$

where the oriented area $\Delta\mathbf{S}$ has magnitude ΔS and is perpendicular to the plane of the loop, pointing in a direction determined by a right-hand grip rule, as shown in Figure 3.3. The SI unit of magnetic dipole moment is $\mathrm{A\,m^2}$.

According to quantum mechanics, each electron in an atom or molecule also has an intrinsic spin, and this has an intrinsic magnetic dipole moment associated with it. So each electron in an atom makes two contributions to the net magnetic moment of the atom, one from its orbital motion and one from its spin. The resultant magnetic moment is simply the vector sum of the two contributions from each of the atom's electrons. Some atoms have no permanent magnetic moment because the resultant moment is zero. However, there are many types of atom where the cancellation is incomplete, and these atoms have a **permanent magnetic moment**.

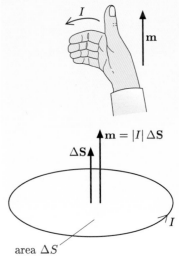

Figure 3.3   The direction of the magnetic moment **m** of a small current loop is related to the direction of current flow by a right-hand grip rule.

43

3.1.1   Permanent magnetic dipoles

We shall consider first a gas of molecules, each of which has a permanent magnetic dipole moment of magnitude m. In the absence of an applied magnetic field, these dipoles are randomly oriented, but when a field is applied, the magnetic dipoles tend to line up parallel with the field. This is analogous to the behaviour of permanent electric dipoles in an electric field. The analogy extends to the expression for the potential energy of the dipoles, which is the scalar product of the dipole moment and the field, that is, $-\mathbf{m} \cdot \mathbf{B}$ for a magnetic dipole and $-\mathbf{p} \cdot \mathbf{E}$ for an electric dipole. Thus the magnetic energy is lower by $2mB$ when the magnetic dipole is parallel to the field than when it is antiparallel. However, at normal ambient temperature and magnetic field, $k_{\mathrm{B}}T \gg mB$; the thermal energy of the atoms is much greater than the energy associated with alignment with the field. Alignment of the dipoles with the field is therefore hindered by the motion and collisions of atoms, and the time during which a dipole has a positive component of its magnetic moment in the direction of the applied field is only slightly greater than the time that it has a negative component. Thus the average component of the magnetic moment in the direction of the applied field is only a tiny fraction of the magnitude of the magnetic moment carried by each atom.

3.1.2   Induced magnetic dipoles

As well as tending to align any permanent magnetic moments, an applied magnetic field induces magnetic moments in all atoms, just as an electric field induces electric dipole moments in all atoms. When a magnetic field is applied, it induces changes in the currents associated with all of the orbiting electrons; this is an example of Faraday's law in action. The sense of the change in current is given by Lenz's law: increasing the applied field in the $+z$-direction induces changes to the orbital currents that increase the component of the magnetic moment in the $-z$-direction; removing the applied field restores the orbital currents and the magnetic moments to their original values. However, unlike conventional electric circuits, there is no dissipation of energy in atomic orbits, so the induced orbital currents continue to flow for as long as the field is applied.

For each of the electron orbits, whatever the direction of its magnetic moment initially, the change in moment is proportional to the applied field and it is in the opposite direction to the change in field. So even though the net moment of an atom may have been zero in the absence of a magnetic field, the atom acquires an **induced magnetic moment** that is the sum of the changes in the moments of the individual orbits, and the changes in these moments are all in the opposite direction to the field change. Also, the induced magnetic moments resulting from the induced currents are independent of temperature. Removing the magnetic field induces changes to the orbital currents and moments that exactly reverse the changes produced by applying the field, so the induced dipole moments are reduced to zero.

3.2 Macroscopic magnetization

We are generally interested in the combined effect of the magnetic dipoles associated with many atoms or molecules in a solid, a liquid or a gas. This combined effect is characterized by the **magnetization M**, which is the total magnetic dipole moment per unit volume, defined by

$$\mathbf{M} = n\langle\mathbf{m}\rangle, \tag{3.2}$$

where n is the number density of magnetic-dipole-carrying atoms or molecules, and $\langle\mathbf{m}\rangle$ is the average magnetic dipole moment of the atoms or molecules in the material. The SI unit of magnetization is $\mathrm{A\,m^{-1}}$, as should be clear from the definitions in Equations 3.1 and 3.2. Magnetization is a macroscopic concept; it is calculated for a volume that includes millions of atoms, so the rapid spatial and temporal variations in the vicinity of individual moments are averaged out.

● The number density of oxygen molecules at $20\,°\mathrm{C}$ and atmospheric pressure is $2.7 \times 10^{25}\,\mathrm{m^{-3}}$. The magnitude of oxygen's magnetization in a particular field is $0.27\,\mathrm{A\,m^{-1}}$. What is the magnitude of the average magnetic moment of the molecules?

○ The magnitude of the average moment, $|\langle\mathbf{m}\rangle|$, is

$$M/n = 0.27\,\mathrm{A\,m^{-1}}/2.7 \times 10^{25}\,\mathrm{m^{-3}} = 1.0 \times 10^{-26}\,\mathrm{A\,m^2}.$$

3.2.1 Types of magnetic materials

When a dielectric rod is placed parallel to a uniform electric field $\mathbf{E}_0$, it becomes polarized, with (approximately) uniform charge densities on each end surface, as shown in Figure 3.4. The field produced by the polarization charges reduces the applied electric field inside the rod and increases the electric field immediately outside its ends.

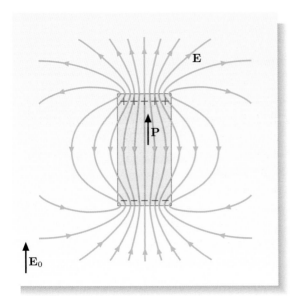

Figure 3.4 The electric field produced by a uniformly polarized dielectric rod.

There are analogous effects when a rod is placed in a magnetic field. Most materials can be classified as either diamagnetic, paramagnetic or ferromagnetic according to their response to an applied magnetic field, and we shall describe these three types of material in turn.

Diamagnetism

In **diamagnetic materials**, the dominant contribution to the magnetization comes from induced dipoles. Since the magnetic moments of induced dipoles always oppose the applied field, because of Lenz's law, the magnetization of a diamagnetic material is in the opposite direction to the magnetic field. The field produced by the magnetization reduces the applied field $\mathbf{B}_0$ inside the material and just outside its ends (Figure 3.5).

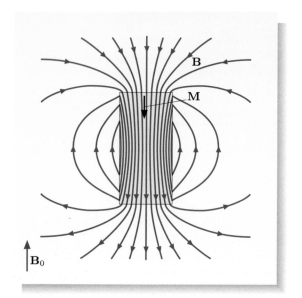

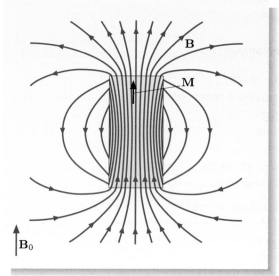

Figure 3.5   The magnetic field produced by a uniformly magnetized diamagnetic rod.

Figure 3.6   The magnetic field produced by uniformly magnetized paramagnetic rod.

Substances that exhibit diamagnetism, such as nitrogen, water, copper and silicon, have atoms or molecules with no permanent magnetic dipole moments; the vector sum of their orbital and spin magnetic moments is zero. In materials that contain atoms with permanent magnetic moments, induced dipoles are still present, but their contribution to the magnetization is generally outweighed by the contribution of the permanent dipole moments.

Paramagnetism

In **paramagnetic materials**, permanent dipole moments associated with the atoms play the dominant role. Since the average magnetic moment of each permanent dipole is in the direction of the applied field, the magnetization of a paramagnetic material is in the direction of the magnetic field. This magnetization increases the applied field $\mathbf{B}_0$ inside the material and outside its ends (Figure 3.6). There will be a contribution to the dipole moment of each atom from induced dipoles, but the mean magnetic moment $\langle \mathbf{m} \rangle$ due to alignment of the permanent moments with the field is generally greater than the induced moment. Examples of paramagnetic materials include oxygen, aluminium, sodium and polythene.

Experiments show that the magnetization of a paramagnetic material is proportional to the applied field and inversely proportional to absolute temperature: $M \propto B/T$. This relationship holds as long as $mB/k_{\mathrm{B}}T \ll 1$, and is a consequence of the competition between the magnetic energy of the dipoles, $\mathbf{m} \cdot \mathbf{B}$, and their thermal energy $k_{\mathrm{B}}T$. Increasing the ratio B/T favours the magnetic energy, so alignment of dipoles with the field increases, and the magnetization increases. Oxygen molecules have a permanent dipole moment of magnitude $2.6 \times 10^{-23}\,\mathrm{A\,m^2}$, and for a 1 T field at 293 K the ratio $mB/k_{\mathrm{B}}T$ is about 6×10^{-3}. So for oxygen, $M \propto B/T$ under these conditions. However, at very high fields or low temperatures, this proportionality breaks down and the magnetization approaches a limiting value that corresponds to all of the permanent dipoles being aligned with the field. Of course, when the applied magnetic field is zero, the magnetization is zero, corresponding to random orientation of dipoles.

Ferromagnetism

The magnetization of diamagnetic and paramagnetic materials is normally small. In contrast, materials such as iron exhibit magnetizations that are several orders of magnitude larger than for paramagnetic materials: such materials are said to be ferromagnetic. **Ferromagnetic materials** have atoms with permanent magnetic dipole moments, and there is a strong quantum mechanical coupling between these atoms that makes it energetically favourable for neighbouring dipoles to be aligned parallel to each other even in the absence of an applied field.

Of course, a piece of iron is not normally strongly magnetized in the absence of a field. This is because dipole alignment occurs over small regions, called **domains**, and a representation of this domain structure in unmagnetized material is shown in Figure 3.7. Domains typically have volumes in the range 10^{-12}–$10^{-8}\,\mathrm{m^3}$, and contain 10^{17}–10^{21} atoms. Within each domain, the permanent dipole moments are aligned parallel to a direction in the crystalline structure in which it is easier to magnetize the material, but the directions of magnetization of neighbouring domains are different. In unmagnetized iron, the net magnetic moment of all of the domains is zero. This arrangement has a lower magnetic energy than if all of the dipoles were aligned in the same direction throughout the material, because the reduction in energy associated with the magnetic field outside the material more than compensates for the increase in energy due to dipoles not being aligned parallel to each other near the domain boundaries. This is analogous to two bar magnets in close proximity to each other having lower energy when their magnetizations are antiparallel than when they are parallel.

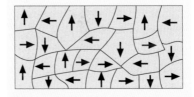

Figure 3.7 The magnetizations of domains in unmagnetized ferromagnetic material are in different directions, and the total magnetic moment is zero.

When an external magnetic field is applied, domains with a component of magnetization parallel to the field tend to grow at the expense of their neighbours, as shown in Figure 3.8 overleaf. Eventually, all of the domains have a magnetization component in the direction of the field, and further increase in the net magnetization requires rotation of the magnetization within each domain to align it with the field. If the applied field is sufficiently strong, all of the permanent moments become aligned in the direction of the field (Figure 3.8c). Thus the saturation magnetization is in the same direction as the applied magnetic field, just as for paramagnetic materials (Figure 3.6), but its magnitude is very much greater because of the complete alignment of the dipoles. Unlike diamagnetic and paramagnetic materials, when the external field is removed, a ferromagnetic material may retain a net magnetization in the direction of the field, so ferromagnetic materials can form permanent magnets.

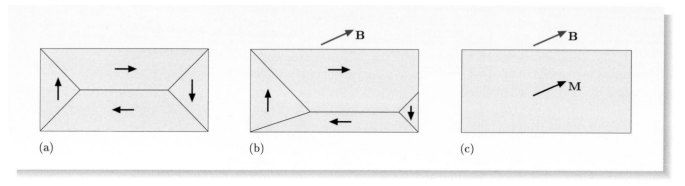

(a)   (b)   (c)

Figure 3.8   Schematic illustration of changes to domains in a ferromagnet when a magnetic field is applied. (a) Zero field, no net magnetization. (b) Domains with a component of magnetization parallel to the field have expanded, and other domains have contracted. (c) Magnetization in each domain has rotated to become aligned with the direction of the applied field.

At normal temperatures, thermal energy is not high enough to disrupt the parallel alignment of neighbouring dipoles within a domain. However, if the temperature of a ferromagnetic material is increased, the thermal energy k_BT eventually becomes large enough to overcome the strong coupling between neighbouring dipoles; the material then loses its spontaneous magnetization and becomes paramagnetic. The temperature at which this transition takes place is known as the **Curie temperature**, and for iron this temperature is about $800\,°C$. This means that the Earth's magnetic field cannot be due to ferromagnetism in the iron core, because the temperature exceeds $800\,°C$ at depths greater than $40\,km$.

Exercise 3.1   Which two of Maxwell's equations explain the crucial difference between Figure 3.4 and Figure 3.6?

Exercise 3.2   Compare and contrast the behaviour of dielectric, diamagnetic and paramagnetic rods by completing Table 3.1. In each blank space, write either 'same' or 'opposite'.   ■

Table 3.1   Comparison of dielectric, diamagnetic and paramagnetic materials.

	Dielectric	Diamagnet	Paramagnet
Relative directions of dipole moment and applied field			
Relative directions of field due to matter and applied field within rod			
Relative directions of field due to matter and applied field just outside ends of rod			

3.2.2   Magnetic susceptibility

For diamagnetic materials, and for many paramagnetic materials at a fixed temperature, the magnetization is proportional to the macroscopic field **B**, and is aligned with it. We can therefore write

$$\mathbf{M} = \chi_B \frac{\mathbf{B}}{\mu_0}, \tag{3.3}$$

where χ_B is known as the **magnetic susceptibility** and depends on the material and factors such as temperature and pressure. Incorporating μ_0, the permeability of free space $(= 4\pi \times 10^{-7} \, \text{T m A}^{-1})$, into this definition means that χ_B is a pure number, since both $\mathbf{M}$ and $\mathbf{B}/\mu_0$ have the same unit (A m^{-1}). Values of χ_B for some common paramagnetic and diamagnetic materials are listed in Table 3.2.

Note that
$1 \, \text{T m A}^{-1} = 1 \, \text{N A}^{-2}$.

Table 3.2   Measured values of magnetic susceptibility χ_B of various materials at $20 \, ^\circ\text{C}$ and atmospheric pressure.

Diamagnetic material	$\chi_B/10^{-6}$	Paramagnetic material	$\chi_B/10^{-6}$
nitrogen	-0.0068	oxygen	$+1.9$
water	-9.0	aluminium	$+22$
copper	-9.6	platinum	$+260$
silicon	-3.7	sodium	$+7.2$
polyvinyl chloride (pvc)	-10	polythene	$+1.9$

The field $\mathbf{B}$ in Equation 3.3 is the macroscopic field within the material. This is the average, over a volume containing millions of atoms, of both the applied field and the field due to the microscopic dipoles. However, because the susceptibility of diamagnetic and paramagnetic materials is very small, the macroscopic field within these materials is essentially the same as the applied $\mathbf{B}$ field.

Note that materials for which Equation 3.3 is valid are said to be LIH (linear, isotropic, homogeneous) magnetic materials: linear because $M \propto B$, isotropic because $\mathbf{M}$ is in the same direction as $\mathbf{B}$, and homogeneous because χ_B is the same throughout the material. There is an analogy here with LIH dielectric materials, which satisfy $\mathbf{P} = \chi_E \varepsilon_0 \mathbf{E}$ (Equation 2.5). Most diamagnetic and paramagnetic materials can be regarded as LIH materials.

For ferromagnetic materials, the relationship between magnetization and the macroscopic field $\mathbf{B}$ is non-linear and dependent on the previous history of magnetization of the specimen. The large magnetization means that the value of χ_B can be very close to 1, but it is not constant, and not uniquely defined by the field. Because of this, the susceptibility is not a very helpful parameter for ferromagnets. We shall discuss an alternative way of describing the magnetization of ferromagnetic materials in Subsection 3.4.1.

3.3   Magnetization currents

When discussing dielectrics in Chapter 2, we showed that polarization of a dielectric produced a surface charge density $\sigma_b = \mathbf{P} \cdot \widehat{\mathbf{n}}$ and a volume charge density $\rho_b = -\,\text{div}\,\mathbf{P}$. We shall now demonstrate that magnetization of an object generates **magnetization currents** on its surface and throughout its volume.

3.3.1 Surface magnetization currents

Let us consider a long cylindrical rod in which the magnetization is uniform (Figure 3.9a). A disc of thickness δz, with faces that are perpendicular to the direction of magnetization, can be divided into small tiles (Figure 3.9b). If the surface area of a tile is δS, then its volume is $\delta S\,\delta z$ and it has a dipole moment equal to $M\,\delta S\,\delta z$. From Equation 3.1 we deduce that the same dipole moment would be produced by a loop of area δS carrying a current $I = M\,\delta z$.

Figure 3.9 (a) A rod, uniformly magnetized parallel to its axis. (b) A transverse slice from the rod, thickness δz, divided into small tiles. (c) Currents $I = M\,\delta z$ flowing around the edges of each tile generate the same magnetic moment as the uniform magnetization.

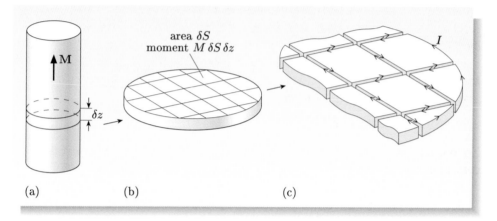

Such current loops can be substituted for every tile in the disc. If the magnetization is uniform, the current is the same for every tile, so at every interior boundary, the oppositely-directed currents from adjacent loops cancel each other out. The array of current loops is therefore equivalent to a single loop, running around the outside of the disc, carrying a current $M\,\delta z$. Thus a uniform magnetization of the slice is equivalent to a current flowing around the surface of the slice, and this is referred to as the **bound surface current**. Dividing by the thickness δz of the disc, we find that the magnitude of the bound surface current *per unit length* of the rod, which we shall denote by i_b, is equal to the magnitude of the magnetization, M. The current flows around the rod in a sense determined by a right-hand rule, so the surface current per unit length can be written as

$$\mathbf{i}_b = \mathbf{M} \times \widehat{\mathbf{n}}, \tag{3.4}$$

where $\widehat{\mathbf{n}}$ is a unit vector in the direction of the outward normal to the surface. Note that $\mathbf{i}_b$ is not a current; it is a vector whose magnitude is the bound current per unit length of surface perpendicular to the direction of current flow and whose direction is the direction of that current flow.

The argument that we used to deduce the existence of the surface current started from the magnetization of small tiles. But we could equally well start from the magnetization of individual atoms that are responsible for the magnetization of these tiles. It is the net effect of the atomic currents that gives rise to the current around the edge of a tile, and hence to the current around the surface of the object. And this is why we refer to this current as a **bound current** — it is the net effect of microscopic currents associated with bound electrons, and no electron is free to travel around the surface of the object. Also, though we derived Equation 3.4 for a situation with uniform magnetization parallel to the surface, it is generally valid as long as $\mathbf{M}$ represents the local magnetization at the point on the surface where the bound surface current is to be determined.

3.3.2 Volume magnetization currents

The discussion in the previous section assumed that the magnetization was uniform, but this is not always the case. If the magnetization depends on position, then we can still divide the material into current loops, but the currents in the loops will vary with the position of the loops. The oppositely-directed currents in adjoining edges of neighbouring loops may not cancel, so there will be a net current density in the volume of the material.

To obtain an expression for the volume current density, consider the two neighbouring current loops shown in Figure 3.10. Loop A lies perpendicular to the z-direction and is centred on the point (x, y, z). It represents part of a slice of thickness δz, and has sides of lengths δx and δy. The z-component of the magnetic moment of this volume element is $M_z(x, y, z)\, \delta x\, \delta y\, \delta z$, so the current that flows around the loop to generate this moment is

$$I(x, y, z) = (\text{magnetic moment})/\text{area} = M_z(x, y, z)\, \delta z.$$

Loop B has the same dimensions but is centred at $(x + \delta x, y, z)$. We can write the current in this loop as

$$I(x + \delta x, y, z) = M_z(x + \delta x, y, z)\, \delta z.$$

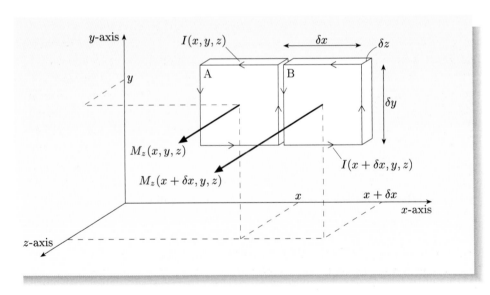

Figure 3.10 Two current loops, A and B, that are equivalent to the magnetic moments of regions with area $\delta x\, \delta y$, thickness δz, centred on points (x, y, z) and $(x + \delta x, y, z)$ in a region of non-uniform magnetization.

The net current in the y-direction at the boundary between the two loops is

$$I(x, y, z) - I(x + \delta x, y, z) = [M_z(x, y, z) - M_z(x + \delta x, y, z)]\, \delta z$$
$$= -(\partial M_z/\partial x)\, \delta x\, \delta z.$$

This current contributes to the y-component of the current density, J_y:

$$J_y = [I(x, y, z) - I(x + \delta x, y, z)]\, /\delta x\, \delta z = -(\partial M_z/\partial x).$$

Thus if M_z depends on x, the current density will have a component in the y-direction.

There will be a second contribution to J_y if the magnetization has a component M_x that depends on the z-coordinate. By considering current loops in a plane perpendicular to the x-axis, and using an argument similar to the one used above, we could show that this second contribution is $J_y = (\partial M_x/\partial z)$. This means that the y-component of the current density is

$$J_y = \left(\frac{\partial M_x}{\partial z} - \frac{\partial M_z}{\partial x} \right) = (\text{curl}\,\mathbf{M})_y.$$

Similar arguments can be used to show that J_x and J_z are equal to the x- and z-components of curl $\mathbf{M}$. So we can represent the magnetization $\mathbf{M}$ of a material by an equivalent **bound current density** $\mathbf{J}_b$ that is related to $\mathbf{M}$ by

$$\mathbf{J}_b = \text{curl}\,\mathbf{M}. \tag{3.5}$$

It is clear from this equation that there will be no bound current density where the magnetization is uniform.

So within the bulk of the rod there is a bound current density given by $\mathbf{J}_b = \text{curl}\,\mathbf{M}$, and at the surface there is a bound surface current per unit length given by $\mathbf{i}_b = \mathbf{M} \times \hat{\mathbf{n}}$, where $\hat{\mathbf{n}}$ is a unit vector in the direction of the outward normal to the surface. $\mathbf{J}_b$ is a current per unit area, where the area is perpendicular to the direction of flow, and $\mathbf{i}_b$ is a current per unit length, where the length is in the plane of the surface and perpendicular to the direction of the surface current. These bound currents are the net effect of the microscopic currents associated with magnetic dipoles.

It is important to note that the relationship $\mathbf{J}_b = \text{curl}\,\mathbf{M}$ implies that the current density must be divergence-free. This can be deduced from the general result, listed with other vector identities inside the back cover, that the divergence of the curl of any vector field is always zero. Thus

$$\text{div}\,\mathbf{J}_b = \text{div}(\text{curl}\,\mathbf{M}) = 0,$$

and this indicates that the bound current always flows in closed loops — there are no sources or sinks of bound current in the material.

Essential skill

Determining bound currents from the magnetization

Worked Example 3.1

The iron block shown in Figure 3.11 has width w, depth d and height h, and its magnetization is given by

$$\mathbf{M} = \left[M_0 + (M_1 - M_0)\frac{y}{w} \right] \mathbf{e}_z.$$

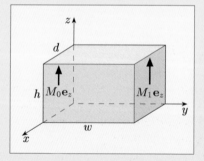

Figure 3.11 A magnetized block of iron. The magnetization is in the z-direction, and its magnitude increases linearly from M_0 on the left face to M_1 on the right face.

(a) Derive an expression for $\mathbf{J}_b$ inside the block.

(b) Derive expressions for $\mathbf{i}_b$ on the left- and right-hand faces of the block.

(c) Hence determine the net magnetization current in the x-direction.

Solution

(a) The symmetry of the problem strongly suggests the use of Cartesian coordinates. The bound current density is $\mathbf{J}_b = \operatorname{curl}\mathbf{M}$, and since $\mathbf{M} = M_z(y)\mathbf{e}_z$, the only non-zero spatial derivative contributing to $\operatorname{curl}\mathbf{M}$ is $\partial M_z/\partial y$. So

$$\mathbf{J}_b = \operatorname{curl}\mathbf{M} = \frac{\partial M_z}{\partial y}\mathbf{e}_x + 0\mathbf{e}_y + 0\mathbf{e}_z = \left(\frac{M_1 - M_0}{w}\right)\mathbf{e}_x.$$

(b) The bound surface current per unit length is $\mathbf{i}_b = \mathbf{M}\times\widehat{\mathbf{n}}$, where $\widehat{\mathbf{n}}$ is the outward normal to the surface. On the left-hand face, $\mathbf{M} = M_0\mathbf{e}_z$ and $\widehat{\mathbf{n}} = -\mathbf{e}_y$, so $\mathbf{i}_b = M_0\mathbf{e}_z\times(-\mathbf{e}_y) = M_0\mathbf{e}_x$. On the right-hand face, $\mathbf{M} = M_1\mathbf{e}_z$ and $\widehat{\mathbf{n}} = \mathbf{e}_y$, so $\mathbf{i}_b = -M_1\mathbf{e}_x$.

(c) $\mathbf{J}_b$ is a current density; it must be multiplied by the cross-sectional area of the block perpendicular to the x-axis, $w\times h$, to obtain a contribution to the total magnetization current in the x-direction. $\mathbf{i}_b$ is a surface current per unit length flowing in the x-direction; to determine the currents on the left- and right-hand faces of the block, values of $\mathbf{i}_b$ for the faces must be multiplied by the length of the faces perpendicular to the current flow, which is the height h of the block. Combining the volume and surface contributions, and noting that the other faces of the block do not contribute to the magnetization surface current in the x-direction, the total magnetization current in the x-direction is

$$wh\left(\frac{M_1 - M_0}{w}\right) + hM_0 - hM_1 = 0.$$

This result should not surprise you; the surface and volume magnetization currents must cancel out, or there would be a steady transport of charge from one side of the block to the other — an impossible state of affairs.

Exercise 3.3 A spherical metal shell has a magnetization vector that is radial and spherically symmetric (i.e. $\mathbf{M}(\mathbf{r}) = M_r(r)\mathbf{e}_r$). By calculating volume and surface magnetization currents, show that this magnetization cannot be detected in the region outside the shell. ◼

3.4 The magnetic intensity H

You have seen that non-uniform magnetization of a material gives rise to a bound current density. This current density generates a magnetic field, in exactly the same way that the free current flowing through a conducting material generates a field. At points that are not on the surface of a material there are no surface currents, and therefore the total current density $\mathbf{J}$ is the sum of the current density due to conduction currents, which we shall call the **free current** density, $\mathbf{J}_f$, and the bound current density $\mathbf{J}_b$. Then according to Ampère's law, the magnetic field is given by

$$\operatorname{curl}\mathbf{B} = \mu_0(\mathbf{J}_f + \mathbf{J}_b).$$

We can use Equation 3.5, $\mathbf{J}_b = \operatorname{curl}\mathbf{M}$, to rewrite this as

$$\operatorname{curl}\mathbf{B} = \mu_0(\mathbf{J}_f + \operatorname{curl}\mathbf{M}).$$

Rearranging this equation to collect the unknown quantities, $\mathbf{B}$ and $\mathbf{J}$, onto the same side, and making use of the fact that the curl operator is linear, we obtain

$$\operatorname{curl}\left(\frac{B}{\mu_0} - M\right) = \mathbf{J}_f. \tag{3.6}$$

We now define a new vector field. The **magnetic intensity** $\mathbf{H}$ is defined by

$$\mathbf{H} = \frac{\mathbf{B}}{\mu_0} - \mathbf{M}. \tag{3.7}$$

This allows us to rewrite Equation 3.6 to give an alternative version of Ampère's law:

$$\operatorname{curl}\mathbf{H} = \mathbf{J}_f. \tag{3.8}$$

Note that the SI unit of $\mathbf{H}$ is $\mathrm{A\,m^{-1}}$, the same as the unit of $\mathbf{M}$.

The definition of $\mathbf{H}$ and this differential version of Ampère's law apply to all materials, and they are not dependent on any assumptions about the relationship between $\mathbf{M}$ and $\mathbf{B}$. The field $\mathbf{H}$ is important because it can be calculated directly from the free current density, without any need to know the bound magnetization currents or the magnetization. However, we still need to determine the field $\mathbf{B}$, because it is $\mathbf{B}$ that determines the forces on moving charges and current-carrying conductors, and we shall show how this can be done in the next subsection.

Equations 3.7 and 3.8 are local relationships, valid at all points for all materials, whether they are LIH materials or not. We can obtain the corresponding integral version of Ampère's law by evaluating the flux of each side of Equation 3.8 over any surface S. Thus

$$\int_S \operatorname{curl}\mathbf{H} \cdot \mathrm{d}\mathbf{S} = \int_S \mathbf{J}_f \cdot \mathrm{d}\mathbf{S}.$$

From the curl theorem, the left-hand side of this equation is equivalent to $\oint_C \mathbf{H} \cdot \mathrm{d}\mathbf{l}$, where the line integral is evaluated around the path C bounding the surface S. The right-hand side is simply the free current I_f passing through the surface S. Thus

$$\oint_C \mathbf{H} \cdot \mathrm{d}\mathbf{l} = \int_S \mathbf{J}_f \cdot \mathrm{d}\mathbf{S} = I_f. \tag{3.9}$$

As usual, the positive direction for the area $\mathrm{d}\mathbf{S}$ is related to the sense of the line integral by a right-hand grip rule. In situations exhibiting a high degree of symmetry, we can use the integral version of Ampère's law to calculate $\mathbf{H}$, even when the magnetization currents are unknown.

To conclude this subsection, here is a warning: the term 'magnetic field' is used to mean both $\mathbf{B}$ and $\mathbf{H}$. This is understandable — both are vector fields and both are 'magnetic' — but can lead to ambiguities and confusion. We have also called $\mathbf{H}$ the 'magnetic intensity', and $\mathbf{B}$ is often called the 'magnetic induction', but these terms are by no means in universal use. Physicists tend to regard $\mathbf{H}$ as an auxiliary quantity — a useful stepping stone to $\mathbf{B}$. When physicists talk about the magnetic field, they are usually referring to **B**. However, **H** is the field that arises directly from the applied free currents, and when engineers talk about the magnetic field, they are likely to mean **H**. Clearly, there is plenty of scope for misunderstanding! However, this can always be avoided by using the symbols; there is no ambiguity if you refer to the field **B** or the field **H**.

Exercise 3.4   A long straight wire of radius a is surrounded by a homogeneous insulating medium. The wire carries a steady current I_f. What is the magnitude of the **H** field at a distance $r > a$ from the axis of the wire? Does your answer depend on whether the surrounding medium is air or glass?   ■

3.4.1   Relative permeability

You have seen in the previous subsection that we can calculate the field **H** from knowledge of the free currents alone — we do not need to know anything about the bound currents. However, there are many situations where we need to determine the field **B** that is produced by free currents that flow through conducting material in the presence of magnetic material. It is **B** that determines the magnetic force on a charged particle ($\mathbf{F} = q\mathbf{v} \times \mathbf{B}$), or the force on an element $\delta \mathbf{l}$ of a current-carrying conductor ($\delta \mathbf{F} = I\,\delta \mathbf{l} \times \mathbf{B}$). **H** is defined as a linear combination of **B** and **M**, so to find **B** we need to make an assumption about the relationship between **B** and **M**. So the next task is to establish a relationship between **B** and **H**, and for diamagnetic and paramagnetic materials this is easily done using the magnetic susceptibility χ_B.

As you have seen in Subsection 3.2.2, the magnetization **M** is related to the field **B** by the equation

$$\mathbf{M} = \chi_B \frac{\mathbf{B}}{\mu_0}, \tag{Eqn 3.3}$$

where the magnetic susceptibility χ_B is independent of **B** for LIH materials. Using this to eliminate **M** from Equation 3.7 gives

$$\mathbf{H} = \frac{\mathbf{B}}{\mu_0} - \chi_B \frac{\mathbf{B}}{\mu_0}.$$

This can be rewritten as

$$\mathbf{B} = \mu \mu_0 \mathbf{H}, \tag{3.10}$$

where we have introduced a new quantity, μ, known as the **relative permeability** of the material, which is related to χ_B by

$$\mu = (1 - \chi_B)^{-1}. \tag{3.11}$$

Like χ_B, μ is a pure number — it has no unit. (Note that some authors define the magnetic susceptibility by the relationship $\mathbf{M} = \chi_H \mathbf{H}$, which leads to $\mu = 1 + \chi_H$. For diamagnetic and paramagnetic materials, μ_B and μ_H are essentially the same, since $\chi_B = \chi_H/(1 + \chi_H) \simeq \chi_H$ when $\chi_H \ll 1$.)

Diamagnetic materials have values of the susceptibility χ_B that are small and negative, so their relative permeabilities are slightly less than unity. In contrast, the susceptibilities of paramagnetic materials are small and positive, so their relative permeabilities are slightly greater than unity. For both types of material,

χ_B and μ are independent of B, so $B \propto H$, and the materials are described as *linear*. Equations 3.3 and 3.10 are true only for *isotropic* materials; for such materials, the susceptibility is the same for all directions of **B**, so **B**, **H** and **M** are all aligned in the same direction. Anisotropic materials are easier to magnetize in some directions than in others, and for such materials **B**, **H** and **M** are not necessarily aligned in the same direction. If μ is independent of position, the material is said to be a *homogeneous* magnetic material.

Ferromagnetic materials have a highly non-linear relationship between B and H. Figure 3.12a shows an example of how the field B inside initially unmagnetized material changes as H is increased. B increases slowly at first, then more rapidly up to the point P, and beyond that the rate of increase slows down until eventually B depends only very weakly on H. The first part of this curve corresponds to shifting the boundaries between domains — those domains that are magnetized in directions close to the direction of **H** grow at the expense of neighbouring domains that are magnetized in opposing directions. At the field corresponding to P, most of the material is magnetized along a direction of easy magnetization that is close to the direction of **H**, and further increase in **B** requires the magnetization to be rotated away from an easy magnetization direction until it eventually lines up with the applied field **H**. The magnetization is then saturated.

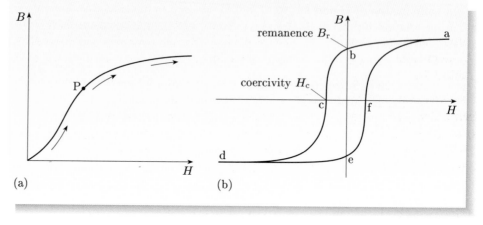

Figure 3.12 (a) Dependence of B on H for an initially unmagnetized ferromagnetic material. (b) Dependence of B on H obtained by applying an alternating **H** field to the same ferromagnetic material as in (a).

If the applied field **H** is now reduced, the curve shown in Figure 3.12a is not retraced. The field B traces out the path abcd shown in Figure 3.12b. At point b there is no applied field ($H = 0$), but there is still a large field B_r in the material, indicating that most of the domains are still magnetized in the direction of the field **H** that produced the saturation magnetization at point a. (This is completely different from diamagnetic and paramagnetic materials, which have B versus H curves that are linear and reversible, so that $B = 0$ when $H = 0$.) The ferromagnetic material is now a 'permanent' magnet, and B_r is known as the **remanence**. Permanent is perhaps a misnomer, because increasing H in the opposite direction, to point c, reduces B to zero. The value of H required to do this is known as the **coercivity**. Increasing H still further in the reverse direction to the original field will lead to saturation of the magnetization in the reverse direction at point d. By sweeping H between the positive and negative limits shown in Figure 3.12b, B traverses the loop abcdefa.

For a ferromagnetic material, the value of μ, as defined by $\mu = B/\mu_0 H$, depends on **H** and on the past magnetization history of the specimen. Equation 3.10 can be used for ferromagnetic materials, but it is necessary to use the appropriate value of μ. Typical values of μ for ferromagnets are 10^3–10^5.

The storage of information on magnetic tapes and disks, and erasing and rewriting that information, is dependent on the properties of B-H loops for magnetic materials. Figure 3.13 shows an image of the surface of a computer hard disk obtained with a magnetic force microscope, which measures the magnetic force on a tiny probe as it is scanned a small distance above the surface. The surface of the disk is coated with a thin layer of ferromagnetic particles. When in operation, the disk spins rapidly and a 'write' head applies a field to a small region containing about 100 particles to magnetize it in one of two opposing directions, corresponding to '0' or '1'. A 'read' head can sense the direction of the magnetization of different regions. The magnetic material requires a large remanence, so that the magnetization corresponding to each bit can be detected reliably, and a coercivity that is large enough that the magnetization is 'permanent' but not so large that it cannot be reversed easily when rewriting data. In 2005, disks could store over $10\,\mathrm{Gb\,cm^{-2}}$ and spin at over $15\,000\,\mathrm{rpm}$, and data could be read and written at over $100\,\mathrm{Mb\,s^{-1}}$, but these values continue to increase rapidly with time.

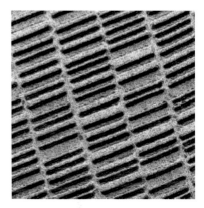

Figure 3.13 The surface of a computer hard disc. The image is about $50\,\mu m$ across.

Exercise 3.5 What happens qualitatively to the magnitude of **B** in a current-carrying solenoid that is initially filled with air when (a) copper, (b) aluminium, and (c) iron, is placed in the interior? (You may need to refer to Table 3.2.)

Exercise 3.6 A long straight wire has radius r_0 and relative permeability $\mu = 2$, and carries a current I_f. The wire is surrounded by air ($\mu_{\mathrm{air}} \simeq 1$). With Ampère's law as your guide, sketch graphs showing how H and B depend on r, the distance from the centre of the wire, from $r = 0$ to $r = 2r_0$. (Assume that the free current density is uniform throughout the wire.) ∎

3.4.2 The Ampère–Maxwell law revisited

Maxwell added an extra term to Ampère's law to show that magnetic fields are generated by changing electric fields as well as by currents, and at the end of the last chapter we showed that in the presence of dielectric material, the Ampère–Maxwell law could be written as

$$\mathrm{curl}\,\mathbf{B} = \mu_0 \left(\mathbf{J}_f + \frac{\partial \mathbf{D}}{\partial t} \right). \tag{Eqn 2.22}$$

However, in deriving this (interim) equation, we did not take account of any bound magnetization current $\mathbf{J}_b$ that may be present. Adding this current density to the right-hand side of the equation, we obtain

$$\mathrm{curl}\,\mathbf{B} = \mu_0 \left(\mathbf{J}_f + \mathbf{J}_b + \frac{\partial \mathbf{D}}{\partial t} \right).$$

We can eliminate $\mathbf{J}_b$ from this equation in exactly the same way that we eliminated it from the differential version of Ampère's law: we use the relationship $\mathbf{J}_b = \text{curl}\,\mathbf{M}$ (Equation 3.5), and combine the $\text{curl}\,\mathbf{M}$ and $\text{curl}\,\mathbf{B}/\mu_0$ terms to obtain

Differential version of Ampère–Maxwell law

$$\text{curl}\,\mathbf{H} = \mathbf{J}_f + \frac{\partial \mathbf{D}}{\partial t}. \tag{3.12}$$

This is the full version of the Ampère–Maxwell law that takes account of dielectric and magnetic properties of materials. As you might expect, there is a corresponding integral version:

Integral version of Ampère–Maxwell law

$$\oint_C \mathbf{H} \cdot \mathrm{dl} = \int_S \left(\mathbf{J}_f + \frac{\partial \mathbf{D}}{\partial t} \right) \cdot \mathrm{d}\mathbf{S}. \tag{3.13}$$

These equations play a major role in the understanding of electromagnetic waves in media.

3.5   Boundary conditions for the $\mathbf{B}$ and $\mathbf{H}$ fields

There are simple **boundary conditions for B and H** at the interface between two different magnetic materials, analogous to the boundary conditions that we derived in Chapter 2 for $\mathbf{D}$ and $\mathbf{E}$ at an interface between dielectric materials.

- Try to recall how the boundary conditions for $\mathbf{D}$ and $\mathbf{E}$ on either side of the boundary between dielectric materials 1 and 2 were derived in Chapter 2.

○ The condition $D_{1\perp} = D_{2\perp}$ was derived by applying the integral version of Gauss's law ($\int_S \mathbf{D} \cdot \mathrm{d}\mathbf{S} = \int_V \rho_f \, \mathrm{d}V$) to a flat pillbox straddling the boundary. The condition $E_{1\parallel} = E_{2\parallel}$ was obtained by applying the relation $\oint_C \mathbf{E} \cdot \mathrm{dl} = 0$, which is valid for electrostatic fields, to a rectangular path straddling the boundary.

We shall derive the conditions obeyed by $\mathbf{B}$ and $\mathbf{H}$ in a similar way, but this time we use the integral version of the no-monopole equation ($\int_S \mathbf{B} \cdot \mathrm{d}\mathbf{S} = 0$) and the integral version of Ampère's law ($\oint_C \mathbf{H} \cdot \mathrm{dl} = I_f$). Note that our use of Ampère's law rather than the Ampère–Maxwell law means that we are not considering time-dependent fields, so the results that we derive will apply to static fields.

Figure 3.14 shows the $\mathbf{B}$ fields in a small region near the boundary between two magnetic materials with relative permeabilities μ_1 and μ_2. We assume that $\mathbf{B}$ is uniform in each of the materials, but that the directions of the fields on either side of the boundary are different.

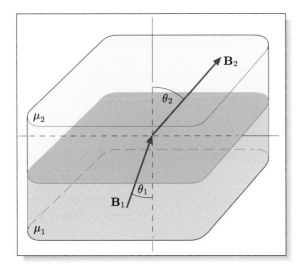
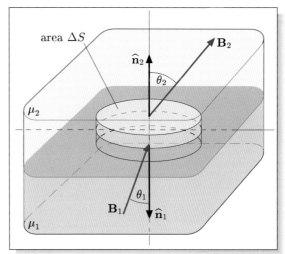

Figure 3.14 Uniform fields $\mathbf{B}_1$ and $\mathbf{B}_2$ on either side of a plane boundary between magnetic materials with relative permeabilities μ_1 and μ_2.

Figure 3.15 Pillbox-shaped surface used to determine a boundary condition on the fields $\mathbf{B}_1$ and $\mathbf{B}_2$ either side of the boundary.

First we apply the no-monopole law to the thin pillbox shown in Figure 3.15. The plane faces of the pillbox lie on either side of the boundary, and both faces are parallel to the boundary. In the limit when the thickness of the pillbox tends to zero, we obtain

$$\int_S \mathbf{B} \cdot \mathrm{d}\mathbf{S} = \mathbf{B}_1 \cdot \widehat{\mathbf{n}}_1 \, \Delta S + \mathbf{B}_2 \cdot \widehat{\mathbf{n}}_2 \, \Delta S = 0,$$

where $\widehat{\mathbf{n}}_1$ and $\widehat{\mathbf{n}}_2$ are outward-pointing unit vectors perpendicular to the plane faces of the pillbox in materials 1 and 2, and ΔS is the area of these faces.

Writing this in terms of the components of $\mathbf{B}$ in the two materials in the $\widehat{\mathbf{n}}_2$ direction, perpendicular to the boundary, $B_{1\perp}$ and $B_{2\perp}$, we obtain $-B_{1\perp} \, \Delta S + B_{2\perp} \, \Delta S = 0$. Hence

Boundary condition for perpendicular field component

$$B_{1\perp} = B_{2\perp}. \tag{3.14}$$

The component of the $\mathbf{B}$ field perpendicular to the boundary remains the same across a boundary.

We shall now use the integral version of Ampère's law, $\oint \mathbf{H} \cdot \mathrm{d}\mathbf{l} = I_\mathrm{f}$ (Equation 3.9), to derive a boundary condition for the $\mathbf{H}$ field. Consider the rectangular path shown in Figure 3.16, which has its two longer sides, $\delta \mathbf{l}_1$ and $\delta \mathbf{l}_2$, parallel to the boundary between materials 1 and 2.

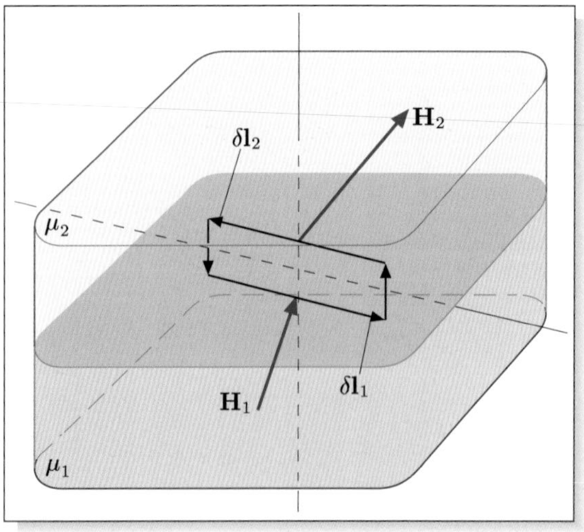

Figure 3.16   Rectangular path used to determine a boundary condition on the fields $\mathbf{H}_1$ and $\mathbf{H}_2$ either side of the boundary between materials with relative permeabilities μ_1 and μ_2.

We take the limit where the lengths of the two shorter sides tend to zero, so that their contribution to the line integral of $\mathbf{H}$ around the loop can be neglected. Since the area of the loop also tends to zero, the current I_f passing through it tends to zero, and the line integral becomes

$$\oint_C \mathbf{H} \cdot d\mathbf{l} = \mathbf{H}_1 \cdot \delta \mathbf{l}_1 + \mathbf{H}_2 \cdot \delta \mathbf{l}_2 = 0.$$

Since $\delta \mathbf{l}_2 = -\delta \mathbf{l}_1$, we can rewrite this as

$$(\mathbf{H}_1 - \mathbf{H}_2) \cdot \delta \mathbf{l}_1 = 0,$$

and this equation indicates that the components of $\mathbf{H}_1$ and $\mathbf{H}_2$ in the direction of $\delta \mathbf{l}_1$ must be equal. Now this result must be true whatever direction parallel to the surface we choose for $\delta \mathbf{l}_1$, and this means that the components of the $\mathbf{H}$ field parallel to the boundary, $H_{1\parallel}$ and $H_{2\parallel}$, must have the same magnitude and be in the same direction:

Boundary condition for parallel field component

$$H_{1\parallel} = H_{2\parallel}. \tag{3.15}$$

The component of the $\mathbf{H}$ field parallel to the boundary remains the same across a boundary.

It is worth reiterating the point that was made about the derivation of the boundary conditions for electrostatic fields. We have assumed a planar boundary, and uniform fields on either side of the boundary. However, whatever the shape of the boundary and whatever the form of the fields on either side of it, we can always make the pillbox in Figure 3.15 and the path in Figure 3.16 small enough so that the boundary enclosed is essentially plane and the fields within them are uniform. Thus the results that we obtained are local relations that apply at any point on any boundary between two magnetic materials.

We have shown that the perpendicular components of $\mathbf{B}$ and the parallel components of $\mathbf{H}$ are continuous across a boundary. These conditions are consequences of the no-monopole law and Ampère's law. To proceed further, we need to assume a form for the relationship between **B** and **H**. As usual, we shall restrict our attention to LIH materials, for which $\mathbf{B} = \mu\mu_0\mathbf{H}$, so **B** and **H** are in the same direction in each material. Using this relationship, we can determine the boundary conditions for the parallel components of **B** and the perpendicular components of **H**, and we can determine the relationship between the angles θ_1 and θ_2 that the fields make with the normal to the interface. The derivations are similar to those for dielectric boundaries in Section 2.5, and lead to the following results:

$$\frac{B_{1\parallel}}{\mu_1} = \frac{B_{2\parallel}}{\mu_2}; \quad \mu_1 H_{1\perp} = \mu_2 H_{2\perp}; \quad \frac{\tan\theta_1}{\tan\theta_2} = \frac{\mu_1}{\mu_2}. \tag{3.16}$$

So the parallel components of **B** and the perpendicular component of **H** are *dis*continuous at surfaces separating media of different relative permeabilities. These discontinuities are very small at interfaces between diamagnetic or paramagnetic materials ($\mu \sim 1$), but large for ferromagnetic materials ($\mu \gg 1$).

The boundary conditions for **B** and **H** find an immediate application in the design of magnetically shielded enclosures. Figure 3.17 shows the magnetic field lines for a spherical shell of iron that has been placed in an originally uniform magnetic field. The relative permeability of iron ($\mu \simeq 1000$) is much greater than that of air ($\mu \simeq 1$), so the field lines in the iron are at much larger angles to the normal to the surface than are the field lines in air, as indicated by Equation 3.16. The field lines are deflected away from the normal to the surface, leaving the central region almost free of field. Some alloys of nickel and iron have relative permeabilities as high as 10^5. These materials are used to construct magnetically shielded rooms (Figure 3.18) in which the tiny magnetic fields due to brain activity can be measured, free from any outside disturbances.

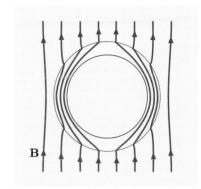

Figure 3.17 Lines of magnetic field **B** in the vicinity of a spherical iron shell.

Figure 3.18 A room constructed from several layers of mu-metal, a nickel–iron alloy, which screen the inside from unwanted fields.

Worked Example 3.2

A thin flat plate, with a large surface area and relative permeability μ_p, is oriented perpendicular to a uniform magnetic field. In the air surrounding the plate, the magnetic field is $\mathbf{B}_0$. Derive expressions for $\mathbf{B}_p$, $\mathbf{H}_p$ and $\mathbf{M}_p$ inside the plate but not close to its perimeter.

Essential skill

Applying the boundary conditions for **H** and **B**

Solution

Outside the plate, the magnetic field is $\mathbf{B}_0$ and the magnetic intensity is $\mathbf{H}_0 = \mathbf{B}_0/\mu_0$ (taking $\mu_{\text{air}} = 1$). To find the fields inside the plate, we use the fact that the perpendicular components of **B** and the parallel components of **H** are continuous across any boundary.

For a point just inside the plate, continuity of $B_\perp$ means that $B_{p\perp} = B_{\text{air}\perp} = B_0$. Continuity of $H_\parallel$ means that $H_{p\parallel} = H_{\text{air}\parallel} = 0$, and hence $B_{p\parallel} = \mu\mu_0 H_{p\parallel} = 0$. Thus $\mathbf{B}_p = \mathbf{B}_0$. The values of $\mathbf{H}_p$ and $\mathbf{M}_p$ then follow from Equations 3.10 and 3.7:

$$\mathbf{H}_p = \mathbf{B}_0/\mu_p\mu_0, \quad \mathbf{M}_p = (\mu_p - 1)\mathbf{B}_0/\mu_p\mu_0.$$

Exercise 3.7   A square plate measuring $1\,\text{m} \times 1\,\text{m} \times 1\,\text{mm}$ is made of mu-metal, a nickel–iron alloy. Assuming that the permeability of the mu-metal is 50 000 in this situation, show that the plate effectively shields the region immediately behind it from static magnetic fields that are at angles of more than about one degree to the normal to its surface.

Exercise 3.8   A long thin cylinder, with relative permeability μ_c, is aligned with its axis parallel to a uniform magnetic field $\mathbf{B}_0$. Estimate the values of $\mathbf{B}_c$, $\mathbf{H}_c$ and $\mathbf{M}_c$ at a point inside the cylinder, near its centre.

Exercise 3.9   Why are the $\mathbf{B}$ field lines shown at the ends of the rods in Figures 3.5 and 3.6 apparently undeviated at the boundaries between a diamagnetic material and air, and between a paramagnetic material and air?   ■

3.6   Electromagnets

Current-carrying coils that are designed to produce magnetic fields are known as **electromagnets** (Figure 3.19). The $\mathbf{H}$ field produced by an electromagnet depends only on the free current in the coil, and is independent of any magnetic materials in the vicinity. However, inserting ferromagnetic material in a coil greatly enhances the $\mathbf{B}$ field, by a factor of μ, which may be 1000 or more. This is why many powerful electromagnets incorporate ferromagnetic material (Figure 3.1b). We shall consider a very simple electromagnet with a ferromagnetic core to illustrate some basic physical principles that arise in magnet design.

Figure 3.19   The world's largest electromagnet at CERN has a similar mass to the Eiffel Tower, and can produce a field of 0.5 T. There are 168 octagonal turns in the coils, which have an average radius of 6.4 m, carry a current of 30 kA and dissipate over 4 MW of power. The magnet will produce a field around the detectors for an experiment that will study collisions between lead nuclei with energy of up to 1150 TeV. Scientists hope to recreate a state of matter thought to have existed in the first few microseconds after the Big Bang, and to find evidence for the existence of the Higgs boson, which theorists have postulated to account for the fact that particles have mass.

Figure 3.20a shows a toroidal coil with N turns that are tightly-wound on magnetic material with relative permeability μ. We first apply Ampère's law to the two circular paths indicated by broken lines, in order to show that the field $\mathbf{H}$ is restricted to the region inside the torus. By symmetry, the magnitude of $\mathbf{H}$ is constant along each of the circular paths, and its direction is everywhere

tangential to the paths. Thus for the path inside the torus,

$$\oint \mathbf{H} \cdot d\mathbf{l} = 2\pi r H = NI,$$

since the path encloses N turns of the coil, each carrying a (free) current I. So

$$H = \frac{NI}{2\pi r}$$

for the circular path within the torus. However, for the circular path outside the torus $H = 0$ because this path encloses no net current. Since $\mathbf{B} = \mu\mu_0\mathbf{H}$, the $\mathbf{B}$ field inside the toroid is

$$B = \frac{\mu\mu_0 NI}{2\pi r}. \tag{3.17}$$

Thus $\mathbf{H}$ does not depend on what magnetic material fills the coil, but $\mathbf{B}$ is greatly enhanced if the coil is filled with ferromagnetic material.

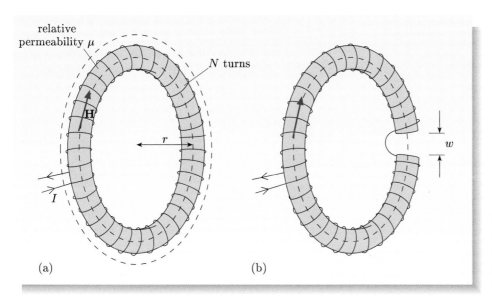

(a)   (b)

Figure 3.20 (a) A toroidal current-carrying coil filled with magnetic material. (b) The same coil with a small air gap in the toroidal magnetic material.

We now create a small gap of width w in the magnetic material (Figure 3.20b). To a first approximation we can assume that the $\mathbf{H}$ field remains tangential to the circular path shown in the figure, and has a constant magnitude, within the material. At the interfaces between the air gap and the material, the normal component of $\mathbf{B}$ must be continuous (Equation 3.14), and since there is no other component of $\mathbf{B}$, we deduce that the magnitude B is the same in the material and in the gap. If the material has a relative permeability μ and we take the relative permeability of air to be unity, then the magnetic intensity inside the material, H_{in}, and in the gap, H_{gap}, are

$$H_{\text{in}} = B/\mu\mu_0 \quad \text{and} \quad H_{\text{gap}} = B/\mu_0.$$

Then applying Ampère's law to the circular path in Figure 3.20b, we find

$$\oint \mathbf{H} \cdot d\mathbf{l} = (2\pi r - w)\frac{B}{\mu\mu_0} + w\frac{B}{\mu_0} = NI,$$

and rearranging this leads to

$$B = \frac{\mu\mu_0 NI}{2\pi r - w + w\mu}. \tag{3.18}$$

Figure 3.21   This electromagnet can lift several tonnes of ferromagnetic material.

For a ferromagnetic material with $\mu \sim 1000$ and w not too small, we need retain only the $w\mu$ term in the denominator, so

$$B \simeq \frac{\mu_0 NI}{w}.$$

This shows that the field in the gap is significantly enhanced compared to its value in an empty coil, $\mu_0 NI/2\pi r$.

We conclude that when (almost) filled with a ferromagnetic material such as iron or steel, the toroidal coil gives a much larger magnetic field **B** than could be obtained from the same coil carrying the same current in the absence of the ferromagnetic core. Figure 3.21 shows an example of how this effect is put to use.

Exercise 3.10   A ferromagnetic ring, mean radius 0.20 m, has a gap of width 1.0 cm cut in it, and 400 turns of wire wound around it. Calculate the coil current required to produce a field $B = 1$ T in the gap. Assume that $H = 1000$ A m^{-1} when $B = 1$ T in this material.   ■

> You can reinforce your understanding of electromagnets by viewing the video sequence *A Grip of Iron* on the course DVD.

Summary of Chapter 3

Section 3.1   A current I flowing in a loop with area ΔS has magnetic dipole moment $\mathbf{m} = |I|\,\Delta\mathbf{S}$, where the direction of the oriented area $\Delta\mathbf{S}$ is related to the current circulation by a right-hand grip rule. Magnetic fields tend to align permanent dipole moments that are present, and they induce dipole moments in all atoms in a sense that opposes the applied field.

Section 3.2   The magnetization **M** is the net magnetic dipole moment per unit volume, and is related to the number density of dipoles n and the average magnetic moment per dipole $\langle\mathbf{m}\rangle$ by $\mathbf{M} = n\langle\mathbf{m}\rangle$. Diamagnetism occurs in materials whose molecules have no permanent magnetic moments. In an applied field, these molecules acquire induced moments in the opposite direction to the applied field, so **M** is in the opposite direction to **B**. Paramagnetism occurs in materials whose molecules have permanent magnetic moments. Alignment of the magnetic dipoles with the field is frustrated by thermal motion and collisions, and the magnetization increases as the ratio of magnetic potential energy to thermal energy, $mB/k_\mathrm{B}T$, increases. The resulting magnetization is parallel to the applied field. In ferromagnetic materials, permanent magnetic dipoles spontaneously align in the same direction within small domains. Application of an increasing external field causes the magnetization of different domains to become progressively more aligned with the field.

The magnetic susceptibility χ_B is defined by $\mathbf{M} = \chi_B\mathbf{B}/\mu_0$, where χ_B is small and negative for diamagnetic materials, and small and positive for paramagnetic materials. For linear, isotropic, homogeneous (LIH) materials, which include most diamagnetic and paramagnetic substances, χ_B is independent of **B**, **M** is in the same direction as **B**, and χ_B is independent of position. For non-linear materials (e.g. ferromagnetic substances), χ_B depends on **B** and on the past history of the specimen.

Section 3.3 The magnetization of the atoms or molecules in a material is equivalent to a bound current density $\mathbf{J}_b = \text{curl}\,\mathbf{M}$, together with a bound surface current per unit length $\mathbf{i}_b = \mathbf{M} \times \hat{\mathbf{n}}$, where $\hat{\mathbf{n}}$ is the outward normal to the surface.

Section 3.4 The magnetic intensity, $\mathbf{H} = \mathbf{B}/\mu_0 - \mathbf{M}$, is related to the free current density $\mathbf{J}_f$ by the versions of Ampère's law used for materials:

$$\text{curl}\,\mathbf{H} = \mathbf{J}_f \quad \text{and} \quad \oint_C \mathbf{H} \cdot d\mathbf{l} = \int_S \mathbf{J}_f \cdot d\mathbf{S} = I_f.$$

The relative permeability μ of a material is defined by $\mathbf{B} = \mu\mu_0\mathbf{H}$. For LIH materials, μ is independent of $\mathbf{H}$ and position. For ferromagnetic materials, μ depends on H.

The Ampère–Maxwell law can also be expressed in terms of $\mathbf{H}$:

$$\text{curl}\,\mathbf{H} = \mathbf{J}_f + \frac{\partial \mathbf{D}}{\partial t} \quad \text{and} \quad \oint_C \mathbf{H} \cdot d\mathbf{l} = \int_S \left(\mathbf{J}_f + \frac{\partial \mathbf{D}}{\partial t} \right) \cdot d\mathbf{S}.$$

Section 3.5 At the interface between two materials, 1 and 2, the fields $\mathbf{B}$ and $\mathbf{H}$ satisfy the boundary conditions $B_{1\perp} = B_{2\perp}$ and $H_{1\parallel} = H_{2\parallel}$.

Section 3.6 In an electromagnet, an $\mathbf{H}$ field is generated by passing a current through a coil. The $\mathbf{H}$ field is concentrated in the region inside the coil. The $\mathbf{B}$ field is amplified by (almost) filling the coil with a ferromagnetic core. Since the normal component of $\mathbf{B}$ is continuous, a large $\mathbf{B}$ field is produced in the air outside the ends of the ferromagnetic material.

Achievements from Chapter 3

After studying this chapter you should be able to do the following.

3.1 Explain the meanings of the newly defined (emboldened) terms and symbols, and use them appropriately.

3.2 Describe the microscopic origins of diamagnetism, paramagnetism and ferromagnetism.

3.3 Explain how the magnetization of a material can be represented by a surface current density and a volume current density, recall how these current densities are related to the magnetization, and calculate these current densities when the magnetization is specified.

3.4 Recall the relationship between $\mathbf{H}$, $\mathbf{B}$ and $\mathbf{M}$, and make use of these relationships to solve problems.

3.5 Derive, recall and apply the differential and integral versions of Ampère's law that involve the field $\mathbf{H}$.

3.6 Derive and recall the boundary conditions on $\mathbf{B}$ and $\mathbf{H}$ at a boundary between two materials, and use these boundary conditions to solve problems.

3.7 Recall the Ampère–Maxwell law for dielectric and magnetic materials.

3.8 Explain how an electromagnet generates a large $\mathbf{B}$ field, and use relationships between $\mathbf{B}$ and other parameters for an electromagnet to solve problems.

Chapter 4   Electrostatic field calculations

Calculations of the electrostatic potential and electric field are of considerable practical importance. Engineers and scientists need to do such calculations when developing new silicon chips (Figures 2.2 and 2.15) or display panels for plasma screens (Figure 4.1a). On a somewhat larger scale, such calculations are done when designing the electron gun for an electron microscope (Figure 3 of the Introduction), or when investigating the possibility of electrical breakdown around high-voltage overhead power lines (Figure 4.1b).

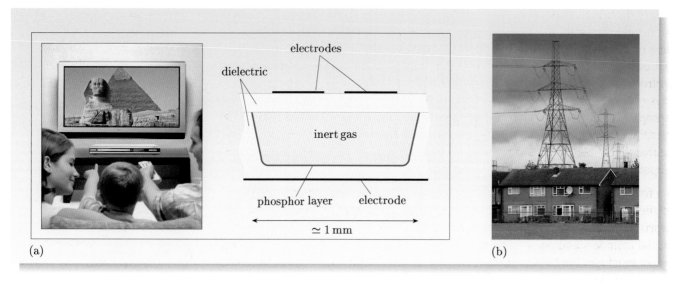

(a)   (b)

Figure 4.1   (a) Plasma display panel, and cross-section through one cell of the display. A voltage difference between the two electrodes at the top causes breakdown of the gas in the cell. The resulting plasma emits ultraviolet photons, which strike the phosphor layer and cause emission of red, green or blue photons, depending on the cell. By computing the potential, the field between the electrodes can be determined, and the voltage difference required for breakdown calculated. (b) Engineers compute the potential and field around power lines to ensure that there is minimal risk of electrical discharges.

You should already be familiar with a number of methods of determining electrostatic fields and potentials. One method is to use the Coulomb field of a point charge as a building block: the field produced by many point charges, or a continuous distribution of charge, is the vector sum of the fields due to each of the constituent point charges. However, it is often more straightforward to first determine the potential V due to the charges, again by adding the Coulomb potentials of the constituent point charges, and then calculating the field $\mathbf{E}$ using the relationship $\mathbf{E} = -\operatorname{grad} V$. The advantage of starting with the potential is that the summation involves scalar quantities, rather than the vector quantities involved when electric fields are added. Another familiar method for determining electric fields involves using the integral version of Gauss's law, which relates the electric flux across a closed surface to the charge contained within that surface. However, you will be aware that this method is restricted to situations with high degrees of symmetry. We shall briefly review these methods in Section 4.1.

Calculating electrostatic fields and potentials from their sources — electric charges — has a number of limitations. Consider, for example, the situation shown in Figure 4.2a, where two conducting spheres have net charges of $+Q$ and $-Q$. If these charges were uniformly distributed over the surfaces of each sphere, then it would be possible to calculate the potential (or field) at any point P by subdividing the surfaces of the spheres into many small elements and adding the potentials (or fields) produced at P by each of the elements. However, the forces between the charges on the spheres lead to non-uniform surface distributions, as indicated in Figure 4.2a, and these distributions can be determined only when the field or potential in the surrounding region is known. The potential cannot be calculated if only the net charge on each sphere is known.

The more important limitation is that there are very many situations where known potentials are applied to conductors, and nothing is known about the charge on the conductors. For example, the electron gun in Figure 4.2b has three electrodes, each maintained at a different potential. Each electrode will have a net charge, but neither the net charges nor their distribution over the electrodes are known, so they cannot be used to determine the electric field in the region traversed by the electron beam.

Clearly there is a need to be able to determine potentials and fields for situations like the electron gun, where it is the potentials of the conductors that are specified. Most of this chapter will discuss how this type of problem can be solved. In Section 4.2 we derive a second-order differential equation that is satisfied by the electrostatic potential, and in the remainder of the chapter we discuss a number of ways of finding solutions to this equation. Acceptable solutions must match appropriate boundary conditions for a particular situation, for example, the potential must match the known potentials on conducting surfaces, and you will see that there is always a unique solution that satisfies the differential equation for the potential *and* meets the specified boundary conditions.

In a few cases with high symmetry it is possible to solve the differential equation satisfied by the potential by direct integration, and you will probably not be surprised that we illustrate this method with familiar examples involving spheres, coaxial cylinders and planes. We also discuss a couple of other methods of finding the potential and the field. However, most practical problems are not soluble by analytic methods, and it is necessary to use numerical methods to find the electrostatic potential, implemented on a computer. We shall conclude this chapter by outlining one method for doing this.

Throughout this chapter we shall be assuming that the electrostatic field is conservative, so that the field and potential are related by $\mathbf{E} = -\operatorname{grad} V$. This is always true for electrostatic problems. Non-conservative fields produced by changing magnetic fields cannot be calculated by the methods described here.

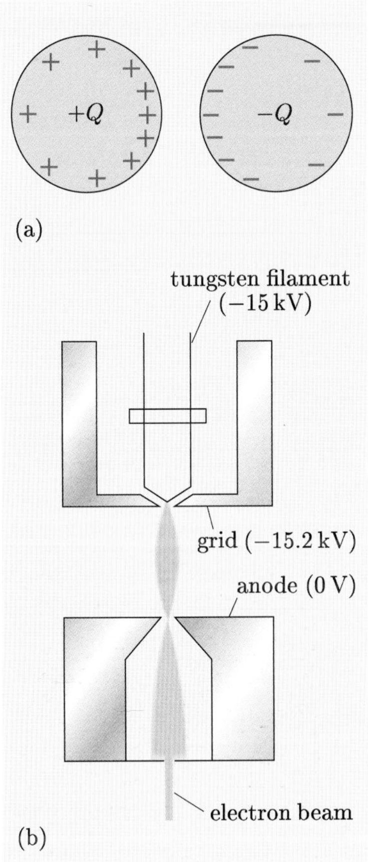

(a)

(b)

Figure 4.2 (a) Conducting spheres with net charges $+Q$ and $-Q$. (b) Electron gun for an electron microscope, showing three electrodes maintained at different potentials.

4.1 Coulomb's law and Gauss's law revisited

4.1.1 Using Coulomb's law to calculate electric fields

Calculating the electric field for a known charge distribution is simple in principle. For a collection of point charges $q_1, q_2, \ldots$ at positions $\mathbf{r}_1, \mathbf{r}_2, \ldots$ in a vacuum, the field at position $\mathbf{r}$ is the superposition of the fields due to the individual charges, each given by Coulomb's law:

$$\mathbf{E}(\mathbf{r}) = \frac{1}{4\pi\varepsilon_0} \sum_i \frac{q_i(\mathbf{r} - \mathbf{r}_i)}{|\mathbf{r} - \mathbf{r}_i|^3}. \tag{4.1}$$

This is a vector sum, so each term has to be decomposed into three components, then the contributions from each component are separately summed, and the three resultant components are recombined to obtain the resultant field.

We have denoted the volume element by $\delta\tau$ here (rather than δV) to avoid any confusion with the use of the symbol V for the electrostatic potential.

A more common situation is a continuous charge distribution described by a charge density $\rho(\mathbf{r})$. Not surprisingly, the field in this situation is given by an expression analogous to Equation 4.1, but with the point charges q_i replaced by the charge distribution $\rho(\mathbf{r})$ and the summation replaced by integration. If we subdivide the charge distribution into small volumes $\delta\tau_i$ within which the charge density $\rho(\mathbf{r}_i)$ is essentially constant, then the field due to all of the elements is

$$\mathbf{E}(\mathbf{r}) = \frac{1}{4\pi\varepsilon_0} \sum_i \frac{\rho(\mathbf{r}_i)\,\delta\tau_i\,(\mathbf{r} - \mathbf{r}_i)}{|\mathbf{r} - \mathbf{r}_i|^3}.$$

In the limit when the region where the charge exists is subdivided into an infinite number of infinitesimal volume elements, we can replace the summation by integration:

$$\mathbf{E}(\mathbf{r}) = \frac{1}{4\pi\varepsilon_0} \int \frac{\rho(\mathbf{r}')(\mathbf{r} - \mathbf{r}')}{|\mathbf{r} - \mathbf{r}'|^3}\,\mathrm{d}\tau'. \tag{4.2}$$

Note that we use primes with the coordinates (and volumes) associated with the charge distribution to distinguish them from the coordinates of the points where the fields and potentials are measured. Thus in Equation 4.2, $\mathbf{r}'$ (pronounced 'are prime') is the position of the volume element $\mathrm{d}\tau'$ within which the charge density is $\rho(\mathbf{r}')$, $\mathbf{r}$ is the position at which the field is evaluated, and $(\mathbf{r} - \mathbf{r}')$ is a vector from the charge to the field point. Again, because the integrand is a vector, it must be decomposed into three components, which are each integrated separately and then recombined to obtain the resultant field.

The complications associated with summing or integrating vectors mean that it is often more straightforward to calculate the electrostatic potential V. For a set of point charges, the potential $V(\mathbf{r})$ is

$$V(\mathbf{r}) = \frac{1}{4\pi\varepsilon_0} \sum_i \frac{q_i}{|\mathbf{r} - \mathbf{r}_i|}, \tag{4.3}$$

and for a charge density $\rho(\mathbf{r}')$ the potential is

$$V(\mathbf{r}) = \frac{1}{4\pi\varepsilon_0} \int \frac{\rho(\mathbf{r}')}{|\mathbf{r} - \mathbf{r}'|}\,\mathrm{d}\tau', \tag{4.4}$$

where the potential is usually taken to be zero at an infinite distance from the charges. In general, V is simpler to calculate than $\mathbf{E}$ because it involves a sum or integral of scalar terms. This means that if you want to calculate the electric field, it is often preferable to calculate the potential first and then calculate the field using the electrostatic relationship,

$$\mathbf{E} = -\operatorname{grad} V, \tag{4.5}$$

rather than evaluating the field directly.

4.1.2   Using Gauss's law to calculate electric fields

In Book 1, Gauss's law was used to calculate the electric field due to various charge distributions that have a high degree of symmetry. Figure 4.3 shows how this is done for distributions with spherical, cylindrical and planar symmetry. In each case the symmetry of the electric field can be deduced from the symmetry of the charge distribution. A Gaussian surface can then be chosen such that the field has constant magnitude on the surface, and its direction is perpendicular to the surface everywhere, except possibly for some parts of the surface where the field is parallel to the surface. The integral version of Gauss's law equates the electric flux through the Gaussian surface to the total charge enclosed divided by the permittivity of free space, and this allows the electric field to be determined.

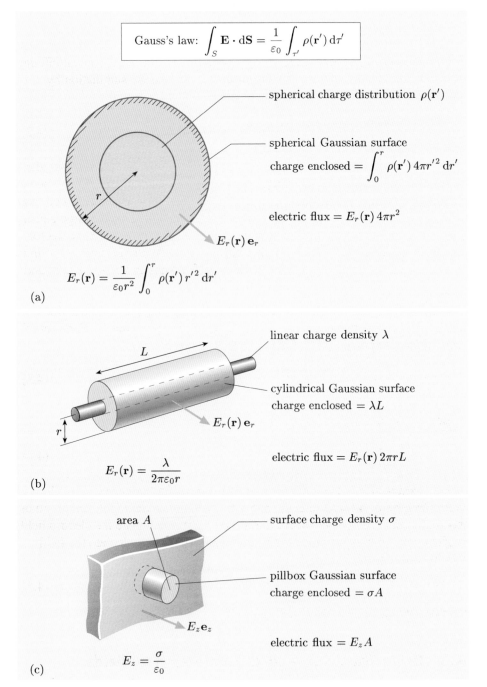

Gauss's law: $\displaystyle\int_S \mathbf{E} \cdot d\mathbf{S} = \frac{1}{\varepsilon_0} \int_{\tau'} \rho(\mathbf{r}')\, d\tau'$

spherical charge distribution $\rho(\mathbf{r}')$

spherical Gaussian surface

charge enclosed $= \displaystyle\int_0^r \rho(\mathbf{r}')\, 4\pi r'^2 \, dr'$

electric flux $= E_r(\mathbf{r})\, 4\pi r^2$

$E_r(\mathbf{r}) \mathbf{e}_r$

$E_r(\mathbf{r}) = \dfrac{1}{\varepsilon_0 r^2} \displaystyle\int_0^r \rho(\mathbf{r}')\, r'^2 \, dr'$

(a)

linear charge density λ

cylindrical Gaussian surface

charge enclosed $= \lambda L$

$E_r(\mathbf{r}) \mathbf{e}_r$

electric flux $= E_r(\mathbf{r})\, 2\pi r L$

$E_r(\mathbf{r}) = \dfrac{\lambda}{2\pi\varepsilon_0 r}$

(b)

area A

surface charge density σ

pillbox Gaussian surface

charge enclosed $= \sigma A$

$E_z \mathbf{e}_z$

electric flux $= E_z A$

$E_z = \dfrac{\sigma}{\varepsilon_0}$

(c)

Figure 4.3   Using Gauss's law to determine the electric field produced by charge distributions with high symmetry: (a) spherical charge distribution, (b) cylindrical charge distribution, (c) planar charge distribution.

This form of Gauss's law is not very useful in the presence of dielectric materials, because the charge density in the integral includes both the free charge and the bound polarization charge on dielectric materials that are present, and we cannot specify the polarization charges until we know the potential or the field. However, as you saw in Chapter 2, we can get around this problem by using the electric displacement $\mathbf{D}$.

Gauss's law can be expressed in terms of $\mathbf{D}$ and the free charge density ρ_f as

$$\int_S \mathbf{D} \cdot d\mathbf{S} = \int_{\tau'} \rho_f \, d\tau',$$

where τ' is the volume enclosed by the surface S. If we consider only LIH dielectric materials, then the electric field can be obtained from the relationship

$$\mathbf{D} = \varepsilon\varepsilon_0 \mathbf{E},$$

where the relative permittivity ε is a constant.

For the Gauss's law method to be feasible, you must be able to identify a Gaussian surface over which the field strength is constant and the field direction is everywhere perpendicular or parallel to the surface. This is a very restrictive condition, which limits the use of Gauss's law for calculating electric fields to situations with symmetries similar to those shown in Figure 4.3. In the next section we shall show how the limitations of the methods of determining potentials and fields based on direct use of Coulomb's law or Gauss's law can be overcome.

4.2 Poisson's and Laplace's equations

The important equations for the electrostatic potential that we shall derive in this section involve an operator, the Laplacian ∇^2, which appears in many branches of physics and mathematics. We shall explain the meaning of this operator before discussing its role in electrostatics.

4.2.1 The Laplacian operator

∇^2 is pronounced 'del-squared', or sometimes 'nabla-squared'.

The **Laplacian operator**, ∇^2, is the name and notation given to the combination of operators div grad. Thus

$$\nabla^2 f \equiv \operatorname{div}(\operatorname{grad} f). \tag{4.6}$$

If we use Cartesian coordinates,

$$
\begin{aligned}
\nabla^2 f = \operatorname{div}(\operatorname{grad} f) &= \frac{\partial}{\partial x}(\operatorname{grad} f)_x + \frac{\partial}{\partial y}(\operatorname{grad} f)_y + \frac{\partial}{\partial z}(\operatorname{grad} f)_z \\
&= \frac{\partial}{\partial x}\left(\frac{\partial f}{\partial x}\right) + \frac{\partial}{\partial y}\left(\frac{\partial f}{\partial y}\right) + \frac{\partial}{\partial z}\left(\frac{\partial f}{\partial z}\right) \\
&= \frac{\partial^2 f}{\partial x^2} + \frac{\partial^2 f}{\partial y^2} + \frac{\partial^2 f}{\partial z^2} \\
&= \left(\frac{\partial^2}{\partial x^2} + \frac{\partial^2}{\partial y^2} + \frac{\partial^2}{\partial z^2}\right) f.
\end{aligned}
$$

So, in Cartesian coordinates,

$$\nabla^2 \equiv \text{div grad} \equiv \frac{\partial^2}{\partial x^2} + \frac{\partial^2}{\partial y^2} + \frac{\partial^2}{\partial z^2}. \tag{4.7}$$

The symbol ∇^2 follows from the use of the ∇ symbol ('del') as an alternative way to represent the div and grad operators. We have

$$\text{div } \mathbf{F} \equiv \nabla \cdot \mathbf{F} \quad \text{and} \quad \text{grad } f \equiv \nabla f,$$

so $\quad \text{div}(\text{grad } f) \equiv \nabla \cdot \nabla f \equiv \nabla^2 f.$

We use div $\mathbf{F}$, grad f and curl $\mathbf{F}$ in this book to represent the divergence, gradient and curl operators, rather than $\nabla \cdot \mathbf{F}$, ∇f and $\nabla \times \mathbf{F}$, but we shall use the more compact ∇^2 notation to represent the Laplacian.

Just as the forms of the expressions for div, grad and curl are different for each coordinate system, the expressions for $\nabla^2 \equiv \text{div grad}$ are different in Cartesian, spherical and cylindrical coordinates. We showed how the expression for ∇^2 in Cartesian coordinates (Equation 4.7) is derived, but we shall not attempt to derive the equivalent expressions for spherical and cylindrical coordinates. These expressions are listed inside the back cover; there is no need to remember them — you can look them up when you need to use them. For the symmetrical situations considered in this book, the expressions for ∇^2 often reduce to simpler forms. Thus for a problem with spherical symmetry, the Laplacian reduces to

$$\nabla^2 = \frac{1}{r^2} \frac{d}{dr} \left(r^2 \frac{d}{dr} \right),$$

since there is no dependence on θ or ϕ.

The Laplacian operator can also be applied to a vector field. In Cartesian coordinates, its operation on a vector field is defined by

$$\nabla^2 \mathbf{F} = \nabla^2 F_x \, \mathbf{e}_x + \nabla^2 F_y \, \mathbf{e}_y + \nabla^2 F_z \, \mathbf{e}_z.$$

The expressions for $\nabla^2 \mathbf{F}$ in spherical and cylindrical coordinates are more complicated, and we shall not be concerned with them in this book.

The Laplacian operator ∇^2

The Laplacian operator ∇^2 acting on a scalar field f is defined by

$$\nabla^2 f = \text{div}(\text{grad } f). \tag{Eqn 4.6}$$

In Cartesian coordinates,

$$\nabla^2 = \frac{\partial^2}{\partial x^2} + \frac{\partial^2}{\partial y^2} + \frac{\partial^2}{\partial z^2}. \tag{Eqn 4.7}$$

4.2.2 Deriving Poisson's and Laplace's equations

The differential version of Gauss's law,

$$\text{div } \mathbf{E} = \frac{1}{\varepsilon_0} \rho,$$

is a good starting point for tackling problems in which we want to determine the electric field and there is not a high degree of symmetry. Since we are considering *electrostatic* problems, the field $\mathbf{E}$ and potential V are related by

$$\mathbf{E} = -\operatorname{grad} V, \tag{Eqn 4.5}$$

and substituting this expression for $\mathbf{E}$ into the equation for Gauss's law, we obtain

$$\operatorname{div} \mathbf{E} = -\operatorname{div}(\operatorname{grad} V) = \frac{1}{\varepsilon_0}\rho. \tag{4.8}$$

We can use the ∇^2 operator to rewrite Equation 4.8 as

$$\nabla^2 V = -\frac{1}{\varepsilon_0}\rho, \tag{4.9}$$

and this is known as *Poisson's equation*. To determine the electrostatic potential, we need to solve this second-order partial differential equation. Once we have a solution for V, we can use Equation 4.5 to find the electric field $\mathbf{E}$.

You have already met the general solution to Poisson's equation: it is given by Equation 4.4. This solution is not usually very useful, however, because the charge density in the integral includes both the free charge and the polarization charge on dielectric materials that are present, and we cannot specify the polarization charges until we know the potential or the field. However, as you saw in Chapter 2, we can get around this problem by using the electric displacement $\mathbf{D}$.

Gauss's law can be written in terms of $\mathbf{D}$ and the free charge density ρ_f as

$$\operatorname{div} \mathbf{D} = \rho_f.$$

For LIH dielectric materials, $\mathbf{D} = \varepsilon\varepsilon_0\mathbf{E}$, so

$$\operatorname{div} \mathbf{E} = \frac{1}{\varepsilon\varepsilon_0}\rho_f. \tag{4.10}$$

Substituting $\mathbf{E} = -\operatorname{grad} V$, and recalling that $\operatorname{div}\operatorname{grad} \equiv \nabla^2$, we obtain the form of **Poisson's equation** that relates the potential to the free charge:

$$\nabla^2 V = -\frac{1}{\varepsilon\varepsilon_0}\rho_f. \tag{4.11}$$

In the absence of any free charge, Equation 4.11 reduces to

$$\nabla^2 V = 0, \tag{4.12}$$

which is known as **Laplace's equation**.

Poisson's and Laplace's equations in electrostatics

The electrostatic potential V satisfies Poisson's equation,

$$\nabla^2 V = -\frac{1}{\varepsilon\varepsilon_0}\rho_f. \tag{Eqn 4.11}$$

If the free charge density ρ_f is zero, then this reduces to Laplace's equation,

$$\nabla^2 V = 0. \tag{Eqn 4.12}$$

Poisson's equation and Laplace's equation are valid for all coordinate systems. However, you must remember to use the appropriate form of the Laplacian operator ∇^2, as listed inside the back cover for easy reference.

Poisson's equation can be used in two ways. If you know the form of the potential $V(\mathbf{r})$, then you can use the equation to deduce the distribution of free charge $\rho_f(\mathbf{r})$. Alternatively, and of more importance, if the distribution of free charge is known, and you also know the boundary conditions for the potential in the region of interest, then Poisson's equation can be solved to obtain the potential function. In particular, in regions outside conductors where there is no free charge, Laplace's equation can be solved without the need for any information about the distribution of free charge on the conductors. We give below an example of how $\rho_f(\mathbf{r})$ is calculated from $V(\mathbf{r})$. In the following sections we shall discuss the reverse procedure.

Worked Example 4.1

The electrostatic potential in a dielectric material with relative permittivity ε is given by

$$V(x, y, z) = a(x^3 - 3xy^2),$$

where a is a constant. What is the free charge density in this region?

Solution

The free charge density ρ_f is related to the potential by Poisson's equation, $\nabla^2 V = -\rho_f/\varepsilon\varepsilon_0$. Since $V(x, y, z) = a(x^3 - 3xy^2)$, we have

$$\frac{\partial V}{\partial x} = a(3x^2 - 3y^2), \quad \frac{\partial V}{\partial y} = -6axy, \quad \frac{\partial V}{\partial z} = 0,$$

and

$$\frac{\partial^2 V}{\partial x^2} = 6ax, \quad \frac{\partial^2 V}{\partial y^2} = -6ax, \quad \frac{\partial^2 V}{\partial z^2} = 0.$$

Therefore

$$\nabla^2 V = \frac{\partial^2 V}{\partial x^2} + \frac{\partial^2 V}{\partial y^2} + \frac{\partial^2 V}{\partial z^2} = 6ax - 6ax + 0 = 0,$$

so $\rho_f = -\varepsilon\varepsilon_0 \nabla^2 V = 0$, i.e. there is no free charge in this region.

Essential skill

Using Poisson's equation to determine the free charge density

Exercise 4.1   The electrostatic potential in a region is

$$V(\mathbf{r}) = A\mathrm{e}^{-r/a},$$

where r is the distance from the origin. What is the free charge density ρ_f in this region, assuming that the space is filled with a material with relative permittivity ε? ■

4.2.3   Solving Laplace's equation by direct integration

In problems with high symmetry, Poisson's equation and Laplace's equation can be solved by direct integration. In other cases, numerical methods have to be adopted, and a suitable method will be outlined in Section 4.4. But in all cases, regardless of how we solve the differential equation in a given region, the values of V at the boundary of the region are of central importance. Indeed, we shall see in the next section that if V is specified at all points on the boundary, then there exists a *unique* value of V at each point in the region enclosed by the boundary. The following example shows the general approach to solving Laplace's equation by direct integration.

Essential skill

Solving Laplace's equation by direct integration

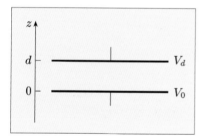

Figure 4.4   Parallel plate capacitor.

Worked Example 4.2

A capacitor has two parallel plates, separation d, with a vacuum between them. One plate is at a potential V_0, the other at V_d. Find an expression for the electrostatic potential $V(\mathbf{r})$ between the plates.

Solution

We shall assume that the linear dimensions of the plates are large compared with their spacing, so that we have planar symmetry, and we shall therefore use Cartesian coordinates. The charge density is zero between the plates of the capacitor, so the electrostatic potential V satisfies Laplace's equation:

$$\frac{\partial^2 V}{\partial x^2} + \frac{\partial^2 V}{\partial y^2} + \frac{\partial^2 V}{\partial z^2} = 0.$$

We choose the z-axis to be perpendicular to the plates of the capacitor (see Figure 4.4), and the planar symmetry then means that the electrostatic potential has no x- or y-dependence, i.e. $V = V(z)$. So, between the plates, Laplace's equation simplifies to

$$\frac{\mathrm{d}^2 V}{\mathrm{d}z^2} = 0.$$

We can solve this equation by direct integration to give

$$\frac{\mathrm{d}V}{\mathrm{d}z} = A$$

and

$$V(z) = Az + B, \tag{4.13}$$

where A and B are constants of integration. This is the general solution of the differential equation. However, to determine V, we need to know the constants A and B, and these are determined by the boundary conditions on V. In this case, the boundaries of the region between the plates are the plates themselves at $z = 0$ and $z = d$, at which the potentials are $V(0) = V_0$ and $V(d) = V_d$.

Using the boundary condition $V(0) = V_0$ in Equation 4.13, we have

$$V_0 = B.$$

The second boundary condition, $V(d) = V_d$, gives

$$V_d = Ad + B,$$

and substituting $B = V_0$ in this equation leads to

$$A = \frac{V_d - V_0}{d}.$$

So the particular solution of Laplace's equation for the region between the plates is

$$V(z) = V_0 + \left(\frac{V_d - V_0}{d}\right) z. \qquad (4.14)$$

Exercise 4.2   Find the electrostatic field $\mathbf{E}$ between the plates of a parallel plate capacitor, given that the electrostatic potential $V(x)$ is given by Equation 4.14.   ■

Using the simplifying assumption that the plates of the capacitor are (effectively) infinite in extent, we have solved Laplace's equation to show that the electrostatic field lines are as shown in Figure 4.5a. These familiar results could have been obtained by more straightforward methods. The true power of Laplace's equation is revealed only in less simple cases.

For finite plates, the field lines are as shown in Figure 4.5b. There are considerable differences between the field lines in the neighbourhood of the edges of the plates, as you might expect. These differences are called *edge effects*, and in order to calculate the field in these regions you would need to use the numerical methods developed later in this chapter.

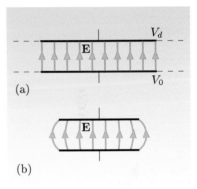

Figure 4.5   Electric field lines for a parallel plate capacitor with (a) infinite width plates, (b) finite width plates.

Worked Example 4.3

A long coaxial cable has an inner conductor with radius r_1 and an outer conductor with internal radius r_2, as shown in Figure 4.6. The region between the two conductors is filled with an LIH dielectric material of relative permittivity ε. The inner conductor is at potential V_1, and the outer conductor is at potential V_2.

Essential skill

Solving Laplace's equation by direct integration

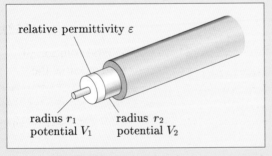

Figure 4.6   A coaxial cable.

(a)   Find an expression for the electrostatic potential in the region between the two conductors.

(b)   Hence find the electric field in this region.

Solution

(a) In the dielectric there is no free charge density, so the electrostatic potential V satisfies Laplace's equation,

$$\nabla^2 V = 0.$$

Because of the cylindrical symmetry of the situation, we use cylindrical coordinates, with the z-axis along the axis of the cable. We therefore need to use the form of Laplace's equation for cylindrical coordinates, and this is given for reference inside the back cover:

$$\frac{1}{r} \frac{\partial}{\partial r} \left(r \frac{\partial V}{\partial r} \right) + \frac{1}{r^2} \frac{\partial^2 V}{\partial \phi^2} + \frac{\partial^2 V}{\partial z^2} = 0.$$

The cylindrical symmetry means that the electrostatic potential V has no dependence on ϕ, and, assuming that the cable is infinitely long so that there are no end effects, the potential V also has no dependence on z. So $V = V(r)$, and Laplace's equation reduces to the differential equation

$$\frac{1}{r} \frac{d}{dr} \left(r \frac{dV}{dr} \right) = 0.$$

Integrating once, we obtain

$$r \frac{dV}{dr} = A, \quad \text{or} \quad \frac{dV}{dr} = \frac{A}{r},$$

where A is a constant of integration. Integrating again, we obtain the general solution

$$V(r) = A \ln r + B,$$

where B is a second constant of integration. The two constants are found by using the boundary conditions $V(r_1) = V_1$ and $V(r_2) = V_2$. Thus

$$V_1 = A \ln r_1 + B,$$

$$V_2 = A \ln r_2 + B.$$

Solving these two simultaneous equations for A and B gives

$$A = \frac{V_2 - V_1}{\ln r_2 - \ln r_1} = \frac{V_2 - V_1}{\ln(r_2/r_1)},$$

$$B = \frac{V_1 \ln r_2 - V_2 \ln r_1}{\ln(r_2/r_1)}.$$

Hence

$$\begin{aligned} V(r) &= \frac{V_2 - V_1}{\ln(r_2/r_1)} \ln r + \frac{V_1 \ln r_2 - V_2 \ln r_1}{\ln(r_2/r_1)} \\ &= \frac{V_2 \ln(r/r_1) - V_1 \ln(r/r_2)}{\ln(r_2/r_1)}. \end{aligned}$$

(b) We find the electrostatic field $\mathbf{E}$ by using $\mathbf{E} = -\operatorname{grad} V$. The expression for $\operatorname{grad} V$ in cylindrical coordinates (from the list inside the back cover) is

$$\mathbf{E} = -\frac{\partial V}{\partial r} \mathbf{e}_r - \frac{1}{r} \frac{\partial V}{\partial \phi} \mathbf{e}_\phi - \frac{\partial V}{\partial z} \mathbf{e}_z,$$

and as $V = V(r)$ has no dependence on ϕ or z,

$$\mathbf{E} = -\frac{\mathrm{d}V}{\mathrm{d}r}\,\mathbf{e}_r.$$

Substituting the expression for $V(r)$ from part (a), we obtain

$$\mathbf{E} = -\frac{V_2 - V_1}{\ln(r_2/r_1)}\frac{1}{r}\,\mathbf{e}_r.$$

Note that this result does not depend on the permittivity of the dielectric. This is because the boundary conditions fix the potentials of the two conductors, and therefore the field $\mathbf{E}(r)$ between them. If the charges on the conductors had been specified instead, then the field strength $E(r)$ in the dielectric would be proportional to ε^{-1}, as you saw in Chapter 2.

Exercise 4.3   A capacitor consists of two concentric conducting spherical surfaces of radii r_1 and r_2 (where $r_2 > r_1$). The inner sphere is maintained at a potential V_1, and the outer sphere at a potential V_2. There is a vacuum between the two spheres.

(a) Find an expression for the electrostatic potential between the two surfaces.

(b) Hence find the electric field in this region.   ■

Boundary conditions revisited

In all the worked examples and exercises that we have met so far in this chapter, the boundaries have been conductors. The potential is constant everywhere on the boundary of a conductor, and this means that there is no component of $\mathrm{grad}\,V$ parallel to the boundary, so the electric field is normal to the surface of a conductor. Sometimes the region of interest is not completely bounded by conductors, and for charge distributions that have finite extent, an appropriate boundary condition is that $V \to 0$ as $r \to \infty$.

Another commonly occurring situation is a boundary between two dielectrics. At such a boundary, the conditions derived in Chapter 2 apply:

- The component of $\mathbf{D}$ perpendicular to a boundary remains the same across a boundary that carries no free charge: $D_{1\perp} = D_{2\perp}$. If there is free charge with surface density σ_{f} at the boundary, then $D_{2\perp} - D_{1\perp} = \sigma_{\mathrm{f}}$.

- The component of $\mathbf{E}$ parallel to a boundary remains the same across a boundary: $E_{1\parallel} = E_{2\parallel}$.

When solving Laplace's equation for the potential, we need to express the boundary conditions in terms of the potential. One condition is fairly obvious: the potential must be continuous across the boundary, since if it were not continuous, the relationship $\mathbf{E} = -\,\mathrm{grad}\,V$ would predict an infinite field perpendicular to the boundary, which is not physically possible. The continuity of V across the boundary implies that $E_\parallel = -[\mathrm{grad}\,V]_\parallel$ must be the same on either side of the boundary, so this is not an independent boundary condition.

The boundary condition for $D_\perp$ can also be expressed in terms of the potential. If we consider only LIH materials, then

$$\mathbf{D} = \varepsilon \varepsilon_0 \mathbf{E} = -\varepsilon \varepsilon_0 \operatorname{grad} V.$$

So the condition that $D_{1\perp} = D_{2\perp}$, which applies when there is no free charge at the boundary, can be written in terms of the potentials either side of the boundary as

$$\varepsilon_1 [\operatorname{grad} V_1]_\perp = \varepsilon_2 [\operatorname{grad} V_2]_\perp, \tag{4.15}$$

where $[\operatorname{grad} V_1]_\perp$ is the component of the vector field $\operatorname{grad} V_1$ in the direction perpendicular to the boundary. In summary, we have the following.

> **Boundary conditions for V at the interface between dielectrics**
>
> - $V_1 = V_2$: the potential remains the same across the boundary.
> - $\varepsilon_1 [\operatorname{grad} V_1]_\perp = \varepsilon_2 [\operatorname{grad} V_2]_\perp$: the product of the perpendicular component of the potential and the relative permittivity remains the same across the boundary.

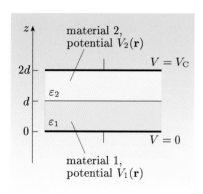

Figure 4.7   Parallel plate capacitor filled with two dielectric slabs.

Exercise 4.4   The parallel plate capacitor shown in Figure 4.7 has conducting plates at $z = 0$ and $z = 2d$, which are maintained at potentials zero and V_C, respectively. The space between the plates is filled with slabs of two dielectric materials, with equal thicknesses d and relative permittivities ε_1 and ε_2. There is no free charge in the dielectrics. The dimensions of the plates are large compared with their spacing, so edge effects can be ignored.

(a) Write down the differential equations that are satisfied by the electrostatic potentials V_1 and V_2 in materials 1 and 2.

(b) Use the result from Worked Example 4.2 to write down the general solutions to these differential equations in the two materials.

(c) Write down equations for the four boundary conditions satisfied by the potentials V_1 and V_2 at the two plates and at the boundary between the dielectrics. (There is no need to wade through the algebra to solve these equations.) ∎

4.3   The uniqueness theorem

In the previous section we showed that solving problems in electrostatics can be reduced to finding the solution of Poisson's equation or Laplace's equation. However, so far our examples and exercises have all been situations with a high degree of symmetry, which could have been solved more easily by methods that we introduced earlier. Nevertheless, these examples and exercises have reinforced the importance of choosing the appropriate coordinate system and the importance of the boundary conditions!

Unfortunately, direct integration of Poisson's equation or Laplace's equation is often impossible, and in this section and the next section we shall introduce several alternative techniques that can be used. However, we need to be sure that the solution that we obtain to a particular problem not only satisfies the boundary conditions but also is the only possible solution. Fortunately, this is guaranteed by the **uniqueness theorem**, which is stated below.

The uniqueness theorem

Any solution of Poisson's equation

$$\nabla^2 V = -\frac{1}{\varepsilon \varepsilon_0} \rho_f(\mathbf{r}),$$
(Eqn 4.11)

or Laplace's equation

$$\nabla^2 V = 0,$$
(Eqn 4.12)

that satisfies the boundary conditions for a particular problem is unique. There is only one possible potential function, $V(\mathbf{r})$, that satisfies both the differential equation *and* the boundary conditions for the region of interest.

Physically it is not surprising that the solution for the potential is unique. If we have a specified set of conductors surrounding a region of interest, and apply specified potentials to the conductors, then we would expect the potential at any point in the region to have the same value each time we apply the boundary potentials. More specifically, we would expect the same distribution of potential in a parallel plate capacitor each time we apply specified potentials to the two plates. The uniqueness theorem can be proved mathematically using some subtle vector calculus manipulations, but we shall not show this derivation here. We shall simply assume that it always applies.

The uniqueness theorem has the following important consequence: if we find a solution to Laplace's equation, say, and this solution satisfies all of the boundary conditions for the problem, then we need look no further — this is the only solution to the problem. This means that it doesn't matter how you find a solution — and it may just be found by guesswork, inspired perhaps by some knowledge of electromagnetism — you can be confident that it is the unique solution.

To show the power of the uniqueness theorem, the next exercise asks you to consider the example of a Faraday cage, a conducting enclosure surrounding a region of space.

Exercise 4.5   Inside a conducting enclosure, the electrostatic potential V satisfies Laplace's equation, $\nabla^2 V = 0$. On the surface of the enclosure, the electrostatic potential takes the constant value V_0.

(a) Write down a solution for the potential inside the enclosure. (This is *not* a trick question!)

(b) How do you know that your solution is the correct one?   ■

4.3.1   The method of images

The uniqueness theorem provides the underpinning for the **method of images**, a technique that can be used to determine the electrostatic potential and field in

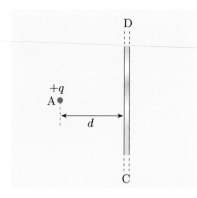

Figure 4.8   Point charge in front of a conducting plate.

certain situations. When a conductor is placed in an electric field, induced charges appear on the surface of the conductor. The surface of the conductor is an equipotential surface, and the uniqueness theorem tells us that there is only one possible solution for the field outside the conductor. However, the potential is difficult to calculate since we don't know how the charge is distributed over the surface. In certain cases, it is possible to replace the conductor by one or more point charges in such a way that the former position of the conducting surface remains an equipotential surface at the same potential. As the boundary conditions remain the same, the electric field for the two systems will be the same in the region outside the conductor. The benefit of making this replacement is that the potential can easily be calculated for this system of charges. We illustrate this by an example.

Suppose that we wish to find the electric field of the system shown in Figure 4.8, which consists of a point charge q at a point A, which is a distance d from an infinite conducting plate CD. Without loss of generality, we assume that the conducting plate is at zero potential. The boundary conditions for the electrostatic potential for this system are:

- $V = 0$ on the conducting plate CD;

- V tends to zero at large distances;

- $V \simeq q/4\pi\varepsilon_0 r_1$ in the immediate neighbourhood of the point charge at A, where r_1 is the distance from the point A.

Now imagine that we remove the conducting plate and replace it with a point charge $-q$ at point B, which is at a distance d behind the original position of the plate, as shown in Figure 4.9. The electrostatic potential at a point P is given by

$$V = \frac{q}{4\pi\varepsilon_0}\frac{1}{r_1} - \frac{q}{4\pi\varepsilon_0}\frac{1}{r_2}, \tag{4.16}$$

where r_1 and r_2 are the distances from P to the charges at points A and B, respectively. When point P is on the plane CD, $r_1 = r_2$, so $V = 0$. For large values of r_1 and r_2, the potential tends to zero. And for small values of r_1, the potential is $V \simeq q/4\pi\varepsilon_0 r_1$. Therefore the electrostatic potential in Equation 4.16 satisfies all three of the boundary conditions listed above for our original problem.

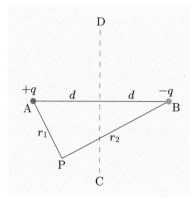

Figure 4.9   The plate CD in Figure 4.8 is replaced by a charge $-q$ at B.

The uniqueness theorem tells us that Equation 4.16 must be the solution for the potential in the original problem — a point charge placed in front of an infinite conducting plate. The field lines and equipotential surfaces for the charges at points A and B are shown in Figure 4.10, and the uniqueness theorem tells us that the left half of this diagram represents the field lines and equipotentials for the original problem of the point charge and the conducting plate.

In summary, the electrostatic potential due to a point charge q placed at a point A in front of an infinite conducting plate CD at zero potential is the same as if the conducting plate were removed and replaced by a charge $-q$ at B. This charge is called the **image charge** of the charge q in the plane. The image charge is only a calculational device and has no existence in reality, just as an optical image has no existence in reality. Of course, for the situation illustrated in Figure 4.8, Equation 4.16 only gives the potential to the left of the conducting plate. On the right of the plate, the potential is zero in the absence of other charges in this region.

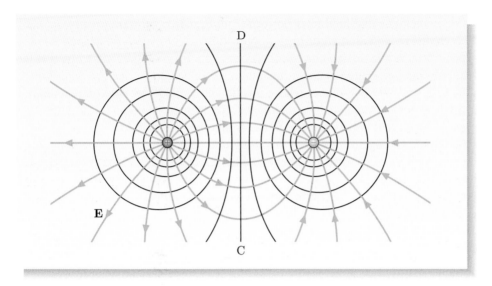

Figure 4.10   Field lines (orange) and equipotentials (black) for point charges $+q$ and $-q$.

A similar method can be used to solve problems involving line charges or cylinders that lie parallel to a conducting plate. Suppose that an infinite line charge, with linear charge density λ, is placed parallel to an infinite conducting plate and at distance d from it. The plate is at zero potential, and we want to determine the potential in the region between the line and the plate.

The success of the method of images with the point charge and conducting plate problem suggests that we try replacing the plate with an image line charge, with linear charge density $-\lambda$, at distance d behind the position of the plate, as shown in Figure 4.11. If the potential due to the two line charges can match the boundary conditions for the line charge plus conducting plate problem, then we shall have found the unique solution for the potential for this problem.

The electrostatic potential at distance r from an isolated infinite line charge is

$$V = -\lambda \ln r / 2\pi\varepsilon_0 + V_0,$$

where the constant V_0 depends on the choice of location for the zero of potential. (Since we have an infinite line charge, we cannot use the normal convention of letting $V = 0$ at infinity.) The potential at point P due to the line charge and the image charge is

$$V = -\frac{\lambda}{2\pi\varepsilon_0}\ln r_1 + \frac{\lambda}{2\pi\varepsilon_0}\ln r_2 + V_0 = \frac{\lambda}{2\pi\varepsilon_0}\ln\frac{r_2}{r_1} + V_0, \qquad (4.17)$$

where r_1 is the distance from the original line charge and r_2 is the distance from its image, and V_0 depends on the choice of location for the zero of potential. This potential satisfies Laplace's equation and can match the boundary conditions, as you can verify in the next exercise.

Exercise 4.6   (a) What property of Laplace's equation allows the superposition of two separate solutions to obtain a new solution?

(b) Verify that the potential in Equation 4.17 can satisfy the boundary conditions in the region of the plate and in the region close to the original line charge. ■

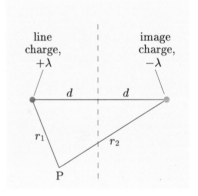

Figure 4.11   Cross-section through line charge $(+\lambda)$ and its image line charge $(-\lambda)$. The broken line is the position of the conducting plate.

The equipotentials and field lines derived from Equation 4.17 are shown in Figure 4.12. Note that all of the equipotentials are circles in the plane perpendicular to the line charge, so the equipotential surfaces are cylinders that lie parallel to the line charge. This means that if we replaced the line charge in this figure by a conducting cylinder whose position coincided with the equipotential labelled V_c, for example, and we maintained the cylinder at potential V_c, then the potential in the region between this cylinder and the plate would still be as shown in the figure. A range of problems involving charged cylinders and conducting planes, and pairs of charged cylinders, can be solved by calculating potentials produced by line charges: if the line charges give rise to potentials that match the boundary conditions at the conductors, then they provide the unique solution to the problem.

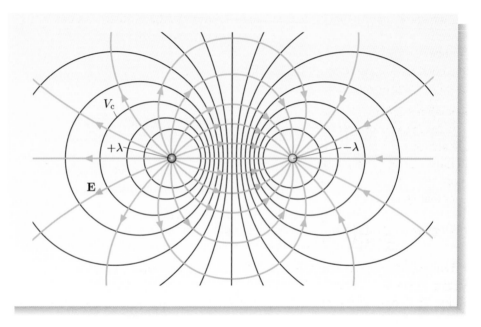

Figure 4.12   Equipotentials and field lines for line charges $+\lambda$ and $-\lambda$. The left half of the diagram represents field lines (orange) and equipotentials (black) for the $+\lambda$ line charge and a conducting plate.

Exercise 4.7   Charge q at point A in Figure 4.13 is near two semi-infinite perpendicular conducting plates, OX and OY, which are at zero potential. Use the method of images to write down an expression for the electrostatic potential in the region between the two plates. (*Hint*: If you stand in front of two mirrors that are perpendicular to each other, you will see *three* images of yourself. So in this case, you will need more than one image charge!) ◼

So far, our discussion of the method of images has been confined to charges near conducting planes. However, the method of images can also be used for conducting cylinders and spheres. In these cases it is not so obvious where the image charges should be placed.

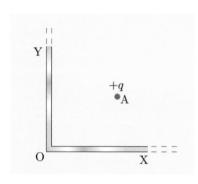

Figure 4.13   A point charge in front of two perpendicular conducting plates.

Consider the example shown in Figure 4.14, where charge q is at a point A which is at a distance d from the centre O of a conducting sphere of radius R, which is at zero potential. We require an image charge (or charges) that in combination with the charge at A produces zero potential on the surface of the sphere. By symmetry, any such charge must lie along the horizontal axis through O and A. In fact, it can be shown that a charge $q' = -qR/d$ at a point B which is a distance $b = R^2/d$ from the point O on the line OA (Figure 4.14) satisfies this requirement: the potentials due to q and q' (with no conducting sphere present) are zero on the spherical surface. So the potential due to a point charge q outside a conducting sphere at zero potential is identical to that of the original point charge and an image point charge q', as described above.

4.3.2 Fitting known solutions to the boundary conditions

The importance of the uniqueness theorem is that as long as we can find a solution to Laplace's equation that satisfies the boundary conditions, by whatever means, then we know that this is the one and only solution to the problem. In this subsection we shall see how this can be used in situations that have azimuthal symmetry, so that V is independent of ϕ. The two problems that we shall tackle are a conducting sphere placed in a uniform electric field and a dielectric sphere placed in a uniform field.

We shall use spherical coordinates, with their origin at the centre of the sphere and the polar (z) axis in the direction of the uniform applied field. The symmetry then indicates that the electric field and the potential are independent of ϕ. The form of the Laplacian in spherical coordinates is given inside the back cover. If we ignore the term involving $\partial^2 V/\partial\phi^2$, then Laplace's equation for situations with azimuthal symmetry is

$$\nabla^2 V = \frac{1}{r^2}\frac{\partial}{\partial r}\left(r^2\frac{\partial V}{\partial r}\right) + \frac{1}{r^2\sin\theta}\frac{\partial}{\partial\theta}\left(\sin\theta\frac{\partial V}{\partial\theta}\right) = 0. \tag{4.18}$$

Deriving solutions to this differential equation would involve a diversion from the electromagnetism problems of interest, so we shall simply quote some of the results. The possibly solutions all involve the product of a term that depends on r and a term that depends on $\cos\theta$, and the simplest four solutions are:

$$A_0 + \frac{B_0}{r}, \tag{4.19}$$

$$\left(A_1 r + \frac{B_1}{r^2}\right)\cos\theta, \tag{4.20}$$

$$\left(A_2 r^2 + \frac{B_2}{r^3}\right)\frac{3\cos^2\theta - 1}{2}, \tag{4.21}$$

$$\left(A_3 r^3 + \frac{B_3}{r^4}\right)\frac{5\cos^3\theta - 3\cos\theta}{2}. \tag{4.22}$$

The general solution to a problem with azimuthal symmetry is a linear combination of the four solutions listed and the other higher-order solutions, with the constants A_i and B_i chosen to fit the boundary conditions. Fortunately, it is not necessary to go to such lengths for the problems that we shall tackle. We can make an educated guess at the simplest solution that appears consistent with the boundary conditions, and then check whether the constants A_i, B_i can be chosen to match the boundary conditions.

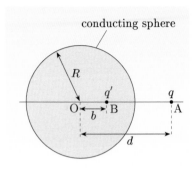

Figure 4.14 A charge q outside a conducting sphere, and the image charge q'.

Conducting sphere in a uniform field

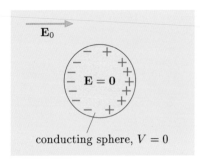

Figure 4.15 A conducting sphere in an initially uniform electric field.

The first situation that we consider is shown in Figure 4.15 — a conducting sphere, radius R, placed in a uniform electric field $\mathbf{E}_0$. The field within the sphere is zero, and this is achieved by an induced charge distribution on the surface which produces a field that cancels the applied field within the sphere. Outside the sphere, the surface charge distorts the initially uniform field in the neighbourhood of the sphere, but at large distances the effect of the sphere becomes negligible and the field has the uniform value $\mathbf{E}_0$. Our aim is to find a solution for Laplace's equation in the region outside the sphere, from which it should be possible to calculate the electric field.

Outside the sphere, the potential must satisfy the form of Laplace's equation given in Equation 4.18, and the solution for V must be some combination of terms like those in Equations 4.19–4.22 that satisfies the boundary conditions. What are the boundary conditions for this problem? The sphere is a conductor, so it must have a uniform potential, and we can take this to be zero. The symmetry then indicates that outside the sphere, the potential across the complete equatorial plane, $\theta = \pi/2$, must be zero. The potential corresponding to the uniform electric field $\mathbf{E}_0$ is

$$V = -E_0 z = -E_0 r \cos\theta.$$

So the boundary conditions are:

- $V = 0$ when $r = R$ for all values of θ and ϕ;

- $V \simeq -E_0 r \cos\theta$ for $r \gg R$.

● Which of the expressions in Equations 4.19–4.22 can satisfy the second of these boundary conditions?

○ The expression in Equation 4.20,

$$\left(A_1 r + \frac{B_1}{r^2}\right) \cos\theta,$$

varies as $r \cos\theta$ when r is large, which satisfies the second boundary condition.

We require that

$$\left(A_1 r + \frac{B_1}{r^2}\right) \cos\theta = -E_0 r \cos\theta$$

when r is large, which means that $A_1 = -E_0$. Our first boundary condition, that $V = 0$ at $r = R$, requires

$$\left(-E_0 R + \frac{B_1}{R^2}\right) \cos\theta = 0$$

for all values of θ, so

$$B_1 = E_0 R^3.$$

With these values of the constants A_1 and B_1, the expression for the potential becomes

$$V = -E_0 r \cos\theta + \frac{E_0 R^3 \cos\theta}{r^2} \quad \text{for } r \geq R. \tag{4.23}$$

This function is a solution of Laplace's equation and satisfies the two boundary conditions. According to the uniqueness theorem, this must be the *only* solution to our problem. The equipotentials and field lines for the potential given by Equation 4.23 are shown in Figure 4.16.

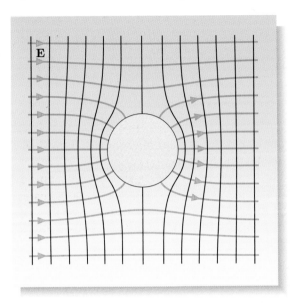

Figure 4.16 Equipotentials and field lines for a conducting sphere in a uniform field.

The first term in Equation 4.23 represents the uniform field $\mathbf{E}_0$, and the second term, $E_0 R^3 \cos\theta/r^2$, represents the field due to the induced surface charge on the conducting sphere. In Book 1 we showed that the potential of an electric dipole $\mathbf{p}$ is $p\cos\theta/4\pi\varepsilon_0 r^2$, so the sphere has the same effect as a dipole of moment $\mathbf{p} = 4\pi\varepsilon_0 R^3 \mathbf{E}_0$.

Dielectric sphere in a uniform field

We shall now consider the case where the conducting sphere is replaced by a dielectric sphere with relative permittivity ε and no net charge (Figure 4.17). There are two distinct regions to consider in this problem, outside and inside the sphere, and we shall denote the electrostatic potentials in these two regions by $V_1(\mathbf{r})$ and $V_2(\mathbf{r})$, respectively. The potential in each region must satisfy Laplace's equation, with the following boundary conditions:

(i) $V_1 \simeq -E_0 r \cos\theta$ for large values of r;

(ii) $V_1 = V_2$ for $r = R$;

(iii) $\dfrac{\partial V_1}{\partial r} = \varepsilon \dfrac{\partial V_2}{\partial r}$ for $r = R$;

(iv) in addition, we require that V_2 remains finite at $r = 0$.

Boundary condition (i) is the same as for the conducting sphere, so this suggests that outside the sphere we again try a potential of the form in Equation 4.20,

$$V_1 = A_1 r \cos\theta + \frac{B_1 \cos\theta}{r^2} \quad \text{for } r \geq R.$$

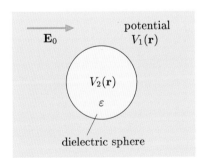

Figure 4.17 A dielectric sphere in a uniform field.

Boundary condition (ii) indicates that we need to match the potentials V_1 and V_2 at the surface of the sphere for all values of θ. This suggests that V_2 has the same dependence on $\cos\theta$ as V_1, so we try the function

$$V_2 = A_2 r \cos\theta + \frac{B_2 \cos\theta}{r^2} \quad \text{for } r \leq R.$$

If we can satisfy all four boundary conditions by appropriate choices of the four constants A_1, B_1, A_2 and B_2, then the uniqueness theorem tells us that we have solved the problem.

Exercise 4.8   (a) Use boundary condition (i) to deduce the value of A_1, and condition (iv) to deduce the value of B_2.

(b) Use conditions (ii) and (iii) to find values for A_2 and B_2.   ∎

Using the values of the constants calculated in Exercise 4.8, the electrostatic potentials for a dielectric sphere in an initially uniform field are

$$V_1 = -E_0 r \cos\theta + \frac{\varepsilon - 1}{\varepsilon + 2} \frac{E_0 R^3 \cos\theta}{r^2} \quad (r \geq R),$$

$$V_2 = -\frac{3}{\varepsilon + 2} E_0 r \cos\theta \quad (r \leq R).$$

The equipotentials and field lines are shown in Figure 4.18. Note that the electric field is uniform inside the sphere, and is smaller than the external field because of the opposing field due to the polarization of the dielectric.

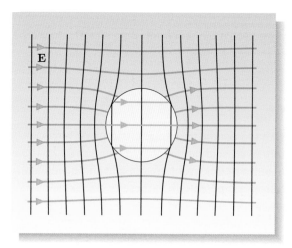

Figure 4.18   Equipotentials and electric field lines for a dielectric sphere in an initially uniform electric field.

4.4   Numerical solutions

We can generally obtain solutions to Poisson's equation or Laplace's equation by direct integration, or by the other methods discussed earlier in this chapter, only in situations where there is a high degree of symmetry. But we may wish to know the electric field in the electron gun of an electron microscope (see Figure 4.2b), given that the electrodes are at some specified potentials. The geometry here is so complicated that none of the methods previously discussed could be used. The situation is even worse if Poisson's equation must be solved with a complicated charge density function. In such cases, numerical methods are used, almost always implemented on a computer. In this section we shall outline briefly the basis of numerical methods that are suitable for solving Laplace's and Poisson's equations.

An important type of numerical method for the solution of boundary-value problems is the **finite difference method**. For simplicity, we shall show how the method can be applied to Laplace's equation in two dimensions.

We want to find the function $V(x, y)$ that satisfies

$$\nabla^2 V = \frac{\partial^2 V}{\partial x^2} + \frac{\partial^2 V}{\partial y^2} = 0. \tag{4.24}$$

First, we divide up the xy-plane to obtain a rectangular grid, as shown in Figure 4.19. Each point of intersection on the grid is called (unsurprisingly) a grid point, and these points are spaced by Δx in the x-direction and by Δy in the y-direction. It is usually the case that smaller values of Δx and Δy lead to a more accurate solution. If the coordinates of a grid point are x_i and y_j, where i and j are integers, then the value of V at that grid point is $V(x_i, y_j)$.

Next, we write the derivatives in Equation 4.24 in an approximate form, known as the **finite difference form**. Consider $\partial^2 V / \partial x^2$. This can be rewritten as $\partial(\partial V / \partial x)/\partial x$, which is the rate of change of $\partial V / \partial x$ with respect to x. To the left of (x_i, y_j), $\partial V / \partial x$ can be approximated in finite difference form as

$$\left(\frac{\partial V}{\partial x}\right)_{\text{left}} \simeq \frac{\Delta V}{\Delta x} = \frac{V(x_i, y_j) - V(x_{i-1}, y_j)}{\Delta x}.$$

This equation is the approximation to $\partial V / \partial x$ at the point midway between the grid points (x_{i-1}, y_j) and (x_i, y_j).

Likewise, at the point midway between the grid points (x_i, y_j) and (x_{i+1}, y_j), the approximation to $\partial V / \partial x$ is

$$\left(\frac{\partial V}{\partial x}\right)_{\text{right}} \simeq \frac{V(x_{i+1}, y_j) - V(x_i, y_j)}{\Delta x}.$$

So, at the grid point (x_i, y_j),

$$\frac{\partial^2 V}{\partial x^2} = \frac{\partial}{\partial x}\left(\frac{\partial V}{\partial x}\right) \simeq \frac{(\partial V/\partial x)_{\text{right}} - (\partial V/\partial x)_{\text{left}}}{\Delta x}$$

$$\simeq \frac{V(x_{i+1}, y_j) - 2V(x_i, y_j) + V(x_{i-1}, y_j)}{(\Delta x)^2}.$$

Similarly, at this grid point,

$$\frac{\partial^2 V}{\partial y^2} \simeq \frac{V(x_i, y_{j+1}) - 2V(x_i, y_j) + V(x_i, y_{j-1})}{(\Delta y)^2}.$$

Thus Equation 4.24 can now be written in finite difference form as

$$\nabla^2 V = \frac{V(x_{i+1}, y_j) - 2V(x_i, y_j) + V(x_{i-1}, y_j)}{(\Delta x)^2}$$

$$+ \frac{V(x_i, y_{j+1}) - 2V(x_i, y_j) + V(x_i, y_{j-1})}{(\Delta y)^2} = 0. \tag{4.25}$$

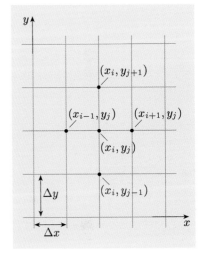

Figure 4.19 A grid for the finite difference method.

An equation like this is written down for every grid point. Some of these grid points will be near, or at, the boundary. At such points, we know the boundary values of V, and we include these in the equations. We then end up with a large number of simultaneous equations, which we can solve to obtain $V(x_i, y_j)$ at each point (x_i, y_j). This is usually done by an iterative method using a computer.

We shall illustrate the type of method used by a simple example, with only a small number of grid points. Let us take the step lengths Δx and Δy to be equal. Then Equation 4.25 reduces to

$$V(x_{i+1}, y_j) + V(x_i, y_{j+1}) - 4V(x_i, y_j) + V(x_i, y_{j-1}) + V(x_{i-1}, y_j) = 0,$$

which can be rewritten as

$$V(x_i, y_i) = \tfrac{1}{4}[V(x_{i+1}, y_j) + V(x_i, y_{j+1}) + V(x_i, y_{j-1}) + V(x_{i-1}, y_j)]. \quad (4.26)$$

Equation 4.26 says that the value of V at any grid point is the average of the values of V at the four closest neighbouring grid points (see Figure 4.19). This forms the basis of a simple, but reasonably efficient, iterative method of solution, known as the *Jacobi relaxation method*.

This procedure is as follows.

1. Draw a square grid covering the region.

2. Use the boundary conditions to allocate values to $V(x_i, y_j)$ for all grid points on, or adjacent to, the boundary.

3. Guess values for $V(x_i, y_j)$ at all other points.

4. Find a better guess V_{new} for $V(x_i, y_j)$ at all the internal grid points, by using the equation

$$V_{\text{new}}(x_i, y_j) = \tfrac{1}{4}[V_{\text{old}}(x_{i+1}, y_j) + V_{\text{old}}(x_i, y_{j+1})$$
$$+ V_{\text{old}}(x_i, y_{j-1}) + V_{\text{old}}(x_{i-1}, y_j)], \quad (4.27)$$

where on the right-hand side we use the previous values V_{old}.

5. Repeat step 4 until $V_{\text{new}} = V_{\text{old}}$ to the required accuracy.

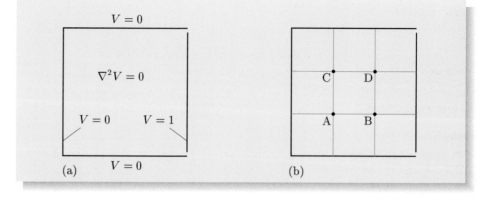

Figure 4.20   (a) Problem to be solved by the finite difference method. (b) Grid for the finite difference method.

To illustrate this procedure, consider a square region with $V = 0$ on three of the sides and $V = 1$ on the fourth, as shown in Figure 4.20a. We shall use a grid with four internal grid points, as shown in Figure 4.20b. We know the values of V at the grid points on the boundaries of the region, but to start the iterative process, we need to make guesses for the values of V at the internal grid points A, B, C, D.

Let us take $V_A = 0.5$, $V_B = 0.5$, $V_C = 0.5$ and $V_D = 0.5$. These initial values are shown in Figure 4.21. We now use Equation 4.27 iteratively to improve on our estimates of V at the grid points.

So our next estimates for the values of V are

$$V_A = \tfrac{1}{4}(0.5 + 0.5 + 0 + 0) = 0.25,$$

$$V_B = \tfrac{1}{4}(1 + 0.5 + 0 + 0.5) = 0.5,$$

$$V_C = \tfrac{1}{4}(0.5 + 0 + 0.5 + 0) = 0.25,$$

$$V_D = \tfrac{1}{4}(1 + 0 + 0.5 + 0.5) = 0.5.$$

These values are shown in Figure 4.22.

Exercise 4.9   Use Equation 4.27 and the values of V shown in Figure 4.22 to find even better estimates for V_A, V_B, V_C and V_D. ■

The values of V from the second iteration are shown in Figure 4.23. We can continue this process until it converges. After a further five iterations, we arrive at values which are accurate to 3 significant figures, namely

$$V_A = 0.125, \quad V_B = 0.375, \quad V_C = 0.125, \quad V_D = 0.375.$$

In fact, these are the exact solutions of the simultaneous equations. In practice, we would use a finer grid and a more efficient iterative technique, but the simple example above illustrates the underlying technique. An example of computed equipotentials for a lens used to focus an ion beam is shown in Figure 4.24.

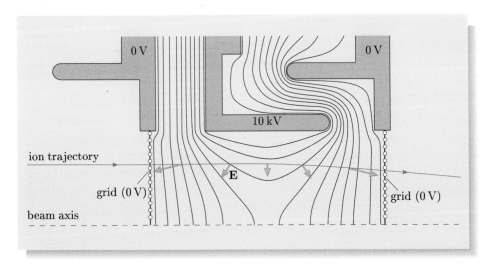

Figure 4.24   Part of an axially-symmetric electrostatic lens, designed to focus a beam of positive lead ions for the laser ion source for the LHC at CERN. Grids of thin wires across the apertures, held at zero volts, restrict the field to the region between the electrodes. Note that the electric field, which is perpendicular to the equipotentials, always has a component directed towards the axis of the lens, acting to focus the beam.

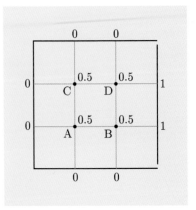

Figure 4.21   Starting values for finite difference method.

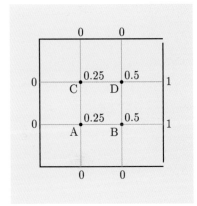

Figure 4.22   First iteration of the finite difference method.

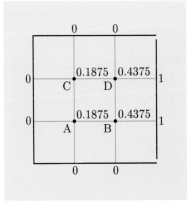

Figure 4.23   Second iteration of the finite difference method.

Summary of Chapter 4

Section 4.1   Coulomb's law can be used to calculate the electric field and electrostatic potential if the distribution of charge is known. It is often more straightforward to calculate the (scalar) electrostatic potential first, and then calculate the (vector) electric field using the relationship $\mathbf{E} = -\operatorname{grad} V$. For problems with high symmetry, the electric field can sometimes be calculated using the integral version of Gauss's law.

Section 4.2   In a region containing a linear isotropic homogeneous (LIH) dielectric, the electrostatic potential V satisfies Poisson's equation,

$$\nabla^2 V = -\frac{1}{\varepsilon \varepsilon_0}\rho_{\mathrm{f}},$$

where ρ_{f} is the free charge density and ε is the relative permittivity. In any region where $\rho_{\mathrm{f}} = 0$, Poisson's equation reduces to Laplace's equation,

$$\nabla^2 V = 0.$$

The operator ∇^2 is known as the Laplacian, and is equivalent to the combined div grad operation. In Cartesian coordinates,

$$\nabla^2 V = \operatorname{div}(\operatorname{grad} V) = \frac{\partial^2 V}{\partial x^2} + \frac{\partial^2 V}{\partial y^2} + \frac{\partial^2 V}{\partial z^2}.$$

In systems with a high degree of symmetry, it may be possible to solve Poisson's equation, or Laplace's equation, by direct integration. At a boundary between two dielectric materials, the potential must remain the same across the boundary, and the perpendicular component of $\varepsilon \operatorname{grad} V$ must remain constant.

Section 4.3   If the value of V is specified on the boundaries of a region, then the solution of Poisson's equation, or Laplace's equation, that matches the boundary conditions is the unique solution. This means that if a solution is found, by whatever means, we can be confident that it is the only solution.

The method of images can sometimes be used to determine the electrostatic potential and field in a system consisting of point, or line, charges and conducting surfaces. The conducting surfaces are replaced by image charges in such a way that the potential and field match the boundary conditions for the original system. Another method is to use solutions to Laplace's equation that have the appropriate symmetry to try to match the boundary conditions for a particular situation.

Section 4.4   In many cases, Laplace's and Poisson's equations cannot be solved analytically, and numerical methods are used. An important type of numerical method for the solution of such differential equations is the finite difference method. The region of interest is divided up by a grid, and simultaneous equations are set up for the potential V at each grid point in terms of the potential at neighbouring points. These equations are solved iteratively, constrained by the values of V on the boundary grid points.

Achievements from Chapter 4

After studying this chapter you should be able to do the following.

4.1 Explain the meanings of the newly defined (emboldened) terms and symbols, and use them appropriately.

4.2 State Poisson's equation and Laplace's equation for the electrostatic potential V, and use them in appropriate situations.

4.3 Integrate Poisson's and Laplace's equations directly to find the electrostatic potential V and the electrostatic field $\mathbf{E}$ in simple systems with a high degree of symmetry.

4.4 Describe the uniqueness theorem for Laplace's equation and Poisson's equation, and explain its relevance to the solution of electrostatic problems.

4.5 Use the method of images in simple situations to find the electrostatic potential and field for a system consisting of charges and conducting surfaces.

4.6 Given the general form of the solution, use the boundary conditions to find a particular solution for the potential and field in an electrostatic problem.

4.7 Use the finite difference method to find a numerical solution of Laplace's equation in simple cases.

Chapter 5 Magnetostatic field calculations

In Chapter 4 you saw how to calculate the electric field for a given distribution of stationary electric charges. In this chapter we shall explore ways of calculating the magnetic field for a given distribution of steady currents. You should already be familiar with the use of the integral version of Ampère's law for magnetic field calculations (Section 1.5), but Ampère's law can be applied usefully only to situations with high degrees of symmetry. The Biot–Savart law provides an alternative basis for magnetic field calculation. In this chapter, we shall discuss a number of examples of its use that go beyond the line current systems you have already met. Much of the emphasis will be on systems that are soluble analytically. However, in many cases analytic solutions are not possible, and brute-force computer calculations are employed. The systems that we discuss can provide the building blocks for such numerically-based calculations.

The ability to calculate the magnetic field produced by a given configuration of currents, and to design a configuration of currents that will produce a required magnetic field, is important for many scientific and technological applications. The electromagnet, electron microscope, MRI scanner and particle accelerator shown in Figures 2, 3, 5 and 6 in the Introduction to this book all depend for their operation on magnetic fields produced by current-carrying coils. Current–field relationships are important too in the natural world. The Earth's magnetic field is determined by currents in the molten core and by currents, like the so-called *ring current*, in regions high above the atmosphere, whilst electrical activity within the human body produces magnetic fields that can be used for diagnosis of various medical conditions.

One of the pleasing aspects of electromagnetism is the similarity between the mathematics describing electric and magnetic phenomena. In this chapter we shall make use of these similarities to simplify the discussion.

Most of this chapter is concerned with methods of calculating the magnetic fields produced by steady electric currents. But does it work the other way round? Can we measure the magnetic field and then work out the current distribution that gives rise to it? This is a so-called 'inverse problem', and you will see that, in this case, it cannot be solved fully. However, if there is additional information about the current distribution, it may be possible to find a solution that is consistent with both the magnetic field data and the additional information. These conditional solutions have a number of useful applications, including the determination of sites of electrical activity in the human brain from measurements of magnetic fields outside the skull (Figure 5.1).

You should note that, strictly speaking, the results in this chapter apply to the fields from steady currents — currents that do not vary in time. This is because Ampère's law and the Biot–Savart law are only strictly true when there is no time dependence. However, in practice, currents and fields have to change very rapidly — at frequencies typical of electromagnetic waves — for any deviations from Ampère's law to be apparent, or we have to be interested in fields at very large distances from the currents.

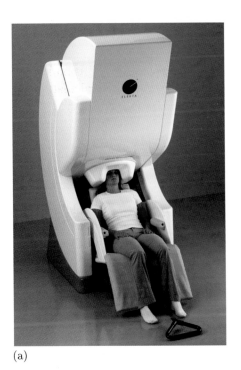

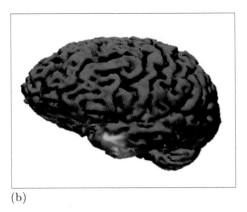

(b)

(a)

Figure 5.1 (a) An ultrasensitive magnetometer with which the brain's magnetic field can be measured continuously at many points on an external helmet-shaped surface. (b) An image of the electrical activity in the cortex superimposed on an anatomical magnetic resonance image. In this case, the main activity — indicated by the lightest colour — is in the left temporal lobe. Activity in this location is characteristic of 'semantic processing', through which language acquires meaning.

Thus, for example, the currents generated by the brain are certainly not steady, but we can regard them as being **quasistatic** since the results for magnetostatics apply with negligible error. To save repetition, in the rest of this chapter all references to fields and currents will mean fields and currents that vary slowly enough that the magnetostatic relationships between current and field can be used.

5.1 The relationship between magnetic field and current

In Section 1.5, the relationship between steady electric currents and magnetic fields was succinctly expressed by Ampère's law, either in the integral version

$$\oint_C \mathbf{B} \cdot d\mathbf{l} = \mu_0 \int_S \mathbf{J} \cdot d\mathbf{S}, \tag{5.1}$$

where the line integral is taken around a closed loop C that bounds an open surface S, or in the differential version

$$\operatorname{curl} \mathbf{B} = \mu_0 \mathbf{J}. \tag{5.2}$$

In Chapter 3 we showed that in the presence of magnetic materials these results could be written in the alternative forms

$$\oint_C \mathbf{H} \cdot d\mathbf{l} = \int_S \mathbf{J}_f \cdot d\mathbf{S} \quad \text{and} \quad \operatorname{curl} \mathbf{H} = \mathbf{J}_f,$$

where $\mathbf{H}$ is the magnetic intensity, $\mathbf{J}_f$ is the free current density, and $\mathbf{B} = \mu\mu_0\mathbf{H}$ for LIH materials. In the present chapter, we are concerned primarily with calculating the magnetic fields produced by currents, and we shall generally assume that there are no magnetic materials present. This is equivalent to assuming that the relative permeability μ is unity in the region of interest, which

Ampère's law: $\int_C \mathbf{B} \cdot d\mathbf{l} = \mu_0 \int_S \mathbf{J} \cdot d\mathbf{S} = \mu_0 I$

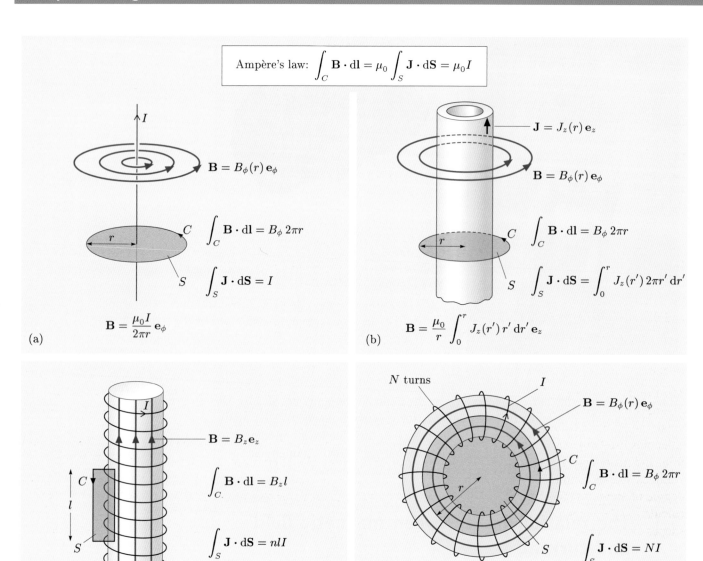

(a)

$\mathbf{B} = B_\phi(r)\,\mathbf{e}_\phi$

$\int_C \mathbf{B} \cdot d\mathbf{l} = B_\phi\, 2\pi r$

$\int_S \mathbf{J} \cdot d\mathbf{S} = I$

$\mathbf{B} = \dfrac{\mu_0 I}{2\pi r}\,\mathbf{e}_\phi$

(b)

$\mathbf{J} = J_z(r)\,\mathbf{e}_z$

$\mathbf{B} = B_\phi(r)\,\mathbf{e}_\phi$

$\int_C \mathbf{B} \cdot d\mathbf{l} = B_\phi\, 2\pi r$

$\int_S \mathbf{J} \cdot d\mathbf{S} = \int_0^r J_z(r')\, 2\pi r'\, dr'$

$\mathbf{B} = \dfrac{\mu_0}{r} \int_0^r J_z(r')\, r'\, dr'\,\mathbf{e}_z$

(c)

$\mathbf{B} = B_z\,\mathbf{e}_z$

$\int_C \mathbf{B} \cdot d\mathbf{l} = B_z\, l$

$\int_S \mathbf{J} \cdot d\mathbf{S} = nl I$

$\mathbf{B} = \mu_0 n I\,\mathbf{e}_z$

(d)

N turns I

$\mathbf{B} = B_\phi(r)\,\mathbf{e}_\phi$

$\int_C \mathbf{B} \cdot d\mathbf{l} = B_\phi\, 2\pi r$

$\int_S \mathbf{J} \cdot d\mathbf{S} = NI$

$\mathbf{B} = \dfrac{\mu_0 N I}{2\pi r}\,\mathbf{e}_\phi$

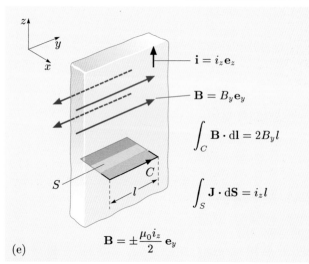

(e)

$\mathbf{i} = i_z\,\mathbf{e}_z$

$\mathbf{B} = B_y\,\mathbf{e}_y$

$\int_C \mathbf{B} \cdot d\mathbf{l} = 2B_y l$

$\int_S \mathbf{J} \cdot d\mathbf{S} = i_z l$

$\mathbf{B} = \pm \dfrac{\mu_0 i_z}{2}\,\mathbf{e}_y$

Figure 5.2 Using the integral version of Ampère's law to determine the magnetic fields produced by currents with high symmetry. (a) Long straight wire. (b) Cylindrical tube. (c) Long solenoid. (d) Toroidal coil. (e) Large thin plate carrying a uniform current per unit length.

means that there are no bound currents (so $\mathbf{J} = \mathbf{J}_f$) and that $\mathbf{B} = \mu_0\mathbf{H}$. Consequently, we can use the forms of Ampère's law in Equations 5.1 and 5.2.

As you saw in Book 1, Ampère's law can be used to calculate the field due to currents that have a high degree of symmetry. Figure 5.2 summarizes a number of important cases. Consider, for example, the long cylindrical tube in part (b) of the figure. Because steady currents only produce magnetic fields perpendicular to the current flow and, in this case, the flow has axial symmetry and translational symmetry in the z-direction, the field generated must be of the form $\mathbf{B} = B_\phi(r)\mathbf{e}_\phi$. The field lines are circles centred on the axis of the tube. So the field at radius r is determined by evaluating the line integral of the field along a circular path of radius r centred on the axis of the tube ($B_\phi \times 2\pi r$), and equating this to $\mu_0 \int_0^r J_z(r')2\pi r'\,\mathrm{d}r'$, which is the current flowing along the tube.

In each of the cases shown in Figure 5.2, the symmetry of the magnetic field can be deduced from the symmetry of the current. This allows us to choose a path for the line integral along which the magnetic field is of simple form, e.g. is constant and directed along the path, or else constant for part of the path and zero for the remainder. The current passing through a surface bounded by the line integral is also easily calculated, either from the known currents in the wires that cross the surface or by integrating a specified current density across the surface.

Most of the current distributions that are of practical importance for generating magnetic fields do not have the high symmetry that is required to use the integral version of Ampère's law to calculate the magnetic field. For example, most solenoids used to generate magnetic fields are short and fat rather than long and thin, and many coils have a non-uniform number of turns per unit length or have complex shapes. Similarly, wires are rarely infinitely long, even to an acceptable degree of approximation. There is clearly a need for a more general method of calculating the magnetic fields due to, say, electromagnetic coils with arbitrary shapes or the electric currents that keep our hearts beating (Figure 5.3).

Figure 5.3 (a) Installation of one of a number of coils used to generate a magnetic field in CERN's LHCb apparatus, which will attempt to detect tiny differences between matter and antimatter. (b) The electrical activity of the heart is rhythmic and self-sustaining. A wave of electrical activity, indicated by the arrows, sweeps round the ventricles as part of the process of muscular contraction that pumps oxygen-rich blood (red) around the body and deoxygenated blood (blue) to the lungs. (c) A typical electrocardiogram recorded using electrodes on the skin of the chest. The signal is caused by the currents set up in the body by the synchronous excitation of the heart muscle cells. The large bipolar deflection corresponds to the contraction of the ventricles, the high-pressure parts of the heart pump.

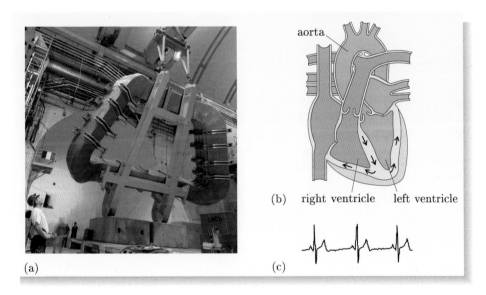

(a)

(b) right ventricle   left ventricle

(c)

5.2   Calculating magnetostatic fields

The Biot–Savart law, which was introduced in Book 1, provides an alternative approach to determining the field produced by a distribution of current. According to this law, the field $\delta\mathbf{B}$ produced by a steady current element $I\,\delta\mathbf{l}'$ — that is, a steady current I flowing along an infinitesimal path element $\delta\mathbf{l}'$ — is given by the following expression:

Biot–Savart law for a current element

$$\delta\mathbf{B}(\mathbf{r}) = \frac{\mu_0 I}{4\pi}\frac{\delta\mathbf{l}' \times (\mathbf{r} - \mathbf{r}')}{|\mathbf{r} - \mathbf{r}'|^3}, \tag{5.3}$$

where $\mathbf{r}$ is the point at which the field is measured, and $\mathbf{r}'$ is the position of the current element. Note that we use primes for the coordinates of current elements (for example, $\mathbf{r}', x', y', z'$) to distinguish them from the coordinates of the point where the field is determined, which have no primes. The spatial relationship between the field $\delta\mathbf{B}$ and the vectors $I\,\delta\mathbf{l}'$ and $(\mathbf{r} - \mathbf{r}')$ is given by the right-hand rule for vector products and is shown in Figure 5.4. Note that $I\,\delta\mathbf{l}'$ and $(\mathbf{r} - \mathbf{r}')$ lie in the plane of the figure, and $\delta\mathbf{B}$ is perpendicular to this plane, pointing away from you.

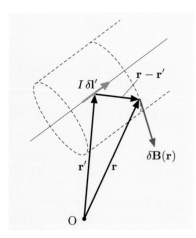

Figure 5.4   The field $\delta\mathbf{B}$ due to the current element $I\,\delta\mathbf{l}'$ is perpendicular to both $\delta\mathbf{l}'$ and $(\mathbf{r} - \mathbf{r}')$.

Exercise 5.1   Describe in words the overall form (i.e. the direction and strength) of the magnetic field $\delta\mathbf{B}$ generated by the current element $I\,\delta\mathbf{l}'$ in Figure 5.4.   ■

We are normally interested in the magnetic field produced by a current I that flows in an extended circuit, such as a coil of arbitrary shape, and this is found by integrating Equation 5.3 along a path that corresponds to the circuit.

You will see an example of how an integral like this can be evaluated in the next subsection.

Biot–Savart law for an extended circuit

$$\mathbf{B}(\mathbf{r}) = \frac{\mu_0 I}{4\pi}\int_{\text{circuit}} \frac{d\mathbf{l}' \times (\mathbf{r} - \mathbf{r}')}{|\mathbf{r} - \mathbf{r}'|^3}. \tag{5.4}$$

This integral version of the Biot–Savart law needs tweaking slightly if we want to calculate the field produced by a volume current density $\mathbf{J}(\mathbf{r}')$ — for example, the field produced by a human heart. We simply replace the linear current element $I\,\delta\mathbf{l}'$ by a volume current element $\mathbf{J}(\mathbf{r}')\,d\tau'$:

Biot–Savart law for a continuous current distribution

$$\mathbf{B}(\mathbf{r}) = \frac{\mu_0}{4\pi}\int_{\tau'} \frac{\mathbf{J}(\mathbf{r}') \times (\mathbf{r} - \mathbf{r}')\,d\tau'}{|\mathbf{r} - \mathbf{r}'|^3}. \tag{5.5}$$

In Book 1 we showed a couple of examples of the use of the Biot–Savart law. We calculated the field at the centre of a circular loop and the field along its axis. These two examples were fairly straightforward because in both cases each element $\delta\mathbf{l}'$ around the loop made the same contribution to the total magnetic field as made by each of the other elements.

We now look at some other examples, starting with the field due to a straight wire of finite length. The result we obtain can be applied to a variety of situations, since many current-carrying circuits can be modelled as the sum of a number of straight lines. A square loop is one example that we shall consider in detail.

5.2.1 The magnetic field of a straight line current

The magnetic field of an infinite straight-line current can be calculated using Ampère's law (Figure 5.2a). Here we shall derive an expression for the field of a finite-length current-carrying wire by doing the integration in Equation 5.4.

We use cylindrical coordinates, with the z-axis aligned with the current, as shown in Figure 5.5. We shall integrate over a finite length of current, between z'_A and z'_B.

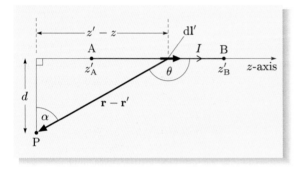

Figure 5.5   Using the Biot–Savart law to calculate the field produced by a straight-line current.

From Equation 5.4,

$$\mathbf{B}(\mathbf{r}) = \frac{\mu_0 I}{4\pi} \int_{\text{line } AB} \frac{\mathrm{d}\mathbf{l}' \times (\mathbf{r} - \mathbf{r}')}{|\mathbf{r} - \mathbf{r}'|^3}. \tag{5.6}$$

This integral does not look very promising, but actually it is not too difficult. The easiest approach is to establish the field direction by inspection of Equation 5.6 and then do the integration to calculate the magnitude.

● What is the direction of the vector product of $\mathrm{d}\mathbf{l}'$ and $(\mathbf{r} - \mathbf{r}')$ for point P in Figure 5.5?

○ $\mathrm{d}\mathbf{l}'$ is in the positive z-direction. Applying the right-hand rule, you should find that the direction of $\mathrm{d}\mathbf{l}' \times (\mathbf{r} - \mathbf{r}')$ is perpendicular to the page, away from you, which is the direction of $\mathbf{e}_\phi$.

This is true for all current elements of the wire, so it must also be true for the integral along the line AB.

Now for the magnitude. The vector product $\mathrm{d}\mathbf{l}' \times (\mathbf{r} - \mathbf{r}')$ in Equation 5.6 can be rewritten as $(\mathrm{d}z' \, \mathbf{e}_z) \times (\mathbf{r} - \mathbf{r}') = \mathrm{d}z' \, |\mathbf{r} - \mathbf{r}'| \sin\theta \, \mathbf{e}_\phi$, where θ is the angle between the direction of the current element and the vector from the element to the point P. So the field strength at P is

$$B = \frac{\mu_0 I}{4\pi} \int_{z'_A}^{z'_B} \frac{\sin\theta \, \mathrm{d}z'}{|\mathbf{r} - \mathbf{r}'|^2}. \tag{5.7}$$

This integral can be evaluated quite easily if we express everything in terms of the angle α in Figure 5.5. We have

$$\sin \theta = \cos \alpha \quad \text{and} \quad |\mathbf{r} - \mathbf{r}'| = d/\cos \alpha.$$

Note the use of italic d for a distance, and roman d for differentials in $\mathrm{d}z'$ and $\mathrm{d}\alpha$.

Also, since $z' - z = d \times \tan \alpha$,

$$\mathrm{d}z' = d \times \sec^2 \alpha \, \mathrm{d}\alpha = \frac{d}{\cos^2 \alpha} \, \mathrm{d}\alpha.$$

The integration limits of z'_A and z'_B for z' correspond to limits of α_A and α_B for α, as shown in Figure 5.6a. Substituting these expressions in Equation 5.7 gives

$$B = \frac{\mu_0 I}{4\pi d} \int_{\alpha_A}^{\alpha_B} \cos \alpha \, \mathrm{d}\alpha,$$

which leads to

$$B = \frac{\mu_0 I}{4\pi d} \left[\sin \alpha_B - \sin \alpha_A \right]. \tag{5.8}$$

Applying this equation requires a little care with the signs of the angles. In Figure 5.6a, both α_A and α_B are measured in the same direction from the perpendicular between P and the line of the current, so both angles are positive. However, in the situation shown in Figure 5.6b, angle α_A is on the other side of the perpendicular and therefore has a *negative* value. So with the values shown,

$$\left[\sin \alpha_B - \sin \alpha_A \right] = \left[\sin 60° - \sin(-30°) \right] = \left[\sin 60° + \sin 30° \right].$$

Figure 5.6 The magnetic fields of line current segments. (a) Integration limits in terms of α for the segment in Figure 5.5. (b) An example with α_A and α_B on opposite sides of the perpendicular line to the current path.

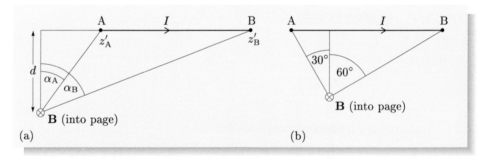

The form of Equation 5.8 tells us that the only pieces of information that we need to calculate the magnetic field strength produced by a line segment are the length d of the perpendicular from the observation point P to the line of the segment, and the angles between this perpendicular line and the lines joining P to the ends of the segment, as shown in Figure 5.6b. The direction of the field is given by the vector product $\delta\mathbf{l}' \times (\mathbf{r} - \mathbf{r}')$, i.e. the field lines are rings around the line of the segment.

● Is the expression in Equation 5.8 consistent with the expression that you have already met for the field of an infinite line current?

○ For an infinite line current, $z'_B \to \infty$, $z'_A \to -\infty$. So $\sin \alpha_B \to 1$, $\sin \alpha_A \to -1$, and

$$B = \frac{\mu_0 I}{2\pi d}, \tag{5.9}$$

which is equivalent to the expression obtained from Ampère's law in Figure 5.2a.

Exercise 5.2   What is the magnetic field **B** at point P in Figure 5.7 due to a 30 A current flowing in the segment of wire between R and S?   ■

In practice, the line segment in Figure 5.6 must be connected in a complete circuit if a steady current is to be maintained, and the field at P will have contributions from all parts of the circuit. However, the expression in Equation 5.8 is useful because we can approximate many circuits by combining straight-line segments. Calculating the field from each segment and then adding the contributions vectorially is often much easier than evaluating the integral in the Biot–Savart law for the path corresponding to the circuit.

5.2.2   Axial field for a square current loop

One of the simplest shapes we can make from line segments is a square current loop. We can use Equation 5.8 to calculate the field anywhere, but to simplify the algebra we shall calculate only the field at a point P on the axis of the loop, as illustrated in Figure 5.8a.

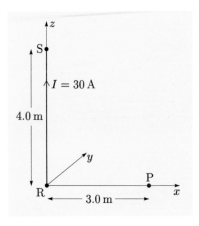

Figure 5.7   What is the magnetic field at P due to the current in RS?

Worked Example 5.1

Derive an expression for the field on the axis of a square current loop.

Solution

The square loop ABCD in Figure 5.8a has sides of length $2a$. We shall find the field at point P on the axis of the loop, at a distance z from the centre. As usual, it is a good idea to see if symmetry arguments can simplify the calculation.

Essential skill

Calculating the field of a loop composed of straight-line segments

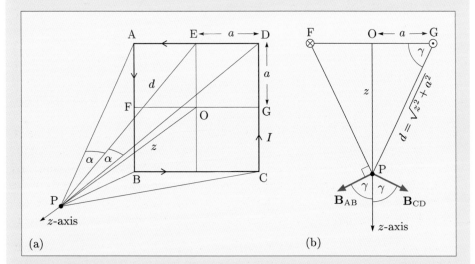

(a)   (b)

Figure 5.8   (a) A point P on the axis of a square coil. (b) The fields $\mathbf{B}_{AB}$ and $\mathbf{B}_{CD}$ at point P due to sides AB and CD.

The four line segments of the square are symmetrically arranged about P, so the magnitudes of the fields they produce at P must be identical; i.e. $B_{AB} = B_{BC} = B_{CD} = B_{DA} = B$. The fields at P due to the current in sides AB and CD are shown in Figure 5.8b: each contribution is perpendicular to the plane containing the line segment and the line between the centre of the segment and point P, and in a direction given by the right-hand grip rule. This direction is at an angle γ to the axis of the coil system. If we decompose these field contributions $\mathbf{B}_{AB}$ and $\mathbf{B}_{CD}$ into components along the axis of the loop and perpendicular to the axis, we find that the perpendicular components cancel, while the axial components reinforce each other. A similar result applies for the fields produced by sides BC and DA.

Thus we conclude that the resultant field is directed along the coil axis, and its magnitude is four times the axial component of the field due to an individual segment, i.e. $B_z = 4B\cos\gamma$. So we need to derive an expression for the axial component for one segment.

Consider the segment DA. The pieces of information that we need in order to calculate the magnitude of the field it produces at P are the length d of the perpendicular from P to AD (PE in Figure 5.8a), and the angles between the lines PE and PA and between PE and PD. From the symmetry, we deduce that E must be the mid-point of DA, so the angles between PE and PA and between PE and PD have the same magnitude α. From the geometry of Figure 5.8a, the perpendicular distance d from P to DA is $d = \sqrt{z^2 + a^2}$. Also,

$$\sin\alpha = \frac{a}{\sqrt{d^2 + a^2}} = \frac{a}{\sqrt{z^2 + a^2 + a^2}} = \frac{a}{\sqrt{z^2 + 2a^2}}.$$

The angles α between the lines PE and PA and the lines PE and PD are on opposite sides of PE, so the term involving the two sines in Equation 5.8 gives

$$\sin\alpha - \sin(-\alpha) = 2\sin\alpha = \frac{2a}{\sqrt{z^2 + 2a^2}}.$$

Substituting this information into Equation 5.8, the magnitude of the magnetic field for segment DA is then

$$B = \frac{\mu_0 I}{4\pi d}[\sin\alpha - \sin(-\alpha)] = \frac{\mu_0 I}{4\pi\sqrt{z^2 + a^2}}\frac{2a}{\sqrt{z^2 + 2a^2}}.$$

The axial component is $B_z = B\cos\gamma$, and from Figure 5.8b,

$$\cos\gamma = \frac{a}{d} = \frac{a}{\sqrt{z^2 + a^2}}. \tag{5.10}$$

So the axial field due to one segment is

$$B_z = \frac{\mu_0 I a^2}{2\pi(z^2 + a^2)\sqrt{z^2 + 2a^2}},$$

and the axial component for the complete square loop is just four times this:

$$B_z = \frac{2\mu_0 I a^2}{\pi(z^2 + a^2)\sqrt{z^2 + 2a^2}}. \tag{5.11}$$

● Write down an expression for the magnitude of the magnetic field on the axis of a square coil when the distance from the coil to the measurement point is very much greater than the coil width ($z \gg 2a$).

○ For $z \gg 2a$, Equation 5.11 becomes

$$B_z \simeq \frac{2\mu_0 I a^2}{\pi z^2 \sqrt{z^2}} = \frac{2\mu_0 I a^2}{\pi z^3}.$$

This result shows that at large distances, the axial field of a square loop with sides of length $2a$ is given by

$$B_z = \frac{\mu_0 I}{2\pi z^3} \times A, \quad \text{where } A = 4a^2 = \text{area of loop.}$$

A similar result was obtained in Book 1 for a circular loop with radius a:

$$B_z = \frac{\mu_0 I a^2}{2z^3} = \frac{\mu_0 I \pi a^2}{2\pi z^3} = \frac{\mu_0 I}{2\pi z^3} \times A, \quad \text{where } A = \pi a^2 = \text{area of loop.}$$

In fact, this result applies for *all* loop shapes at axial distances much greater than the loop dimensions. In Section 3.1 we defined the magnetic dipole moment **m** of a current loop by

$$\mathbf{m} = |I|\, \Delta \mathbf{S},$$

where $\Delta \mathbf{S}$ is a vector with magnitude equal to the area of the loop and pointing in a direction that is related to the direction of current flow by the right-hand grip rule. So the field $\mathbf{B}_{\text{axial}}$ on the axis of a small current loop with magnetic dipole moment **m** at a distance z is

$$\mathbf{B}_{\text{axial}} = \frac{\mu_0 \mathbf{m}}{2\pi z^3}.$$

The approach that we used to calculate the axial field for the square loop could be applied to the calculation of the field on the axis of any coil that is a regular polygon. The calculation is greatly simplified by the fact that the contribution from each side of the polygon is the same. We could use a similar procedure to calculate the field at *any* point in the vicinity of a loop of any shape that we can break down into line segments. The only problem is that the computation of angles and distances must be carried out individually for each segment, and this would be repetitive and rather tedious!

Now, repetitive, tedious calculations are just what computers are good at, and once a computer program has been written, the calculations can be performed in a fraction of a second. A current loop with an arbitrary shape can be approximated with a large number of very short straight segments. The magnetic field can then be calculated at any point within the vicinity of the loop for all the segments. The resultant field at that point is the vector sum of the fields produced by all of the segments. The power of a computer program based on line current segments is that, once written, it will work for all current loops.

Exercise 5.3   The square loop in Figure 5.9 has side length 2.0 m and carries a current of 10 A. Determine approximately the field at point P, which is in the plane of the loop and a distance 1.0 cm from the two closer sides.

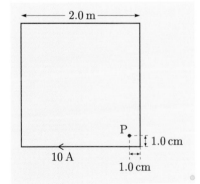

Figure 5.9   What is the magnetic field at point P?

5.2.3   Axial field for a short solenoid

You have seen how the field due to a circuit made up from straight-line segments can be determined by adding the contributions from each of the segments. This method of superposition is not limited to straight line segments, however. It is often possible to break down a circuit into components whose fields are known, and the resultant field is then the superposition of the fields due to the component parts. As an example, we shall calculate the field on the axis of a short closely-wound solenoid.

In Figure 5.2 we showed how the field near the centre of a very long solenoid is determined using Ampère's law. This method works because we can assume that the field is uniform and parallel to the solenoid's axis. For a short solenoid, the field lines spread out towards the ends of the solenoid, as shown in Figure 5.10, so we need an alternative method. We could use the Biot–Savart law and integrate along a path that followed all of the turns of the solenoid, but we can take a short-cut and use the result for the field on the axis of a circular loop, which was derived in Book 1 using the Biot–Savart law:

$$\mathbf{B} = \frac{\mu_0 I a^2}{2(a^2 + z^2)^{3/2}}\,\mathbf{e}_z. \tag{5.12}$$

In this expression, a is the radius of a loop, which has its axis aligned with the z-axis, z is the distance between the measurement point and the centre of the loop, and a positive current I flows in the $\mathbf{e}_\phi$-direction. The field due to the solenoid is the superposition of terms like Equation 5.12, one for each turn and each with a different value of z, and this can be expressed as an integral.

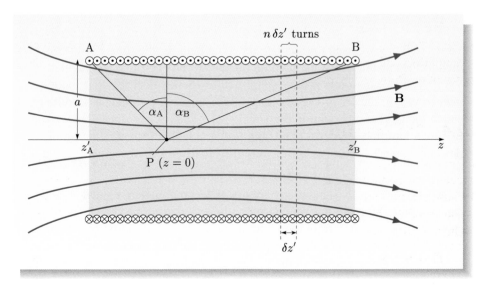

Figure 5.10 Calculating the field on the axis of a short solenoid.

To simplify the mathematics, we shall locate the point P at which the field is measured at the origin, with the ends of the solenoid located at z'_A and z'_B, as shown in Figure 5.10. If the number of turns per unit length is n, then there are $n\,\delta z'$ turns in the range $\delta z'$, and the field on the axis of the solenoid due to all of the turns is

$$\mathbf{B} = \frac{\mu_0 I a^2}{2} \int_{z'_A}^{z'_B} \frac{n\,\mathrm{d}z'}{(a^2 + z'^2)^{3/2}}\,\mathbf{e}_z.$$

Using one of the standard integrals listed inside the back cover, we obtain

$$\mathbf{B} = \frac{\mu_0 I a^2}{2} \left[\frac{nz'}{a^2\sqrt{a^2 + z'^2}} \right]_{z'_A}^{z'_B} \mathbf{e}_z.$$

Now $z'_B / \sqrt{a^2 + z'^2_B} = \sin \alpha_B$, where α_B is defined in Figure 5.10, and there is a similar relationship between z'_A and α_A. We therefore obtain the following expression for the axial field:

$$\mathbf{B} = \frac{\mu_0 n I}{2} \left[\sin \alpha_B - \sin \alpha_A \right] \mathbf{e}_z. \tag{5.13}$$

This is valid for points anywhere on the axis of the solenoid, both inside and outside. However, you should note that if z'_A and/or z'_B are negative, then $\sin \alpha_A$ and/or $\sin \alpha_B$ are negative too.

Note that n is the number of turns per unit length; this gives the right-hand side of the equation the same dimensions as B, namely the dimensions of $\mu_0 I / (\text{length})$, as in Equations 5.8 and 5.12.

● Is Equation 5.13 consistent with the expression for the field inside a very long solenoid (given in Figure 5.2c)?

○ For a long solenoid, α_B and α_A are approximately $\pm 90°$, so $[\sin \alpha_B - \sin \alpha_A] = 2$, and Equation 5.13 reduces to $\mathbf{B} = \mu_0 n I \mathbf{e}_z$, which is the expression that you met earlier for the field inside a very long solenoid.

Exercise 5.4   A solenoid has its length equal to its diameter. What is the ratio of the fields on the axis at the ends of the solenoid and at its centre?

Exercise 5.5   Obtain an expression for the magnetic field at the origin due to current I flowing in the loop shown in Figure 5.11. (The field due to a semicircle is straightforward to calculate if you consider the magnitude and direction of the contribution from each current element.) ■

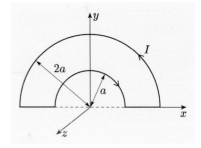

Figure 5.11   Calculating the field of a current-carrying loop.

5.2.4   The magnetic vector potential — an aside

In electrostatics, given a particular change distribution, it is sometimes easier to calculate the electric field from the electrostatic potential than to do so directly. Because electrostatic potential is a scalar, the potential contributions from the various charges can be added algebraically and the electric field calculated as the gradient of the potential,

$$\mathbf{E} = -\operatorname{grad} V. \tag{5.14}$$

Unfortunately, the same tactics are not as helpful in magnetostatics, and as an aside we shall explain why this is so. The explanation will reveal the mathematical similarities between the equations of electrostatics and magnetostatics, and will allow us to introduce the concept of the magnetic vector potential. The discussion will make use of two of the vector identities given inside the back cover. These can be proved by expanding the vector operators, but we shall simply apply them without proof:

$$\operatorname{curl}(\operatorname{grad} f) = \mathbf{0} \quad \text{where } f \text{ is any scalar field;} \tag{5.15}$$

$$\operatorname{div}(\operatorname{curl} \mathbf{F}) = 0 \quad \text{where } \mathbf{F} \text{ is any vector field.} \tag{5.16}$$

The relationship between the electric field and the electrostatic potential in Equation 5.14 is a reflection of the fact that the electrostatic field is a conservative field. For any conservative field, the curl of the field is zero everywhere, and this allows the field to be expressed as the gradient of a scalar function. Thus since $\mathbf{E}$ is conservative, $\mathrm{curl}\,\mathbf{E} = \mathbf{0}$ everywhere, and this allows us to express the electric field as the gradient of a scalar potential, $\mathbf{E} = -\mathrm{grad}\,V$. This relationship is clearly consistent with the irrotational nature of the conservative electrostatic field, since Equation 5.15 shows that $\mathrm{curl}(\mathrm{grad}\,V)$ must be zero.

This electrostatic potential has a simple relationship with the charge distribution:

$$V(\mathbf{r}) = \frac{1}{4\pi\varepsilon_0} \int_{\tau'} \frac{\rho(\mathbf{r}')\,\mathrm{d}\tau'}{|\mathbf{r} - \mathbf{r}'|}, \tag{5.17}$$

where $\mathbf{r}'$ represents the position of a small volume $\mathrm{d}\tau'$ within the charge distribution $\rho(\mathbf{r}')$, τ' is the volume containing the charge distribution, and $\mathbf{r}$ is the point at which the electrostatic potential is evaluated.

Now for the magnetostatic case. Here, the crucial property of magnetic fields is encapsulated in the no-monopole law, that is, $\mathrm{div}\,\mathbf{B} = 0$ everywhere. Any divergence-free field can be expressed as the curl of a vector field, and this means that the magnetic field can be written as

$$\mathbf{B} = \mathrm{curl}\,\mathbf{A}. \tag{5.18}$$

The vector field $\mathbf{A}$ defined by Equation 5.18 is known as the **magnetic vector potential**, or **vector potential** for short. This relationship is clearly consistent with the divergence-free nature of the magnetic field, since Equation 5.16 shows that $\mathrm{div}(\mathrm{curl}\,\mathbf{A})$ must be zero.

The magnetic vector potential too has a fairly simple relationship with its source distribution, in this case the current density in the system:

$$\mathbf{A}(\mathbf{r}) = \frac{\mu_0}{4\pi} \int_{\tau'} \frac{\mathbf{J}(\mathbf{r}')\,\mathrm{d}\tau'}{|\mathbf{r} - \mathbf{r}'|}, \tag{5.19}$$

where $\mathbf{J}(\mathbf{r}')$ is the source current density within the volume τ', and $\mathbf{r}$ is the measurement point. The similarity between Equations 5.17 and 5.19 is clear. In both cases, the potential field is proportional to source strength and inversely proportional to the distance from the source.

Unfortunately, the similarity between the electrostatic potential and the magnetic vector potential does not extend to the latter being useful for calculating magnetic fields. Because $\mathbf{A}$ is a vector, the contributions from its source currents must be added vectorially, which is inherently more difficult than algebraic addition of the contributions to the scalar electrostatic potential. So, little use is made of the magnetic vector potential in magnetostatic calculations.

Given its limited value in magnetostatic calculations, you might be wondering whether the magnetic vector potential is anything more than a mathematical construct. What is the point of introducing it?

There are several answers. First, and most importantly, $\mathbf{A}$ is far more than a mathematical construct. It comes into its own when dealing with dynamic fields and in relativistic analyses, and it is arguably a more fundamental physical quantity than the magnetic field (Figure 5.12). This means that you may encounter the magnetic vector potential in the wider literature, and this brief introduction should help to put it into context. Secondly, the mathematical arguments that underpin the definitions of the electromagnetic fields have an intrinsic aesthetic elegance that can assist understanding of the subject. In particular, it may be helpful to see the similarities and differences between the definitions of, and the relationships between, $\mathbf{E}$ and V on the one hand, and $\mathbf{B}$ and $\mathbf{A}$ on the other. However, since the vector potential is not particularly useful for magnetostatic field calculations, we shall not pursue it further here.

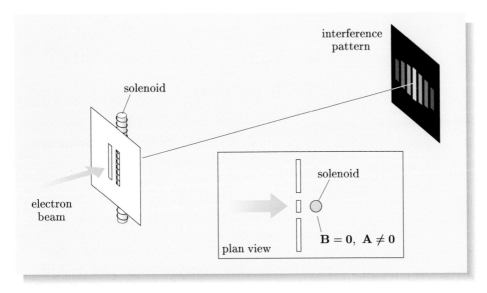

Figure 5.12   The Aharonov–Bohm effect. An electron beam is passed through two slits and produces an interference pattern on a screen. When a current is passed through a long solenoid that is immediately behind the slits, the pattern shifts sideways. There is no magnetic field outside the solenoid, but there is a magnetic vector potential. This suggests that the magnetic vector potential causes real physical effects. It is not just a mathematical construct.

5.2.5   The different methods for calculating magnetic fields

You should now be familiar with three methods of calculating the magnetic field produced by a system of currents. You can

- calculate the field directly from the integral version of Ampère's law (Equation 5.1);

- use the Biot–Savart law to find the total field by integrating the fields due to individual current elements (Equation 5.4);

- model the current pattern with a set of line current segments, work out the field for each segment and then add the fields together.

You often have a choice of which route to take (as you have seen for the infinite line current), and it may be a matter of trial and error to find which is the simplest in a given situation.

In practice, there is only a limited number of circuits and systems for which any of these methods yields results simply. For example, it is relatively easy to calculate the field on the axis of a coil, but it is much more difficult to find the field off-axis. When the symmetry of the system is high, there is the possibility of an analytic solution but, in general, this is not achievable. Instead, we use the analytic methods to establish expressions for the fields generated by building blocks of the system (e.g. the line current segments that can approximate a complicated circuit), and then program computers to perform numerical calculations that add the fields due to the building blocks to obtain the total field. This approach is not elegant but it is practically effective. And we can use the approximate analytic solutions to check the plausibility of the computer results.

5.3   Magnetic fields from biological currents

5.3.1   Electrical currents in the body

Most of the examples discussed so far have involved currents passing through some configuration of thin wires. However, in the natural world we need to deal with magnetic fields generated by current sources that have much more complex distributions. One example is the magnetic fields generated by electric currents within biological organisms.

As you read this page, a tremendous amount of electrical activity is going on within your body. Even if you are sitting still, your heart is beating and your eyes are flicking from side to side following the text. The muscles controlling these actions are governed by charged ions flooding in and out of the excitable cells that make up muscles. As you shift in your seat, the muscles themselves are responding to electrical signals from your brain travelling along nerve fibres. At the same time, the image of the page in front of you is focussed on the retinas in your eyes, and electrical signals from the retinas are transmitted to the visual cortex at the back of your brain where the decoding of the visual signals begins. This processing also manifests itself as electrical activity. Mapping the currents associated with electrical signals in the heart, brain or other parts of the body can give important insights into the physiological functioning of the body, and is a valuable diagnostic tool in medicine.

The most frequently used method of monitoring electrical activity within the human body is to measure electrical potential differences on the skin close to the current source. The electrocardiogram (ecg) is used to measure heart function, and the electroencephalogram (eeg) is used to monitor brain activity. These measurements rely on the fact that the human body is permeated with ionic fluids, which provide a highly conducting medium. A small source of energy (for example, a nerve or muscle cell) acts analogously to a battery. It sets up charge flows within itself and through the conducting fluid in its immediate vicinity. The external flows are known as return currents. They are accompanied by small electric fields, given by $\mathbf{J} = \sigma\mathbf{E}$. The associated potential differences can be detected with electrodes placed on the skin, as shown in Figure 5.13. The highly conducting brain is enclosed within the skull, which has about 80 times lower conductivity. A homogeneous conducting sphere provides a good first approximation to the volume within which return currents flow. However, skin electrode measurements on the scalp are largely detecting the currents that 'leak out' through the eye-sockets and the base of the brain. They provide very limited information about the sources of the underlying activity.

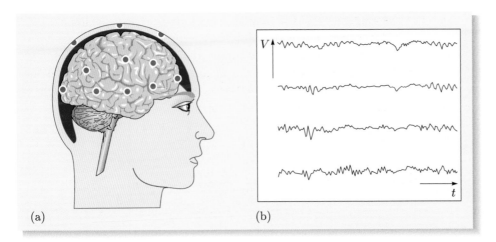

Figure 5.13 (a) Location of eeg electrodes on one side of the head relative to the underlying brain. (b) Eeg traces from four different electrodes.

One problem with these measurements is that the return current paths are distorted by the presence of bones, which are relatively poor conductors. This can make the signals measured at the surface difficult to interpret. A second problem is that reliable measurements are possible only if there is good electrical contact between the skin and the electrodes. This can cause considerable practical difficulty, particularly for measurements on the hairier parts of the body!

Both of these difficulties can be avoided by measuring the magnetic field generated by the currents rather than the electrical potential differences. Biological tissues are paramagnetic or diamagnetic, with relative permeabilities close to unity. Therefore, the tissue has negligible effect on the magnetic fields generated within the body. In addition, the magnetic fields can be measured outside the body, so there need be no contact between the sensing device and the body.

Given these advantages, are biomagnetic field measurements technically feasible? Biological currents are small (unless you are an electric eel), so there is a real question as to whether it is feasible to measure their associated magnetic fields with a sensor placed outside the body. To find the answer, we must estimate the magnetic fields associated with typical biological currents.

5.3.2   Modelling the magnetic field of the human brain

As a specific example, we shall consider the current patterns associated with activity in the human brain. We shall not be too concerned with the physiology here. It is enough to know that this electrical activity is associated with cells called neurons (Figure 5.14a overleaf). The electrical signals can be represented by tiny elements of current, which pass along the neuron (Figure 5.14b). These current elements are often referred to as **current dipoles**, and they can be visualized as tubes of current which draw in charge at one end and expel it at the other. This gives rise to **return currents** in the surrounding conducting fluid that complete the circuit and maintain the flow of charge (Figure 5.14b).

These linear *current* dipoles are quite different from the small current loops that are often referred to as *magnetic* dipoles (see Chapter 3), and both are clearly different from *electric* dipoles (Chapter 2). The meaning of the term 'dipole' should always be clear from the context.

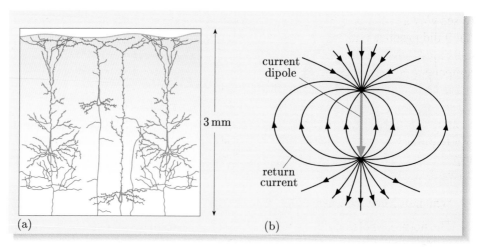

(a)   (b)

Figure 5.14   (a) Idealized view of a small patch of cortex showing alignment of neurons perpendicular to the surface. Their horizontal spacing is greatly exaggerated for clarity. Each neuron can be regarded as a current dipole and because they are parallel, the fields they generate reinforce each other. Together they constitute an effective current dipole that reflects the activity in a small region. (b) Schematic representation of a current dipole with associated volume return currents.

To calculate the magnetic field at some distance from the current dipole, we need to take account of the field due to the dipole itself and also the field due to the return currents. The field due to the dipole itself is easy to calculate from the Biot–Savart law (Equation 5.3), provided that we know the value of $I\,\mathrm{d}\mathbf{l}'$. The product of current and dipole length, $I\,\delta l$, is the strength of the current dipole, and fortunately we can estimate it from other biological measurements.

The field of the volume return current appears initially to be more difficult to calculate. However, in the simplest possible case, in which the surrounding conducting medium is homogeneous and infinite in extent, the return current pattern is the sum of a radial inflow of current at one end of the dipole and a radial outflow at the other end of the dipole, as shown in Figure 5.15. The symmetry of each of these radial current patterns dictates that the magnetic field produced by each pattern is zero, and therefore the field due to their sum must also be zero, as we shall now demonstrate.

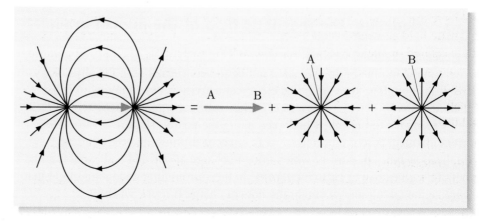

Figure 5.15   Representation of volume return currents from a current dipole.

To see why a radial current flow does *not* generate a magnetic field, first assume that it did produce a magnetic field at a point P at distance r from the current source, as shown in Figure 5.16. The field at P could be decomposed into a radial component B_r along the direction of current flow, and a tangential component B_t that is perpendicular to the current flow. It should be immediately apparent from the spherical symmetry of the current that $B_t = 0$, since a non-zero tangential component of the field could not satisfy spherical symmetry. Spherical symmetry also requires that the radial component B_r has the same magnitude at all points on a spherical surface centred on the end of the current dipole, and is directed outwards at all points or inwards at all points.

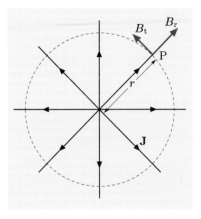

Figure 5.16 Radial current density **J** in an infinite conductor. What are B_r and B_t?

● Which of Maxwell's equations would be violated by such a field?

○ The no-monopole equation, which in integral form states that $\int_S \mathbf{B} \cdot d\mathbf{S} = 0$. If this integral is evaluated over the surface of a sphere where the magnitude of the radial field is constant and directed outwards at all points, then it has a non-zero value, *unless* $B_r = 0$.

If a radial current pattern produces no magnetic field, then the magnetic field of the volume return current in an infinite homogeneous conductor, which is the sum of the two radial patterns shown in Figure 5.15, must also be zero everywhere.

Of course, the brain is not an infinite conductor, so we need to refine our model. A somewhat more realistic approach would be to represent the brain as a large, spherical conductor. The return current paths are then constrained to flow within the boundary of the conductor, so we can no longer think only in terms of radial current patterns.

Although this complicates the mathematics considerably, some of the main characteristics of the fields produced within this model can be derived, with some ingenuity, from arguments already presented. The two most useful simplifying results are as follows.

- A radially-oriented current dipole and its return current produce no magnetic fields outside the sphere.

- Tangentially-oriented dipoles do produce magnetic fields outside the sphere. The radial component of such a magnetic field is produced by the current dipole itself; there is no contribution from the return currents.

The first of these results is fairly easily derived. A radially-oriented current dipole and its return currents constitute an axially symmetric system (Figure 5.17). Any magnetic field generated must reflect that symmetry: it must be tangential to a circle centred on the cylindrical axis through the current dipole, and it must have constant magnitude at all points on any given circle. Using Ampère's law, the integral of this tangential field around the circle is proportional to the total current though any surface bounded by the circle. But this is zero for all of these surfaces, and therefore the field must be zero.

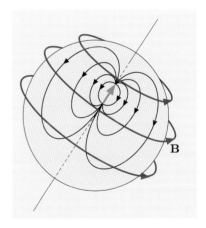

Figure 5.17 A radially-oriented current dipole in a conducting sphere. Symmetry arguments indicate **B** = 0 in this case.

Proving the second result demands more ingenuity. We are interested in the fields generated by the return currents due to a tangentially-oriented dipole (Figure 5.18a). In considering this problem, it does not matter how those return currents were set up, so let us replace the tangential dipole by two radial line current segments joining the centre of the sphere to the positions of the ends of the tangential dipole (Figure 5.18b). Now, we know already that the external field due to a radial line segment plus its return currents is zero. So the sum of the external fields due to the two radial segments and their return currents must also be zero, which means that the external field of the return currents alone is equal but opposite to the external field of the two radial line current segments (Figure 5.18c). It follows that we can reduce the problem of finding the field due to the return currents to the simpler problem of calculating the field due to the two radial line current segments.

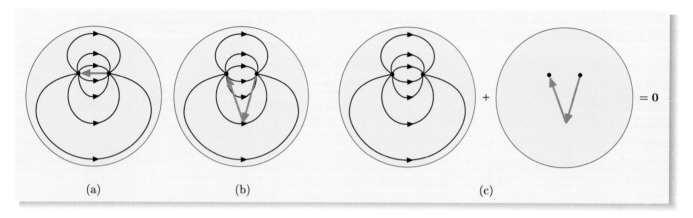

(a)   (b)   (c)

Figure 5.18   (a) A tangentially-oriented current dipole in a conducting sphere. (b) The return currents set up by a tangential current dipole are identical to those set up by two line current segments joining its ends to the centre of the sphere. (c) The total external field due to the two radial line current segments and their accompanying return currents is zero.

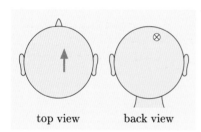

top view   back view

Figure 5.19   Idealized views of the head. The activity is modelled as a current dipole that is just to the right of the mid-line and points forward.

Now the result we are looking for is nearly within our grasp. Using the axial symmetry arguments with which you should by now be familiar, each line current segment produces a field that is in azimuthal directions around the cylindrical axis along which it lies, and therefore this field is tangential to the sphere. So the return currents must also produce tangential fields. This means that the radial component of the field due to a tangential dipole depends on the original current dipole alone, and has no contribution from the return currents.

As any current dipole can be decomposed into a radial and a tangential component, the net radial field that it produces at any point outside the conducting sphere can be calculated by applying the Biot–Savart law to the tangential component.

Exercise 5.6   In a psychology experiment, there is a response from a superficial part of the brain. Assuming that the activity can be modelled in terms of the current dipole shown in Figure 5.19, describe how the radial component of the accompanying magnetic field (that is, the component perpendicular to the spherical surface of the scalp) will vary with position over the scalp.

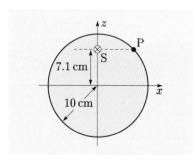

Figure 5.20   What is the field at P due to the dipole at S?

Exercise 5.7   Calculate the radial component of magnetic field at the point P on the surface of a conducting sphere of radius 10 cm shown in Figure 5.20. The source current dipole is at point S on the z-axis, at 7.1 cm from the origin. It is oriented in the positive y-direction, and has magnitude 1.0×10^{-9} A m. ∎

5.3.3 Medical applications of biomagnetic monitoring

The strength of the current dipole associated with activity in a single neuron is typically of order 10^{-13} A m. Ignoring for the moment any physiological or measurement subtleties, is the field due to such a source detectable outside the head? Shorn of its geometrical factors, the Biot–Savart law tells us that the field due to a current dipole of magnitude $I \, \delta l$ at a distance r is of order $10^{-7} \, \mathrm{T \, m \, A^{-1}} \times I \, \delta l / r^2$. Given the thickness of the skull and scalp, we might be able to make a measurement about 3 cm away from a neuron, and at this distance, we might expect a field of 10^{-17} T. None of the existing instruments for measuring magnetic fields, which are called **magnetometers**, have sufficient sensitivity to measure a field this small. However, this is where we get some help from physiology.

In the previous paragraph we chose the phrase 'activity in a single neuron' carefully. As you have seen in Figure 5.14, the brain is organized with some neurons that run parallel to each other and are massively connected. Activity in one neuron is accompanied by activity in others. Although they will not all fire at the same time, they will continue to support longer-lasting background currents throughout the period of activity in that particular part of the brain. Typically, there might be 10^4 to 10^5 neurons with synchronous background activity in a few mm^2 of cortex. The situation is analogous to that found in the heart, where the strongest signal is caused by the synchronous contraction of the muscle cells that make up the ventricles (Figure 5.3). In the present case, the synchronous activity of the large number of neurons in a small area of cortex can give rise to signals that are many orders of magnitude greater than from one neuron alone.

Figure 5.21 shows the magnetic field strengths generated outside the body by a number of biological sources. Also shown are some other natural or technologically relevant fields, and the sensitivity of some magnetometers. The most sensitive type of instrument — a **SQUID magnetometer** — is based on quantum properties of superconducting circuits that incorporate Superconducting Quantum Interference Devices, or SQUIDs. They provide the sensitive elements in the large scanner systems used in **magnetoencephalography**, or MEG, which is the term used for the study of magnetic fields produced by brain activity. In spite of their potential utility, SQUID magnetometers are not in common use in hospitals to measure human electrical activity. This is because mains electricity, small vibrations of nearby metal objects, and even variations in currents in the Earth's ionosphere, all contribute to background fluctuations in the ambient fields. These fluctuations make it very difficult to detect the tiny magnetic fields from bioelectric sources. Sophisticated methods have to be employed to reduce this background 'noise', such as the magnetically screened room shown in Figure 5.22. Inside such rooms, the field noise is reduced typically by a factor of 10^5.

Nevertheless, the technical problems have been gradually overcome, and MEG investigations are now carried out within some large teaching hospitals and research facilities. Typical MEG instruments have several hundred SQUID sensors, enabling them to measure the field simultaneously at many points on a helmet-shaped surface round the head. Frequently, the instruments make use of sensors that are sensitive to the magnetic flux through a circuit that consists of more than one coil. One example is the figure-of-eight arrangement shown

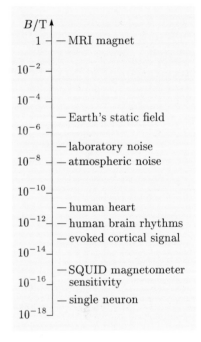

Figure 5.21 Some characteristic magnetic field strengths and magnetometer sensitivities.

Figure 5.22 A magnetically screened room.

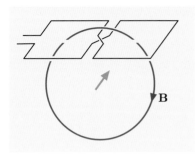

Figure 5.23   A coil system that is most sensitive to directly underlying current in the direction shown.

schematically in Figure 5.23, in which the total magnetic flux through the circuit is the *sum* of the upward flux through the left half and the downward flux though the right half, because of the crossover of the connections in the middle. This arrangement has maximum flux coupling to a current dipole that is directly beneath it, and is oriented as shown in the figure. It is much less sensitive to more distant sources, for which the fluxes through the two halves of the circuit tend to cancel.

One of the most developed uses of such instruments is in preparation for neurosurgery. Although all human brains are broadly similar, the differences are sufficient to create ambiguity about the functional significance of the various cortical folds exposed during surgery. A surgeon carrying out a procedure needs to be able to assess the damage they may cause to brain function, and this is difficult without a functional map. Function can be assessed during the operation by electrically stimulating the cortex, but MEG provides an alternative. By stimulating various parts of the body and observing the MEG signals, it is possible to identify cortical functionality prior to surgery. This technique can be further extended by feeding this coordinate information into 'robotic' systems that guide the surgeon during the operation.

Such techniques are possible when the underlying neural generators can be localized precisely. This is the case for simple sensory and motor (i.e. movement) systems. However, for many brain functions, more sophisticated maps of the activity have to be calculated. This topic is considered further in the next section.

5.4   The magnetic inverse problem

The main focus of this chapter has been on methods of calculating the magnetic field produced by a specified current distribution. This is known as a 'forward' problem, because we are working from cause to effect. In many applications, we need to work in the other direction — given the effect (the magnetic field), can we find the cause (a current distribution)? This is known as an **inverse problem**, and it is very relevant to the biomagnetic measurements discussed in the previous section. Valuable knowledge of how the body is functioning can be obtained if we can use measurements of the magnetic field outside the body to deduce information about the currents within.

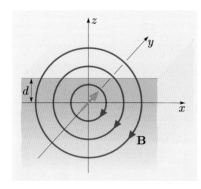

Figure 5.24   A current dipole at depth d below the surface of a conducting material.

A simple example will illustrate the inverse problem method. Suppose that a current dipole lies parallel to the surface of an infinitely wide conducting volume, as shown in Figure 5.24. This arrangement might provide a first approximation to a biological source in the chest. The task is to find that dipole by measuring the perpendicular component of the magnetic field just outside the surface of the conductor.

We choose a Cartesian coordinate system with its origin at the dipole and with the y-axis oriented along the current dipole. You will probably not be too surprised that, by analogy with the conducting sphere discussion, the field component perpendicular to the surface depends only on the current dipole itself: it is not affected by the return currents in the conductor.

Exercise 5.8 Figure 5.24 shows magnetic field lines in the xz-plane associated with the current dipole. Sketch a graph showing qualitatively how the z-component of the field on the surface of the conductor ($z = d$) varies along the x-axis. ■

The next step is to find the x-values of the maximum and minimum. This involves applying the Biot–Savart law. With the geometry in Figure 5.24, Equation 5.3 reduces to

$$\mathbf{B}(\mathbf{r}) = \frac{\mu_0 I \,\delta\mathbf{l}' \times (\mathbf{r} - \mathbf{r}')}{4\pi |\mathbf{r} - \mathbf{r}'|^3} = \frac{\mu_0 I \,\delta l' \, \mathbf{e}_y \times \widehat{\mathbf{r}}}{4\pi r^2}.$$

This field is perpendicular to $\mathbf{r}$ and in the xz-plane, so the z-component of the field is simply

$$B_z = \frac{\mu_0 I \,\delta l'}{4\pi (x^2 + z^2)} \times \frac{-x}{(x^2 + z^2)^{1/2}} = \frac{-\mu_0 I \,\delta l' \, x}{4\pi (x^2 + z^2)^{3/2}}.$$

To find the positions of the maximum and minimum values of B_z, we need to establish where the derivative of B_z with respect to x is zero. Now

$$\frac{\mathrm{d}B_z}{\mathrm{d}x} = \frac{-\mu_0 I \,\delta l'}{4\pi} \left[\frac{(x^2 + z^2)^{3/2} - x \frac{3}{2} 2x \,(x^2 + z^2)^{1/2}}{(x^2 + z^2)^3} \right]$$

$$= \frac{-\mu_0 I \,\delta l'}{4\pi} \left[\frac{(z^2 - 2x^2)(x^2 + z^2)^{1/2}}{(x^2 + z^2)^3} \right].$$

This expression is zero where $(z^2 - 2x^2) = 0$. Since the surface is at $z = d$, the maximum and minimum values of B_z at the surface are at $x = \pm d/\sqrt{2}$, so they are separated by $\sqrt{2}\,d$.

This simple result predicts the positions of the maximum and minimum values of the component of the field perpendicular to the surface from a knowledge of the current source, but it can be used the other way round. If we had measured the perpendicular component of the field and we knew that the source was a small current element, then we could determine its position from the positions of the maximum and minimum. It would lie halfway between these two turning points, at a depth equal to their separation divided by $\sqrt{2}$.

This technique, with numerical modification that reflects the spherical geometry, is used to provide initial estimates of localized sources in the brain. Figure 5.25 shows an example of an MEG signal where the model might be used. In this case, the source was the result of a touch stimulus, and this field pattern was recorded 20 ms after the touch. The red and blue lines are contours of constant field component perpendicular to the scalp. The field is outwards from the scalp where the lines are red, and inwards where they are blue.

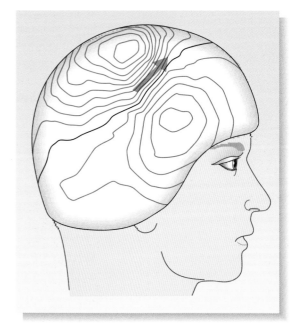

Figure 5.25 An example of a magnetic field whose source might be modelled by a current dipole.

Although the example of an inverse problem presented above is oversimplified, it illustrates one of the most important features of all approaches. We have to make assumptions about the nature of the sources, because the inverse problem is formally insoluble without this additional information. Even if you could measure the field outside a known conductor with infinite accuracy at all points, you could not compute the current sources unambiguously. In fact, there are an infinite number of sources that produce the same external field!

You might be able to suggest why. You have already seen several examples of current distributions that produce no external field, for example, a radial dipole in a conducting sphere. Such a current distribution could be added to any solution without changing the measured field. There are an infinite number of ways of adding radial current sources, so there are an infinite number of solutions. This result is quite general. The problem is further compounded by the existence of source distributions that are very different but produce almost identical external fields. For example, two large oppositely-oriented, but not quite identically located, current dipoles produce almost the same external field as the net current dipole placed at the mid-point between them (Figure 5.26).

These problems can be overcome, or at least minimized, by making assumptions about the sources that are guided by physiological knowledge. For example, we can require the sources to consist of one or more localized current dipoles. This is likely to be appropriate when studying the early stages in the processing of sensory information. However, when more complex brain processing is involved, for example, memory retrieval, decision making, reading, etc., the activity is spread over large areas of the brain. For such situations, we might produce an image showing distributed activity and, in order to avoid the inverse problem ambiguities already discussed, we might choose the solution that corresponds to the lowest electrical power (i.e. with the minimum value of the square of the source current integrated over the conducting volume). This method is widely employed and, with appropriate mathematical implementation, is known to give robust results.

Figure 5.26   These systems produce almost the same magnetic fields outside the spheres.

Summary of Chapter 5

Section 5.1   The relationship between steady currents and magnetic fields is described by Ampère's law:

$$\oint_C \mathbf{B} \cdot d\mathbf{l} = \mu_0 \int_S \mathbf{J} \cdot d\mathbf{S} \quad \text{and} \quad \text{curl}\,\mathbf{B} = \mu_0 \mathbf{J}.$$

The integral version of this law is useful for calculating magnetic fields produced by currents in situations with high symmetry.

Section 5.2   The Biot–Savart law relates the magnetic field to a line integral over a current in a circuit (or a volume integral of a current density):

$$\mathbf{B} = \frac{\mu_0 I}{4\pi} \int_{\text{circuit}} \frac{\delta \mathbf{l}' \times (\mathbf{r} - \mathbf{r}')}{|\mathbf{r} - \mathbf{r}'|^3}.$$

This expression can be used to derive the field of a line current segment, and this is useful for calculating fields due to current loops of complex shapes, and particularly valuable for computer-based calculations.

The existence of a magnetic vector potential **A** is a consequence of the no-monopole equation. **A** is defined by the equation $\mathbf{B} = \text{curl}\,\mathbf{A}$.

Analytic solutions for the field generated by current distributions are generally not possible, and computers are programmed to find solutions using numerical methods.

Section 5.3   Cellular currents in biological organisms produce potential differences that are measured on the surface of the body and (bio)magnetic fields that are measured outside the body. Both provide useful clinical information, but biomagnetic measurements have the advantages that the field is not affected by intervening tissue and there need be no contact between sensing device and the body. The Biot–Savart equation can be used as a simple model of the field produced by intra-cellular currents. This has medical applications in imaging human heart and brain functions.

Section 5.4   The calculation of currents from a knowledge of the associated magnetic fields is known as the magnetic inverse problem. In general, unique solutions to the magnetic inverse problem are not possible unless assumptions are made restricting possible current configurations.

Achievements from Chapter 5

After studying this chapter you should be able to do the following.

5.1   Explain the meanings of the newly defined (emboldened) terms and symbols, and use them appropriately.

5.2   State Ampère's law, and use its integral version to determine magnetic fields in situations with high symmetry.

5.3   Describe qualitatively the relationship between magnetic fields and steady electric currents for simple current patterns.

5.4   State the Biot–Savart law, and use it to calculate the magnetic field for simple current configurations.

5.5   Calculate the magnetic field for current configurations consisting of simple combinations of line current segments and circular loops.

5.6   Recall that the magnetic vector potential **A** is defined by $\mathbf{B} = \text{curl}\,\mathbf{A}$.

5.7   Describe qualitatively how magnetic fields are used in the investigation of bioelectric currents, and describe the fields produced by simple sources in a conducting material.

5.8   Estimate the strength, location and direction of a magnetic dipole from its associated magnetic field in certain specific situations.

Chapter 6   Forces on charged particles

We have discussed in some detail how electric and magnetic fields can be calculated from knowledge of charges and currents. But the main reason that these fields are of interest is that they affect the charges and currents in the regions where they exist. The interaction of charges and currents with electric and magnetic fields gives rise to a wide range of natural phenomena and is the basis for many important technological devices. In this chapter we shall discuss some of these phenomena and devices and the physics necessary to understand them.

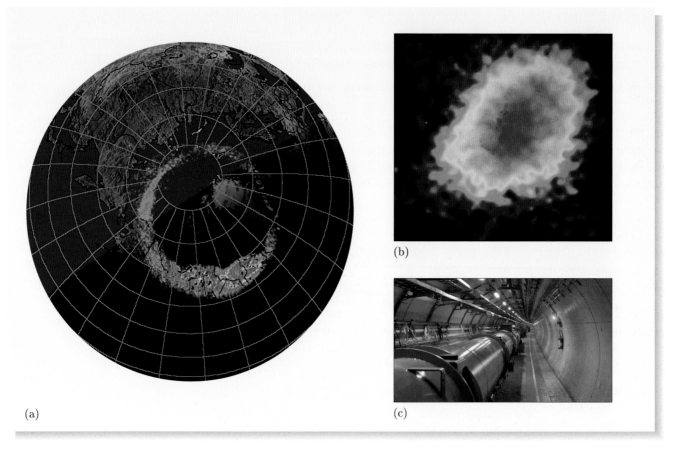

(a)

(b)

(c)

Figure 6.1   Three situations where charged particles interact with electric and/or magnetic fields. (a) The aurora borealis, viewed from space in false colour. (b) The Crab Nebula, imaged by a radio telescope. (c) Part of the Large Hadron Collider (LHC) at CERN, pictured during construction.

In Figure 6.1a, the coloured ring around the north magnetic pole shows where charged particles trapped by the Earth's magnetic field interact with molecules in the atmosphere. The Crab Nebula (Figure 6.1b) is the remnants of a supernova explosion which took place almost 1000 years ago. The radio waves that produced this image were emitted by energetic charged particles as they spiralled around the strong magnetic field associated with a pulsar at the centre of the nebula. In the LHC at CERN (Figure 6.1c), beams of lead nuclei (charge $82e$, energy $575\,\text{TeV}$) will circulate in opposite directions in two concentric rings in the 27 km-long tunnel before they intersect and some of the nuclei collide. Vertical magnetic fields, magnitude $8.5\,\text{T}$ and in opposite directions for the two rings, provide the necessary centripetal force.

We shall first consider some important general properties of the Lorentz force, and then discuss situations that involve only a single uniform field. This will lead to consideration of cases where both electric and magnetic fields are present, and we shall conclude the chapter by looking at examples where particles are moving in non-uniform magnetic fields.

6.1 The Lorentz force law

The interaction between charged particles and electric and magnetic fields is encapsulated in the following important law.

Lorentz force law

$$\mathbf{F} = q(\mathbf{E} + \mathbf{v} \times \mathbf{B}).\tag{6.1}$$

This law specifies the electromagnetic force $\mathbf{F}$ that acts on a particle with charge q moving at velocity $\mathbf{v}$ at a point where there is an electric field $\mathbf{E}$ and a magnetic field $\mathbf{B}$. If we know the electric and magnetic fields, together with the mass, charge and initial position and velocity of a particle, we can use the Lorentz force law to predict the subsequent motion of the particle. Conversely, it is possible to infer what electric and magnetic fields are present in a region by observing the motion of charged particles.

6.1.1 General properties of the Lorentz force

The Lorentz force law is a *local* relationship between the force on a charged particle and the electric field $\mathbf{E}$ and the magnetic field $\mathbf{B}$ *at the point* in space and time where the particle is located. The law applies to both uniform and spatially-varying fields, and to both static and time-dependent fields.

There are several important points to remember about the Lorentz force that are implicit in Equation 6.1. The first is that the electric force $q\mathbf{E}$ is parallel to the electric field $\mathbf{E}$ and is independent of the particle's velocity. Second, the magnetic force $q\mathbf{v} \times \mathbf{B}$ is perpendicular both to the particle's velocity $\mathbf{v}$ and to the magnetic field $\mathbf{B}$, with its direction given by the right-hand rule. The magnitude of the magnetic force is zero for a stationary particle. Generally, the direction of the total Lorentz force is not parallel to $\mathbf{E}$, nor perpendicular to $\mathbf{v}$ and $\mathbf{B}$.

We can make another important general observation about the Lorentz force by considering its scalar product with the particle's velocity, which is the rate at which energy is transferred to the particle:

$$\begin{aligned}\mathbf{F} \cdot \mathbf{v} &= q(\mathbf{E} + \mathbf{v} \times \mathbf{B}) \cdot \mathbf{v} \\ &= q\big(\mathbf{E} \cdot \mathbf{v} + (\mathbf{v} \times \mathbf{B}) \cdot \mathbf{v}\big) \\ &= q\mathbf{E} \cdot \mathbf{v}.\end{aligned}\tag{6.2}$$

The term $(\mathbf{v} \times \mathbf{B}) \cdot \mathbf{v}$ is zero because $\mathbf{v} \times \mathbf{B}$ is perpendicular to $\mathbf{v}$. To demonstrate the significance of Equation 6.2, we use Newton's second law to

The *electronvolt*, abbreviated to eV, is a conveniently-sized unit for expressing energies of electrons, protons, atoms and nuclei. It is the change in energy of an electron when displaced through a potential difference of 1 V. Thus $1\,\text{eV} = 1.6 \times 10^{-19}\,\text{J}$ and $1\,\text{TeV} = 10^{12}\,\text{eV} = 1.6 \times 10^{-7}\,\text{J}$.

rewrite the left-hand side as follows:

$$\mathbf{F} \cdot \mathbf{v} = m\frac{d\mathbf{v}}{dt} \cdot \mathbf{v}$$

$$= m\left(\frac{dv_x}{dt}v_x + \frac{dv_y}{dt}v_y + \frac{dv_z}{dt}v_z\right)$$

$$= \tfrac{1}{2}m\left(\frac{dv_x^2}{dt} + \frac{dv_y^2}{dt} + \frac{dv_z^2}{dt}\right)$$

$$= \tfrac{1}{2}m\frac{d}{dt}(v^2)$$

$$= \frac{d}{dt}\left(\tfrac{1}{2}mv^2\right). \tag{6.3}$$

Comparing Equations 6.2 and 6.3, we obtain

$$\mathbf{F} \cdot \mathbf{v} = \frac{d}{dt}\left(\tfrac{1}{2}mv^2\right) = q\mathbf{E} \cdot \mathbf{v}.$$

This indicates that the rate of change of the particle's kinetic energy is due only to the electric field $\mathbf{E}$, not to the magnetic field $\mathbf{B}$. This is consistent with the fact that the magnetic force $q(\mathbf{v} \times \mathbf{B})$ is always perpendicular to the velocity — it changes only the direction of motion, not the speed. Thus a static magnetic field cannot change the kinetic energy of a charged particle. We shall often make use of this fact in this chapter. However, remember that a *time-dependent* magnetic field gives rise to an electric field (Faraday's law: $\mathrm{curl}\,\mathbf{E} = -\partial\mathbf{B}/\partial t$), and this electric field will change a particle's kinetic energy.

Note that we have used the non-relativistic expression for the force, $\mathbf{F} = m\,d\mathbf{v}/dt$, in the analysis above. For particle speeds that approach the speed of light, we should use the more general expression

$$\mathbf{F} = \frac{d\mathbf{p}}{dt},$$

where $\mathbf{p} = \dfrac{m\mathbf{v}}{\sqrt{1 - (v^2/c^2)}}$ is the relativistic momentum. However, this does not affect the conclusions we reached above. In this chapter we shall be concerned mainly with non-relativistic situations, though we shall point out a number of instances where relativistic effects come into play. Note that for $v < c/10 = 3 \times 10^7$ m s^{-1}, the relativistic correction to the force is less than $\tfrac{1}{2}\%$.

6.2   The Lorentz force in uniform fields

We now consider the Lorentz force acting on a particle moving through electric and magnetic fields that are both *uniform* — that is, independent of position — and *constant* — that is, independent of time. We start by discussing simple situations when either $\mathbf{B}$ or $\mathbf{E}$ is zero.

6.2.1   Uniform electric field

If a charged particle is moving at non-relativistic speeds through a region where $\mathbf{E}$ is uniform and $\mathbf{B} = \mathbf{0}$, then the Lorentz force is simply

$$\mathbf{F} = m\frac{d\mathbf{v}}{dt} = q\mathbf{E}. \tag{6.4}$$

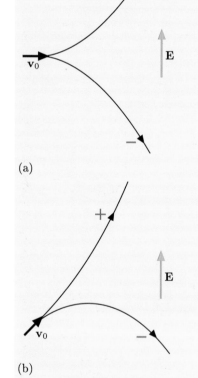

(a)

(b)

Figure 6.2 Parabolic paths followed by charged particles in a uniform electric field.

This equation is analogous to the equation of motion for a mass m in a uniform gravitational field $\mathbf{g}$, namely $\mathbf{F} = m\,d\mathbf{v}/dt = m\mathbf{g}$, and it has solutions, analogous to those for projectile motion, that can be derived from the constant acceleration equations:

$$\mathbf{v} = \mathbf{v}_0 + \frac{q\mathbf{E}}{m}t \quad \text{and} \quad \mathbf{r} = \mathbf{r}_0 + \mathbf{v}_0 t + \tfrac{1}{2}\frac{q\mathbf{E}}{m}t^2.$$

Figure 6.2 shows the parabolic paths of positive and negative charges in a uniform vertical field. The particles have the same mass, the same charge magnitude and the same initial speed v_0, but the direction of the initial velocity $\mathbf{v}_0$ is different in parts (a) and (b) of the figure. The horizontal components of velocity are unaffected by the vertical electric field, but the positively-charged particles accelerate in the direction of the electric field, and the negatively-charged particles accelerate in the opposite direction.

6.2.2 Scanning electron microscope

A scanning electron microscope, like the one shown in Figure 3 of the Introduction to this book, uses a beam of electrons to produce images of the microscopic world that have a far higher resolution than is possible with an optical microscope. The beam is controlled by electric and magnetic fields, which accelerate, focus and steer the electrons between the electron source and the specimen. Figure 6.3 shows some of the main components of a scanning electron microscope.

At the top of the microscope is an **electron gun**, in which electrons are emitted from a heated tungsten filament, the **cathode**, which is held at a large negative potential, and accelerated towards a second electrode, the **anode**, which is at earth potential and therefore at a high positive potential relative to the cathode. For typical scanning electron microscopes this potential difference can be between 1 and 50 kV. The electrons then pass through a series of lenses, which control the brightness of the beam and focus it onto a small spot on the specimen. A proportion of the electrons that strike the specimen are scattered back and are collected by the electron detector, and the resulting current is amplified and provides the input signal to a video monitor. The scanning coils produce magnetic fields in two perpendicular directions, both perpendicular to the beam, and by varying the current in the coils, the beam is scanned across the specimen in a raster pattern that sweeps sequentially along parallel lines to cover a small rectangular area, in the same way that the image on a TV screen is built up (see Figure 6.5 on page 121). The time dependence of the rate at which back-scattered electrons are detected leads to a time-dependent signal at the video display which is converted to a two-dimensional image by synchronizing the raster patterns of the electron beam and the video display. The image magnification is simply the ratio of the width of the video display to the length of a raster line on the specimen.

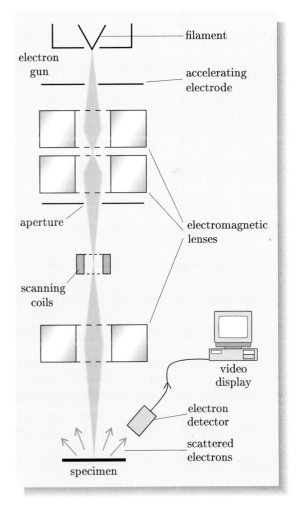

Figure 6.3 Main components of a scanning electron microscope.

In later sections we shall consider the magnetic fields required for the scanning coils, and the focusing effect of magnetic lenses, but the following exercise looks at the acceleration of electrons in the electron gun.

Exercise 6.1   Assume that the cathode of the microscope depicted in Figure 6.3 emits electrons into a region where there is an accelerating electric field of 3.0×10^4 V m^{-1}, which extends over a length of 5.0 cm. What is the speed of the electrons as they leave this field? (Assume that the field is uniform and that the electrons' initial speed is negligible.) ■

6.2.3 Uniform magnetic field

We now consider motion of a charged particle in a uniform magnetic field, but with $\mathbf{E} = \mathbf{0}$. The equation of motion is

$$\mathbf{F} = m\frac{d\mathbf{v}}{dt} = q\mathbf{v} \times \mathbf{B}.$$

If we choose the z-axis to be in the direction of $\mathbf{B}$, i.e. $\mathbf{B} = B\mathbf{e}_z$, we can then write the components of the acceleration as

In this case,

$$\mathbf{v} \times \mathbf{B} = \begin{vmatrix} \mathbf{e}_x & \mathbf{e}_y & \mathbf{e}_z \\ v_x & v_y & v_z \\ 0 & 0 & B \end{vmatrix}.$$

$$\frac{dv_x}{dt} = \frac{q}{m}[\mathbf{v} \times \mathbf{B}]_x = \frac{qB}{m}v_y,$$

$$\frac{dv_y}{dt} = \frac{q}{m}[\mathbf{v} \times \mathbf{B}]_y = -\frac{qB}{m}v_x, \tag{6.5}$$

$$\frac{dv_z}{dt} = 0.$$

As you might have anticipated from the comments in Subsection 6.1.1, there is no acceleration in the direction of the magnetic field, the z-direction.

The differential equations involving v_x and v_y in Equations 6.5 are coupled, but if we differentiate them with respect to time, then we obtain

$$\frac{d^2v_x}{dt^2} = \frac{qB}{m}\frac{dv_y}{dt} = -\left(\frac{qB}{m}\right)^2 v_x, \quad \frac{d^2v_y}{dt^2} = -\frac{qB}{m}\frac{dv_x}{dt} = -\left(\frac{qB}{m}\right)^2 v_y.$$

These differential equations have simple solutions. Both v_x and v_y vary sinusoidally with time with angular frequency qB/m, and the phases of the two sinusoidal functions are linked by Equations 6.5. The general solution is

$$\mathbf{v} = v_\perp \sin\left(\frac{qB}{m}t + \phi_0\right)\mathbf{e}_x + v_\perp \cos\left(\frac{qB}{m}t + \phi_0\right)\mathbf{e}_y + v_\parallel\mathbf{e}_z, \tag{6.6}$$

as you can verify by substituting the velocity components into Equations 6.5. Note that $v_x^2 + v_y^2 = v_\perp^2$, so $v_\perp$ represents a constant speed in a plane perpendicular to the field. Also, the velocity component parallel to the field, $v_z = v_\parallel$, is constant, so $v^2 = v_x^2 + v_y^2 + v_z^2$ is also constant. Thus the particle's kinetic energy remains constant, as required for a particle experiencing a magnetic force only. The constant ϕ_0 is a phase that depends on the initial conditions.

It is straightforward to integrate Equation 6.6 to give

$$\mathbf{r} = \left[x_0 - \frac{mv_\perp}{qB}\cos\left(\frac{qB}{m}t + \phi_0\right)\right]\mathbf{e}_x$$

$$+ \left[y_0 + \frac{mv_\perp}{qB}\sin\left(\frac{qB}{m}t + \phi_0\right)\right]\mathbf{e}_y + (z_0 + v_\parallel t)\mathbf{e}_z. \tag{6.7}$$

The x- and y-components of this solution represent uniform circular motion in a plane perpendicular to the field. This circular motion is centred on the point (x_0, y_0) and has an angular frequency qB/m. Superimposed on the circular motion is a drift at uniform velocity in the direction parallel to the field. Thus the path of the charged particle describes a helix in three dimensions, as shown in Figure 6.4.

The angular frequency ω_c of a charged particle's motion in a magnetic field is known as the (angular) **cyclotron frequency** ω_c:

$$\omega_c = \frac{|q|B}{m}. \tag{6.8}$$

We shall explain the origin of the term *cyclotron* in the next subsection. The period corresponding to this frequency is often referred to as the **cyclotron period** T_c,

and is simply $2\pi/\omega_c = 2\pi m/|q|B$. The radius of the particle's circular orbit is known as its **cyclotron radius** r_c,

and is given by the amplitude of the cosine and sine terms in Equation 6.7:

$$r_c = \frac{mv_\perp}{|q|B}. \tag{6.9}$$

Thus particles with greater charge to mass ratios and particles in stronger magnetic fields will have greater cyclotron frequencies (shorter periods). Also, for a given value of $v_\perp$, greater charge to mass ratios and stronger magnetic fields lead to smaller cyclotron radii. However, note that the cyclotron frequency is independent of the particle's speed when relativistic effects can be ignored, because any change in speed is balanced by a corresponding change in the cyclotron radius, so the time required to complete an orbit stays the same. When the particle's speed approaches the speed of light, the m in Equation 6.8 must be replaced by $m/\sqrt{1 - (v^2/c^2)}$, which means that the cyclotron frequency then decreases.

Positively-charged particles spiral around the field direction in the opposite sense to negatively-charged particles.

Exercise 6.2 (a) Use the right-hand rule to determine the sign of the charge of a particle that follows the path shown in Figure 6.4.

(b) By evaluating the x- and y-components of position and velocity when $\omega_c t = 0$ and $\omega_c t = \pi/2$, show that the solution represented by Equations 6.6 and 6.7 for the case where $x_0 = 0$, $y_0 = 0$ and $\phi_0 = 0$ corresponds to a positively-charged particle travelling anticlockwise around the positive z-axis, in the same direction as shown in Figure 6.4.

Exercise 6.3 A scanning electron microscope uses magnetic fields to scan the electron beam in a raster pattern, as discussed in Subsection 6.2.2 and shown in Figure 6.5. The speed of the electrons is 2.3×10^7 m s^{-1}, as calculated in Exercise 6.1. What are the direction and strength of the magnetic field required to deflect the scanning beam a distance of $x_s = 5.0\,\mu$m in the $+x$-direction? You should assume that the coils produce a constant magnetic field over a distance $z_m = 1$ mm along the beam path, and that the specimen is at a distance $z_s = 10$ cm below the scanning coils. ∎

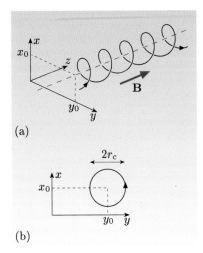

Figure 6.4 (a) With a uniform magnetic field in the z-direction, a charged particle travels in a helical path, with the helix axis in the z-direction. (b) Viewed along the z-direction, the path appears circular.

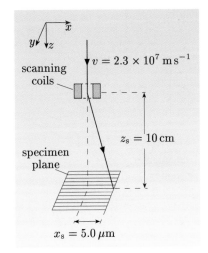

Figure 6.5 Using a magnetic field to scan an electron beam across a specimen in a scanning electron microscope. The parameters are for use in Exercise 6.3.

The direction of deflection of charged particles by a magnetic field can always be determined by using the right-hand rule. However, it is also helpful to remember the following.

> When viewed along the direction that the field vector points, positively-charged particles are always deflected in an anticlockwise direction, whereas negatively-charged particles are always deflected in a clockwise direction.

6.2.4   The cyclotron

The word 'cyclotron' comes from one of the oldest types of particle accelerator, which uses electric fields to accelerate charged particles while they are travelling in circular orbits perpendicular to a magnetic field. The layout of a cyclotron is shown schematically in Figure 6.6a. It is composed of two D-shaped hollow metal sections (dees), with a magnetic field perpendicular to the plane of the dees. Charged particles are injected horizontally near the centre of the cyclotron, and travel in circles with the cyclotron radius $r_c = mv_\perp/|q|B$ at the cyclotron frequency $\omega_c = |q|B/m$.

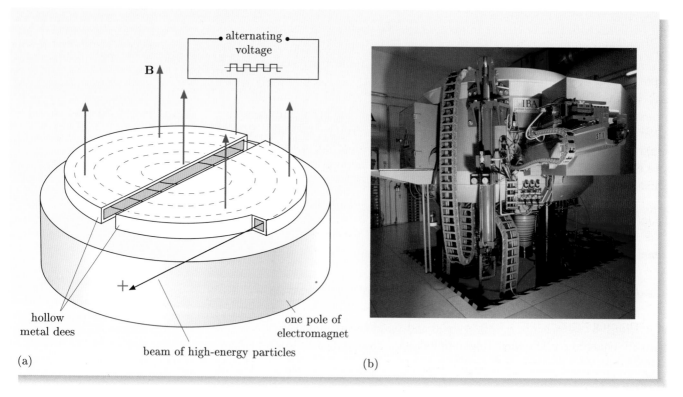

(a)

(b)

Figure 6.6   (a) The particles in a cyclotron follow a spiral path between the injection point, near to the centre, and the exit point. An alternating voltage difference between the dees accelerates the particles each time they cross the gap. (The top pole of the magnet has been omitted for clarity.) (b) A hospital cyclotron.

To accelerate the particles, a large voltage difference is applied between the two dees, so that the electric field produced in the gap between the dees is in the appropriate direction to accelerate the particles at they cross the gap. Within the hollow metal dees there is no electric field, so the particles travel at constant speed in a circular orbit. When the particles are halfway round the dee, the potential difference is reversed, so when the particles cross the gap again, the electric field accelerates them further. By alternating the potential difference at the cyclotron frequency, the energy of the particles is boosted each time they cross the gap. As the energy of the particles increases, the radius of their orbit increases, but the cyclotron frequency remains the same. When the orbit reaches the maximum radius, the particles can be deflected out of the cyclotron by a large electrostatic field.

Cyclotrons are still used to accelerate particles that are then injected into much more powerful particle accelerators. However, they are also increasingly used in hospitals to prepare short-lived radioactive samples. A typical hospital cyclotron (Figure 6.6b) produces 30 MeV protons that strike selected targets to generate radioactive isotopes for use in medical imaging.

Worked Example 6.1

The cyclotron in Figure 6.6b has an outer radius of 1.1 m and produces 30 MeV protons. Calculate

(a) the magnetic field required (assumed uniform),

(b) the angular frequency of the alternating voltage difference applied to the dees,

(c) the time taken to accelerate a proton from 10 keV to 30 MeV, if the alternating voltage difference has an amplitude of 500 V.

Essential skill

Using the Lorentz force law

Solution

(a) For a uniform magnetic field, the radius of the cyclotron orbit increases with the speed and energy of the proton, so the maximum kinetic energy of 30 MeV corresponds to the outer radius of 1.1 m. The orbit radius is $r_c = mv_\perp/|q|B$, and using the relationship between speed and kinetic energy ($v_\perp = \sqrt{2E_{kin}/m}$) to eliminate $v_\perp$, we can obtain an expression for the field needed to maintain an orbit, in terms of the orbit radius and kinetic energy:

$$B = \frac{mv_\perp}{|q|r_c} = \frac{\sqrt{2mE_{kin}}}{|q|r_c}.$$

Substituting the values of the maximum energy and the outer radius, we find

$$B = \frac{(2 \times 1.67 \times 10^{-27}\,\text{kg} \times 3.0 \times 10^7\,\text{eV} \times 1.60 \times 10^{-19}\,\text{J eV}^{-1})^{1/2}}{1.6 \times 10^{-19}\,\text{C} \times 1.1\,\text{m}}$$

$$= 0.72\,\text{T}.$$

Note that we have used the relationship $1\,\text{eV} = 1.6 \times 10^{-19}\,\text{J}$ to convert the proton energy to joules, the SI unit for energy.

(b) The voltage must alternate at the cyclotron frequency; this will ensure that the electric field is in opposite directions for alternate crossings of the gap between the dees, but is always in the direction that accelerates the proton. The angular frequency required is

$$\omega_c = \frac{|q|B}{m} = \frac{1.60 \times 10^{-19}\,\text{C} \times 0.72\,\text{T}}{1.67 \times 10^{-27}\,\text{kg}} = 6.9 \times 10^7\,\text{rad s}^{-1}.$$

(c) In each complete orbit, the proton crosses the gap twice, and on each crossing its energy increases by $q\,\Delta V = 500\,\text{keV}$, i.e. 1 keV per orbit. For the energy to increase from 10 keV to 30 MeV, a difference of 29 990 keV, requires 29 990 orbits. Since the period of the orbit is $2\pi/\omega_c$, the time required is

$$29\,990 \times \frac{2\pi}{\omega_c} = 29\,990 \times \frac{2\pi}{6.9 \times 10^7\,\text{rad s}^{-1}} = 2.7 \times 10^{-3}\,\text{s}.$$

Exercise 6.4   Suppose that the cyclotron magnet described in Worked Example 6.1 is to be used to accelerate negatively-charged deuterium ions, D^-, which have mass twice that of a proton and the same net charge as an electron. What modifications will be required to the frequency of the oscillator, and to the injection and extraction arrangements, and what will be the maximum energy of the emerging ions?   ∎

Relativistic effects limit the maximum energy of the protons delivered by a cyclotron to about 30 MeV. As the protons speed up, their inertia increases by a factor $(1 - v^2/c^2)^{-1/2}$, and their cyclotron frequency therefore decreases. This means that their orbits will not be synchronized with the alternating field, so no further acceleration can occur. This limitation is overcome in the synchrotron, a type of cyclotron in which the frequency of the alternating field is reduced as the proton's energy increases. The Tevatron, at Fermilab in the USA, can accelerate protons to 1 TeV, that is, 10^{12} eV.

6.2.5   Magnetic field parallel to electric field

We now consider the case where both **E** and **B** are uniform and parallel to the z-axis. Since the electric and magnetic fields are parallel, the forces due to these fields must be perpendicular. The electric force acts in the z-direction, so changes only v_z, and the magnetic force is perpendicular to the z-axis, so changes only v_x and v_y. Therefore, the xy part of the solution obtained for a uniform **B** field and **E** = **0** is also the solution for the present case. Likewise, the solution for a uniform **E** field and **B** = **0** is applicable to the motion in the z-direction in this case. Combining the two solutions, the velocity is

$$\mathbf{v} = v_\perp \sin\left(\frac{qB}{m}t + \phi_0\right)\mathbf{e}_x + v_\perp \cos\left(\frac{qB}{m}t + \phi_0\right)\mathbf{e}_y$$

$$+ \left(v_{0\parallel} + \frac{qE}{m}t\right)\mathbf{e}_z, \tag{6.10}$$

where $v_\perp$ is the (constant) speed in the plane perpendicular to **B**, and $v_{0\parallel}$ is the velocity component parallel to **B** (the z-direction) at time $t = 0$.

● How does the path traversed by a particle in this situation differ from the helical path for the **E** = **0** case shown in Figure 6.4?

○ Motion in the xy-plane is unaffected by the field $E\mathbf{e}_z$, so viewed along the z-axis the path will still appear circular. However, Equation 6.10 indicates that there is a uniform acceleration qE/m in the z-direction, and this means that the spacing between successive turns of the spiral increases.

Collimating a particle beam

Using a uniform electric field to accelerate electrons emitted from a heated cathode source will not produce a very narrow beam. The electrons will be emitted in all directions, and will have typical speeds in the plane perpendicular to the electric field of $v_\perp \sim \sqrt{2k_BT/m}$, where k_B is Boltzmann's constant and T is the absolute temperature of the cathode. The motion perpendicular to the electric field will not be affected by the electric field. So the beam will continue to diverge after the electrons have been accelerated.

Thermal energy of the emitted electrons is $\frac{1}{2}m(v_x^2 + v_y^2 + v_z^2) \sim \frac{3}{2}k_BT$, or for motion in the plane perpendicular to the electric field, $\frac{1}{2}m(v_x^2 + v_y^2) = \frac{1}{2}mv_\perp^2 \sim k_BT$.

We can estimate the divergence of the beam by comparing an electron's velocity components in the directions parallel and perpendicular to the axis of the beam. If we ignore the initial velocity component parallel to the field direction, then after being accelerated through a voltage V, the electron's component of velocity parallel to the beam is given by $\frac{1}{2}mv_\parallel^2 = eV$, or $v_\parallel = \sqrt{2eV/m}$, which is about 3×10^7 m s^{-1} for $V = 2.5$ kV. The typical speed in the plane perpendicular to the beam is $v_\perp \sim \sqrt{2k_BT/m} \sim 3 \times 10^5$ m s^{-1}, assuming a source temperature of 2700 K. Thus the ratio $v_\parallel : v_\perp$ is about $100 : 1$, and after the electrons have travelled 50 cm, the beam radius will be about 5 mm.

One way to reduce the divergence of the beam is to apply a magnetic field parallel to the beam.

● What effect will this magnetic field have on the trajectories of electrons initially travelling (a) along the beam axis, and (b) at a small angle to the beam axis?

○ The magnetic field parallel to the axis will have no effect on electrons travelling along the axis, since $\mathbf{v} \times \mathbf{B} = \mathbf{0}$ for parallel vectors. Electrons travelling at an angle to the axis will follow a clockwise helical path parallel to the field direction, with a radius $r_c = mv_\perp/eB$, and an angular frequency $\omega_c = eB/m$.

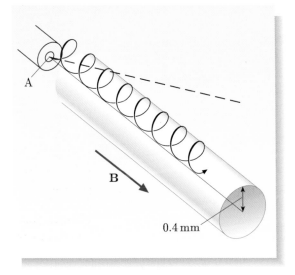

Figure 6.7   Helical path followed by an electron emerging from an electron gun at point A. In the absence of the field $\mathbf{B}$, the electron would follow the linear path shown by the broken line. ($v_\perp/v_\parallel$ is exaggerated for clarity.)

If we used a long solenoid to produce a field of 3×10^{-3} T parallel to the beam, then the cyclotron radius for electrons with $v_\perp \sim 3 \times 10^5$ m s^{-1} would be $r_c \sim 0.2$ mm. The radius of the beam would be twice this value, that is, about 0.4 mm, since the orbits all pass through the beam axis rather than being centred on it. Note that this beam radius is a factor of about ten smaller than the beam radius after 50 cm that we calculated above with no magnetic field. Figure 6.7 compares an electron's helical path in a magnetic field with its linear trajectory in the absence of the field. The field clearly converts the diverging beam of electrons to a parallel beam, a process known as **collimation**. What is more, if we had a sufficiently long solenoid, we could confine the beam within this 0.4 mm radius over any distance required.

Essential skill

Using the Lorentz force law

Worked Example 6.2

Electrons emerge through a small hole in the anode of an electron gun after being accelerated through a potential difference of $1.5\,\mathrm{kV}$. They form a diverging beam, spread over a range of about $\frac{1}{2}^{\circ}$ from the beam's axis. The beam must be focused onto a point $0.25\,\mathrm{m}$ away on the axis of the gun. What uniform magnetic field $\mathbf{B}$ would do this?

Solution

The discussion above indicates that a magnetic field parallel to the beam axis is likely to do the job.

The velocity component $v_{\parallel}$ of the electrons parallel to the axis of the gun obeys $eV = \frac{1}{2}mv_{\parallel}^2$, so $v_{\parallel} = \sqrt{2eV/m}$. All of the electrons have essentially the same value of $v_{\parallel}$ since they have been accelerated by the same electric field, and all of them have the same cyclotron frequency $\omega_{\mathrm{c}} = eB/m$ and therefore the same cyclotron period $T_{\mathrm{c}} = 2\pi/\omega_{\mathrm{c}} = 2\pi m/eB$. This means that all of the electrons that emerge from the anode will complete one cyclotron orbit in time T_{c}, all will travel an axial distance of $v_{\parallel}T_{\mathrm{c}}$ in that time, and all will return to the beam's axis at the same point, irrespective of their value of $v_{\perp}$. We require that point to be a distance $d = 0.25\,\mathrm{m}$ from the anode, where

$$d = v_{\parallel}T_{\mathrm{c}} = \left(\frac{2eV}{m}\right)^{1/2}\frac{2\pi m}{eB} = \frac{2\pi}{B}\left(\frac{2mV}{e}\right)^{1/2}.$$

The field strength B needed is therefore

$$B = \frac{2\pi}{d}\left(\frac{2mV}{e}\right)^{1/2}$$

$$= \frac{2\pi}{0.25\,\mathrm{m}}\left(\frac{2 \times 9.11 \times 10^{-31}\,\mathrm{kg} \times 1.5 \times 10^3\,\mathrm{V}}{1.60 \times 10^{-19}\,\mathrm{C}}\right)^{1/2}$$

$$= 3.3 \times 10^{-3}\,\mathrm{T}.$$

Exercise 6.5   What magnetic field strength is required to collimate electrons from a small source within a beam of radius $5\,\mathrm{mm}$, given that the electrons were generated from a source at a temperature of $10^3\,\mathrm{K}$? ■

You can reinforce your understanding of the Lorentz force law by viewing the video sequence *Bending magnets* on the course DVD, which shows how charged particles were accelerated, steered and focused at the Nuclear Structure Facility at Daresbury.

6.3   Dynamics in non-uniform magnetic fields

Coils and magnets are often designed to produce uniform fields in a particular region. However, there are many situations where magnetic fields are required with specific forms of non-uniformity, for example, to contain charged particles for nuclear fusion experiments. So we now consider some aspects of the dynamics of charged particles in non-uniform magnetic fields. Note that a magnetic field can be non-uniform in strength or in direction, or non-uniform in both strength *and* direction.

In Subsection 6.3.1 we consider a case where the direction of the field varies but its strength is essentially constant, and in Subsection 6.3.2 we consider a field that is uniform in direction but varies in strength. In both cases we assume that the magnetic field has a relatively small spatial gradient, so the field does not change significantly on the scale of a cyclotron radius. You will see that particles still follow spiralling paths, but rather than a path remaining centred around a particular field line, the spiral path drifts slowly in a direction perpendicular to the field lines. Finally, in Subsection 6.3.3, we shall show how non-uniform magnetic fields can be used to produce a 'magnetic bottle' to contain charged particles.

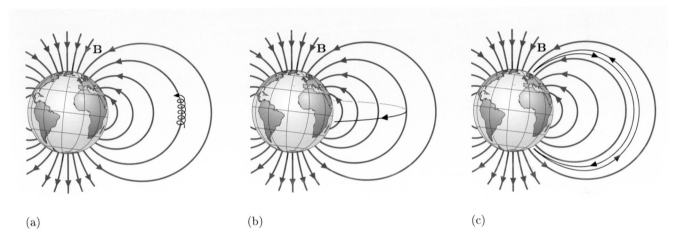

Figure 6.8   Three types of motion of charged particles in the Earth's field: (a) cyclotron motion, (b) transverse drift, (c) bouncing between poles.

All of these effects are illustrated by the motion of charged particles in the magnetic field surrounding the Earth, as shown schematically in Figure 6.8. Electrons and ions spiral around field lines (Figure 6.8a), and because the field lines are curved and the strength depends on position, the helical paths are displaced transversely (Figure 6.8b). In addition, the increase in field strength towards the poles causes the particles to bounce back and forth between the poles (Figure 6.8c). We shall discuss all of these effects in this section.

6.3.1   Magnetic fields with varying direction

We first consider a magnetic field where the field strength is constant along each field line but the direction of the field varies. Specifically, we shall consider the case of a circular field line, radius R_B, centred on the z-axis, as shown in Figure 6.9. Using cylindrical coordinates, the magnetic field vector can be written as $\mathbf{B} = B\mathbf{e}_\phi$. We assume that $R_B \gg r_c$, so the field does not vary appreciably over a distance of a cyclotron radius.

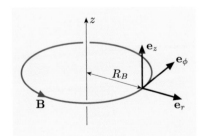

Figure 6.9   A circular field line of radius R_B centred on the z-axis. The local unit vectors $(\mathbf{e}_r, \mathbf{e}_\phi, \mathbf{e}_z)$ of a cylindrical coordinate system are shown.

We shall seek a solution that corresponds to a particle spiralling around this circular magnetic field line. Since the directions of $\mathbf{e}_r$ and $\mathbf{e}_\phi$ depend on the particle's position, the equation of motion is

$$
\begin{aligned}
\frac{d\mathbf{v}}{dt} &= \frac{dv_r}{dt}\mathbf{e}_r + \frac{dv_\phi}{dt}\mathbf{e}_\phi + \frac{dv_z}{dt}\mathbf{e}_z + v_r\frac{d\mathbf{e}_r}{dt} + v_\phi\frac{d\mathbf{e}_\phi}{dt} \\
&= \frac{q}{m}\mathbf{v} \times \mathbf{B} \\
&= \frac{q}{m}(v_r\mathbf{e}_r + v_\phi\mathbf{e}_\phi + v_z\mathbf{e}_z) \times B\mathbf{e}_\phi \\
&= \frac{q}{m}(-v_z B\mathbf{e}_r + v_r B\mathbf{e}_z).
\end{aligned}
\tag{6.11}
$$

Initially, we shall ignore the time dependence of the unit vectors, and this allows us to write the components of Equation 6.11 as

$$
\frac{dv_r}{dt} = -\frac{qB}{m}v_z, \quad \frac{dv_\phi}{dt} = 0, \quad \frac{dv_z}{dt} = \frac{qB}{m}v_r.
\tag{6.12}
$$

These equations have a similar form to Equations 6.5, so describe a spiral motion at the cyclotron frequency, $\omega_c = |q|B/m$, about the magnetic field direction. The particle has a constant speed $v_\phi = v_\parallel$ along the field line, and a constant speed $v_\perp$ in the plane perpendicular to the field line. However, we need to take into account the corrections to this motion which arise because of the time dependence of the unit vectors $\mathbf{e}_r$ and $\mathbf{e}_\phi$. Solving the full equations from scratch is rather laborious, so we shall present a simple physical argument.

For the particle to move around a circular path of radius R_B with velocity component v_ϕ, it must have an additional acceleration, a centripetal acceleration, equal to $-(v_\phi^2/R_B)\mathbf{e}_r$. This requires a force $-m(v_\phi^2/R_B)\mathbf{e}_r$ in addition to the force responsible for the cyclotron motion.

● Suppose that a positively-charged particle spiralling around the field line shown in Figure 6.9 has a slow drift in the $+z$-direction, velocity $v_{zd}\mathbf{e}_z$, superimposed on its cyclotron motion. What is the magnetic force that acts on the particle as a consequence of this drift?

○ The magnetic force due to the drift is

$$
\mathbf{F} = q(v_{zd}\mathbf{e}_z) \times B\mathbf{e}_\phi = -qv_{zd}B\mathbf{e}_r.
$$

This has a constant magnitude and is directed towards the axis on which the circular field line is centred.

So the centripetal force required for the particle to follow an orbit around the z-axis, radius R_B, can be generated if the particle drifts at an appropriate velocity in the $+z$-direction. The required velocity component, v_{zd}, is found by equating the centripetal force to the magnetic force:

$$
-m(v_\phi^2/R_B)\mathbf{e}_r = -qv_{zd}B\mathbf{e}_r,
$$

so

$$
v_{zd} = \frac{mv_\phi^2}{qBR_B}.
$$

The effect of the field lines being circular rather than linear is to superimpose a steady drift in the z-direction onto the spiral motion around the field direction, with the drift velocity $\mathbf{v}_{zd}$ given by

$$\mathbf{v}_{zd} = \frac{mv_\phi^2}{qBR_B}\mathbf{e}_z. \tag{6.13}$$

The curvature of the field lines means that the particle drifts in a direction that is perpendicular to the direction of the field and perpendicular to a vector drawn to the field line from its centre of curvature, as shown in Figure 6.10. The centre of the cyclotron orbit does not follow the field line, but has a component that follows the circular field line and another component corresponding to the drift. For the field shown in Figure 6.9, Equation 6.13 indicates that positively-charged particles drift in the $+z$-direction, and negatively-charged particles drift in the opposite direction. Note that in deriving this result we assumed that the radius of curvature, R_B, of the path is much larger than the particle's cyclotron radius, so the change in field over a cyclotron radius is small.

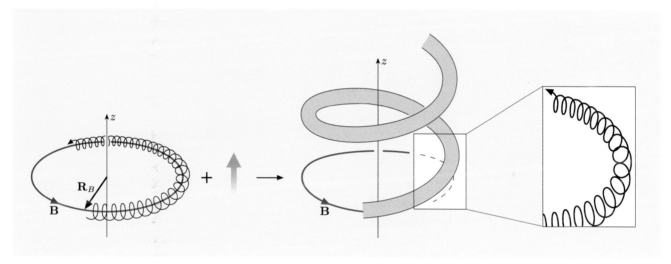

Figure 6.10   The path of a charged particle in a field $\mathbf{B} = B\mathbf{e}_\phi$ is the superposition of cyclotron motion about a circular field line and a steady drift motion perpendicular to both $\mathbf{B}$ and $\mathbf{R}_B$.

We can generalize Equation 6.13 to cover fields and curvatures in any direction. If $\mathbf{R}_B$ is a vector drawn to a point on a field line from the centre of curvature of the line at that point, then the drift velocity $\mathbf{v}_d$ is

$$\mathbf{v}_d = \frac{mv_\parallel^2}{qB^2R_B^2}\mathbf{R}_B \times \mathbf{B} = \frac{mv_\parallel^2}{qBR_B}\widehat{\mathbf{R}}_B \times \widehat{\mathbf{B}}, \tag{6.14}$$

where $v_\parallel$ is the particle's velocity component in the direction of the magnetic field. You should check for yourself that this predicts the same magnitude and direction for the drift velocity as does Equation 6.13 for the situation shown in Figure 6.9.

We have considered the drift of the cyclotron orbits due to the curvature of circular field lines, but Equation 6.14 is a local relation that applies to any 'shape' of the magnetic field lines. Any field line can be broken down into a series of small circular elements, each with its own radius of curvature, and the derivation above can be applied to each element. So at each point in the magnetic field, the motion is a superposition of a spiralling cyclotron orbit with its axis along the field direction and a drift in the direction perpendicular to both the field and its radius of curvature at that point.

The discussion in this subsection has assumed that the change in field over a cyclotron radius is small; we have assumed a constant field strength B over the orbit. In Subsection 6.3.2 we shall see what happens to the cyclotron motion when the field strength depends on position.

Motion of charged particles in the Van Allen belts

The Earth is surrounded by regions containing energetic charged particles, mainly electrons and protons. The regions where these particles are most concentrated form two belts around the Equator, known as the **Van Allen belts** (Figure 6.11).

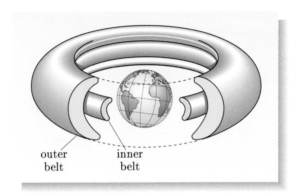

Figure 6.11   The Van Allen radiation belts are high above the Earth's atmosphere, and contain high densities of energetic electrons and protons.

The particles within these belts spiral around the curved field lines of the Earth's magnetic field, as shown in Figure 6.12. To give some idea of the scale of these orbits, the cyclotron radius for 1 MeV protons 3000 km above the Equator, where the field strength is about 10^{-5} T, is about 15 km, and their cyclotron frequency is 10^3 rad s^{-1}. For 1 MeV electrons, which travel at a speed close to that of light, a relativistic correction must be made to Equations 6.9 and 6.8; the radius and frequency of their orbits are about 500 m and 6×10^5 rad s^{-1}, respectively.

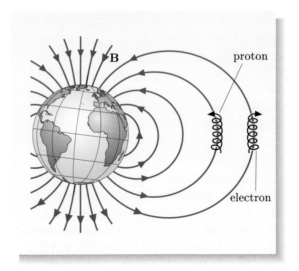

Figure 6.12   Electrons and protons spiral around the curved magnetic field lines in the Van Allen belts. Note the opposite directions of the spirals — clockwise for electrons, anticlockwise for protons, when viewed in the direction of the field.

Exercise 6.6   A proton in the outer Van Allen belt has $v_{\parallel} = 2.0 \times 10^6 \, \text{m s}^{-1}$ and is at a point above the Equator where the field strength is $4.7 \times 10^{-7} \, \text{T}$ and the radius of curvature of the field lines is $8.4 \times 10^6 \, \text{m}$. What is the drift velocity of this particle caused by the changing direction of the field?   ■

Motion of charged particles in the Sun's atmosphere

A more dramatic example of motion of charged particles in magnetic fields can be observed in the coronal region around the Sun. Figure 6.13 is an ultraviolet image of the solar corona, showing lots of loop structures. These loops trace out magnetic field lines that protrude above the surface of the Sun. The gas in the region of these loops is at a temperature above $10^6 \, \text{K}$, sufficient to ensure that its constituent atoms are ionized, and the ions and electrons travel along spiral paths around the field lines. The characteristic frequencies of the spectral lines emitted by the energetic ions depend on their degree of ionization (that is, the number of electrons stripped off), which in turn depends on the temperature. The intensity of the spectral lines depends on the number density of the ions. Thus, as well as showing the magnetic field pattern, these images provide astronomers with a wealth of information about the temperature and composition of the corona.

Figure 6.13   Magnetic field loops in the lower atmosphere of the Sun. This ultraviolet image taken by the TRACE satellite shows the paths of high-energy electrons that spiral around the magnetic field lines. The superimposed image of the Earth indicates the immense scale of these field lines.

Exercise 6.7   Our analysis of the motion of charged particles in non-uniform fields assumes that the magnetic field does not vary significantly over length scales comparable with a cyclotron radius. The magnetic field loop structures observed in the solar atmosphere are thousands, or even hundreds of thousands, of kilometres across. The typical field strength in these loops is $1.0 \times 10^{-3} \, \text{T}$, and the particles have typical kinetic energies, E_{kin}, of $500 \, \text{eV}$ (corresponding to a temperature of several million kelvin). How do the cyclotron radii of electrons and protons with these typical energies compare with the size of these loops?   ■

The solar wind

The fact that energetic charged particles spiral around field lines is crucial for the existence of life on the Earth. The Sun ejects vast numbers of charged particles, mostly protons and electrons, representing a mass loss of about one million tonnes per second. These ejected particles are accelerated by the electric and magnetic fields in the atmosphere of the Sun, often in violent events such as solar flares, by processes that are as yet only barely understood. The particles form what is known as the **solar wind** (Figure 6.14). In the region of the Earth's orbit there are about 5×10^6 particles per cubic metre, and the average wind speed is about $400 \, \text{km} \, \text{s}^{-1}$.

The interaction between the solar wind and the Earth's magnetic field has major effects on both of them, as shown in Figure 6.14. As the charged particles approach the Earth, they reach a region where the Earth's field has a significant effect on their motion. This region is known as the bow shock, because of its similarity to the bow wave of a moving ship. The magnetic field presents an obstacle to the flow of the solar wind, since the charged particles cannot travel transverse to the field. Most of the solar wind is therefore diverted through a region called the *magnetosheath* around the boundary of the Earth's field, so life on the ground is protected from the potentially harmful effects of the energetic charged particles.

The interaction of the solar wind with the Earth's field distorts it from the dipolar form that it has close to the Earth. On the day side of the Earth, the dipolar magnetic field is compressed, as shown in Figure 6.14, and on the night side it is stretched out into an extended tail. The region in which the Earth's field has a significant effect on the solar wind is known as the *magnetosphere*. Though most of the solar wind continues to travel further out into the solar system, small proportions of the particles enter the Van Allen belts and a region within the equatorial plane of the tail, known as the *plasma sheet*, and then contribute to the Earth's ring current and to auroras, which are discussed later in this chapter.

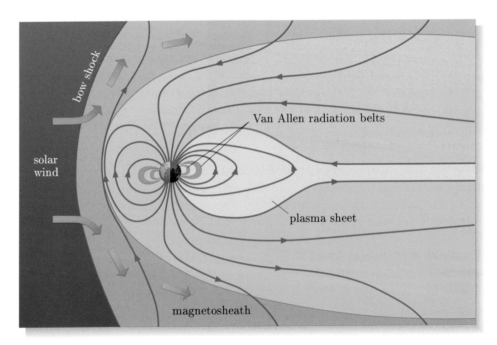

Figure 6.14   The Earth's magnetic field effectively diverts most of the solar wind around the Earth.

6.3.2 Magnetic fields with varying strength

We shall now discuss the motion of charged particles in a magnetic field that has the same direction everywhere, but with strength depending on position. Consider the magnetic field depicted in Figure 6.15, which is in the z-direction everywhere, but its strength depends on the x-coordinate, that is, $\mathbf{B} = B(x)\mathbf{e}_z$. (Note that we cannot choose a field of the form $\mathbf{B} = B(z)\mathbf{e}_z$, because this does not satisfy the no-monopole equation, $\mathrm{div}\,\mathbf{B} = 0$.)

We shall investigate the motion of a particle that is initially spiralling around a field line passing through $x = 0$, $y = 0$. The equations to be solved are similar to Equations 6.5, but with $B = B(x)$:

$$\frac{\mathrm{d}v_x}{\mathrm{d}t} = \frac{qB(x)}{m}v_y, \qquad \frac{\mathrm{d}v_y}{\mathrm{d}t} = -\frac{qB(x)}{m}v_x, \qquad \frac{\mathrm{d}v_z}{\mathrm{d}t} = 0. \qquad (6.15)$$

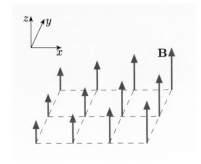

Figure 6.15 A magnetic field in the z-direction, with a gradient of the field strength in the x-direction.

If we assume that the magnetic field varies only slightly on the spatial scale of the particle's cyclotron radius, then we can perform a first-order Taylor expansion of $B(x)$ about $x = 0$:

$$B(x) \simeq B(0) + B'(0)x,$$

where $B'(0)$ is the value of $\mathrm{d}B/\mathrm{d}x$ evaluated at $x = 0$. Using this expansion, the equations of motion can be rewritten as

$$\frac{\mathrm{d}v_x}{\mathrm{d}t} = \frac{qB(0)}{m}v_y + \frac{qB'(0)x}{m}v_y,$$
$$\frac{\mathrm{d}v_y}{\mathrm{d}t} = -\frac{qB(0)}{m}v_x - \frac{qB'(0)x}{m}v_x. \qquad (6.16)$$

We shall assume again that the field changes slowly with position, so $B'(0)x$ is small compared with $B(0)$. Since the terms involving $B'(0)x$ are small, it is a reasonable approximation to substitute the solutions we obtained for a uniform magnetic field (Equations 6.6 and 6.7) for x, v_x and v_y in these terms in Equation 6.16. In this case, $x_0 = 0$ and $y_0 = 0$ since we are considering a particle spiralling around a field line with these coordinates, and we shall choose the origin of the time scale so that $\phi_0 = 0$. We then obtain

$$\frac{\mathrm{d}v_x}{\mathrm{d}t} = \frac{qB(0)}{m}v_y + \left[\frac{qB'(0)}{m} \times \left(-\frac{mv_\perp}{qB(0)}\cos\frac{qB(0)}{m}t\right) \times \left(v_\perp \cos\frac{qB(0)}{m}t\right)\right],$$
$$\frac{\mathrm{d}v_y}{\mathrm{d}t} = -\frac{qB(0)}{m}v_x - \left[\frac{qB'(0)}{m} \times \left(-\frac{mv_\perp}{qB(0)}\cos\frac{qB(0)}{m}t\right) \times \left(v_\perp \sin\frac{qB(0)}{m}t\right)\right].$$

If we now average these equations over a cyclotron period, then $\langle \cos^2 \omega_c t \rangle = \frac{1}{2}$, and $\langle \sin \omega_c t \cos \omega_c t \rangle = 0$, and we find

$$\left\langle \frac{\mathrm{d}v_x}{\mathrm{d}t} \right\rangle = \frac{qB(0)}{m}\langle v_y \rangle - \frac{qB'(0)}{m}\frac{mv_\perp^2}{2qB(0)}, \qquad (6.17)$$

$$\left\langle \frac{\mathrm{d}v_y}{\mathrm{d}t} \right\rangle = -\frac{qB(0)}{m}\langle v_x \rangle. \qquad (6.18)$$

Now the kinetic energy of a particle remains constant in a magnetic field, so the quantities on the left-hand sides of Equations 6.17 and 6.18, the averaged components of the acceleration, must be zero. From Equation 6.18, we deduce that $\langle v_x \rangle = 0$, so there is no drift in the x-direction. However, from Equation 6.17,

$$\langle v_y \rangle = \frac{mv_\perp^2 \, B'(0)}{2qB^2(0)}. \tag{6.19}$$

This means that the orbit of a positively-charged particle will drift in the y-direction, since $B'(0)$ is positive in Figure 6.15. Note that the drift is perpendicular to the direction of the field, and also perpendicular to the direction of the gradient of the field.

We derived this expression for the drift velocity for specific directions of field and field gradient, but it can be generalized to give a vector equation that is valid for all fields and field gradients. The general relationship for the drift velocity $\mathbf{v}_d$ is

$$\mathbf{v}_d = \frac{mv_\perp^2}{2qB^3} \, \mathbf{B} \times \operatorname{grad} B. \tag{6.20}$$

You should check for yourself that this expression predicts the same direction and magnitude for the drift velocity of a positively-charged particle in the magnetic field of Figure 6.15 as does Equation 6.19.

So in a non-uniform magnetic field of constant direction, a particle spirals around the field lines much like it does in a uniform field, but in addition it drifts in the direction perpendicular to both the magnetic field direction and the gradient of the magnetic field's magnitude. Notice that because the drift is perpendicular to the gradient of the field strength, the *average* field strength experienced by the particle remains constant. This means that the frequency and the average radius of the particle's orbit, and the drift speed itself, are constant.

When there is only a small change in magnetic field over the cyclotron radius, the drift transverse to the orbit has the form shown in Figure 6.16a. If the field strength changes much more rapidly with position, so that $\operatorname{grad} B$ is larger, then the orbit could have the form shown in Figure 6.16b. Since $r_c = mv_\perp/|q|B$, a visual comparison of the radii of the loops at the top and bottom of this figure suggests that the field varies by a factor of 10 over the path in Figure 6.16b. Positively-charged particles drift in the opposite direction to negatively-charged particles, so they would drift from right to left in the fields shown in Figure 6.16.

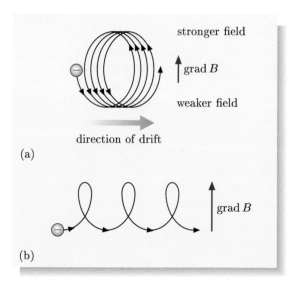

(a)

(b)

Figure 6.16 Paths followed by negatively-charged particles in the plane perpendicular to a **B** field directed out of the page for (a) small and (b) large variations in field over the orbit.

This is a second contribution to the drift of charged particles in non-uniform magnetic fields. In most non-uniform fields, both the magnitude and the direction of the field vary, so the contributions represented by Equations 6.14 and 6.20 must be added to obtain the total drift velocity.

Exercise 6.8   Figure 6.17 shows the circular orbit of a positively-charged particle in a uniform **B** field in the z-direction, which is directed perpendicularly out of the plane of the page. Suppose that a field gradient is superimposed in the x-direction, so that the field remains in the same direction but its strength is slightly weaker at A, and slightly stronger at C, than the strength of the initial, uniform field shown in this figure. By considering the effect of these differences in the field on the cyclotron radii at A and C, explain why the orbit drifts, and deduce the direction of the drift.

Exercise 6.9   Determine the drift velocity due to the gradient in field strength experienced by the proton described in Exercise 6.6. Assume that $v_\perp = v_\parallel = 2.0 \times 10^6 \text{ m s}^{-1}$ (corresponding to energy 40 keV), that the proton is 2.6×10^7 m from the Earth's centre, above the magnetic equator, where the field strength is 4.7×10^{-7} T, and that the field *in the equatorial plane* has a dipolar form, given in spherical coordinates by $\mathbf{B}(\mathbf{r}) = -(C/r^3)\mathbf{e}_\theta$, where C is a constant.

Exercise 6.10   (a) Do particles with opposite charge drift in the same direction or in opposite directions in non-uniform fields?

(b) To what directions is the drift always perpendicular?

(c) For a given kinetic energy and magnetic field configuration, do electrons or protons have the greater drift speed?   ∎

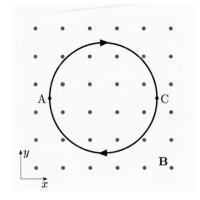

Figure 6.17   Circular orbit of a charged particle in a uniform field (represented by a uniform array of green dots) directed perpendicularly out of the page.

The Earth's ring current

You have seen that the charged particles in the Van Allen belts drift transversely as they spiral around the Earth's magnetic field lines. The gradient in field strength and the curvature of the field lines cause positively-charged particles to drift from east to west, and negatively-charged particles to drift in the opposite direction. Thus particles with both signs of charge contribute to a current in the east–west direction, and this current is known as the Earth's **ring current**.

Figure 6.18 shows part of the Earth's field in a plane through the magnetic equator, as it would appear from high above the northern hemisphere. The green dots represent the field lines emerging perpendicularly out of the page, and they are more closely packed nearer the Earth to indicate that the field is stronger there. The cyclotron radius is therefore smaller closer to the Earth, and this leads to a transverse drift of the orbits, shown here for particles with $v_\parallel = 0$. By using the right-hand rule, you should be able to convince yourself that protons would traverse the path shown in Figure 6.18 from left to right (east to west), while electrons would traverse it from right to left (west to east).

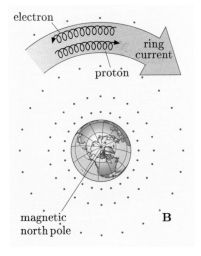

Figure 6.18   Viewed from above the magnetic north pole, which was at 83° N, 114° W in 2005, the transverse drift of charged particles in the Van Allen belts generates a current flowing from east to west.

● What effect will the ring current have at the Earth's surface?

○ The ring current is a large current loop and will generate a magnetic field at the Earth's surface. Application of the right-hand rule indicates that this field points towards the south — the opposite direction to the Earth's internally generated field — so the measured field at the Earth's surface is smaller than it would be in the absence of the ring current.

If the ring current were constant, its contribution to the field would be of little importance. However, during periods of intense solar activity, when the solar wind carries greater numbers of charged particles towards the Earth, the number density of particles in the Van Allen belts is enhanced. The ring current therefore increases, and this leads to a measurable decrease in the magnetic field strength at the Earth's surface. Such decreases in the field are referred to as **magnetic storms**. A typical storm might reduce the Earth's field by $100\,\text{nT}$, and reductions can be as large as $600\,\text{nT}$, which is about 2% of the field strength at the Equator. The field returns to its 'normal' value after about a day. Magnetic storms can also cause major disruption to electrical distribution systems and communications, and space scientists are using instruments on satellites in various regions of the magnetosphere to try to understand the mechanisms responsible for these disruptive events.

Exercise 6.11   Spacecraft measurements indicate that the ring current is carried mainly by charged ions, with energies from a few keV to a few hundred keV, which spiral round field lines that pass over the Equator between about $2.5R_{\text{E}}$ and $7R_{\text{E}}$ from the Earth's centre, where R_{E} is the Earth's radius. Estimate the current required to reduce the field at a point near the Equator by $100\,\text{nT}$. You may assume that the ring current can be modelled by a simple loop in the equatorial plane with radius $4R_{\text{E}}$, that the field this generates at the Earth's surface is approximately the same as the field it generates at the centre of the Earth, and that $R_{\text{E}} = 6 \times 10^{6}\,\text{m}$.   ■

6.3.3   Magnetic bottles

You have seen in Subsection 6.2.5 that a uniform magnetic field can be used to guide a beam of particles. We shall now look at how particles can be trapped, or 'bottled', by a magnetic field. This is relevant to the containment of particles in the Van Allen belts, and to the containment of plasmas in prototypes of fusion reactors.

One of the simplest magnetic field patterns that can be used to trap charged particles is shown in Figure 6.19. This field is produced by a cylindrical coil that has more windings at the ends than at the centre. In the central region, a particle follows a helical path, but as it approaches one of the ends, its component of velocity parallel to the axis decreases and eventually reverses. The particle is reflected, and the point at which it is reflected is known as the mirror point. It then accelerates back towards the other end of the coil, where it is again slowed down and reflected. The particle is trapped by these repeated reflections, and the field responsible for trapping the particle is called a **magnetic bottle**.

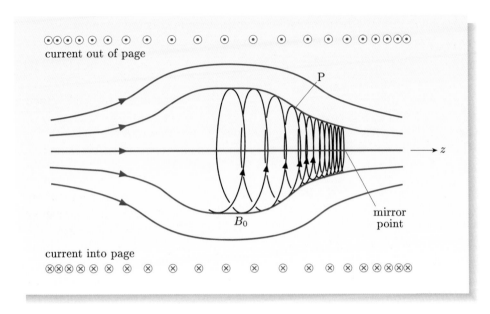

current out of page

P

z

mirror
point

B_0

current into page

Figure 6.19 A magnetic bottle with a magnetic field strength that is least in the middle (B_0) and greatest at the ends.

It is straightforward to explain the reflection process qualitatively. At point P in Figure 6.19, the velocity has a component in the azimuthal direction, and the field has a radial component towards the axis. The right-hand rule indicates that these velocity and field components produce a component of the Lorentz force in the $-z$-direction. This force will reduce the velocity component in the z-direction to zero, then increase the velocity in the opposite direction, and this accounts for the reflection of the particle.

We shall now make this argument more precise. We shall use cylindrical coordinates, with the z-axis along the axis of the bottle. At point P in Figure 6.19, we can write the particle's velocity as $\mathbf{v} = v_\phi \mathbf{e}_\phi + v_z \mathbf{e}_z$, and write the field as $\mathbf{B} = B_r \mathbf{e}_r + B_z \mathbf{e}_z$. The Lorentz force on the particle is then

$$\mathbf{F} = q(v_\phi \mathbf{e}_\phi + v_z \mathbf{e}_z) \times (B_r \mathbf{e}_r + B_z \mathbf{e}_z) = q(v_\phi B_z \mathbf{e}_r + v_z B_r \mathbf{e}_\phi - v_\phi B_r \mathbf{e}_z).$$

When the positive charge shown in Figure 6.19 passes through point P, the components of velocity and field have the following signs: v_ϕ negative, v_z positive, B_r negative, B_z positive. So the radial component of the force, $v_\phi B_z \mathbf{e}_r$, is negative and therefore directed towards the axis; this is the centripetal force required to maintain the (approximately) circular orbit. The azimuthal component of the force, $v_z B_r \mathbf{e}_\phi$, is negative and therefore in the same direction as $v_\phi \mathbf{e}_\phi$; this force acts to increase the magnitude of the azimuthal velocity. The z-component of the force, $-v_\phi B_r \mathbf{e}_z$, is negative, and this is the component that we referred to in the earlier qualitative discussion that reduces the z-component of velocity to zero and then accelerates the particle in the $-z$-direction.

As with all examples of motion of charged particles in magnetic fields, the speed and kinetic energy of the particle must remain constant. So the reduction of the z-component of velocity, v_z, is accompanied by an increase in the azimuthal component, v_ϕ, with $v^2 = v_\phi^2 + v_z^2$ remaining constant.

It is possible to prove that the magnetic moment associated with a charged particle in an orbit remains constant as long as the field changes slowly over a cyclotron radius. Deriving this result would be too much of a detour, and we shall simply make use of it here to explore further the properties of magnetic bottles. Recalling the definition of magnetic moment — its magnitude is the product of the current and the area of the current loop — we can write the magnitude of the magnetic moment of an orbiting particle as

$$I\pi r_c^2 = \frac{|q|}{2\pi/\omega_c}\pi\left(\frac{mv_\phi}{|q|B}\right)^2 = \frac{mv_\phi^2}{2B}, \tag{6.21}$$

where we have substituted v_ϕ for $v_\perp$ in the usual expression for r_c. So constancy of the magnetic moment means that v_ϕ^2/B must remain constant as the particle travels along the path shown in Figure 6.19.

Now, rather than describing a particle's motion in terms of v_z and v_ϕ, it is helpful to use its speed v, which remains constant in the magnetic bottle, and the angle α between the velocity $\mathbf{v}$ and the magnetic field direction, as defined in Figure 6.20. The angle α is known as the **pitch angle** of the motion, and is constant for a uniform helical trajectory. The two descriptions are related by the transformations

$$v^2 = v_z^2 + v_\phi^2, \quad \tan\alpha = v_\phi/v_z,$$

and all four of these parameters remain constant for motion in a uniform magnetic field. Since $v_\phi = v\sin\alpha$, the condition in Equation 6.21 for the magnetic moment to remain constant, $v_\phi^2/B = \text{constant}$, is equivalent to

$$\frac{\sin^2\alpha}{B} = \text{constant}.$$

We now apply this condition to a particle that has pitch angle α_0 while in the middle of the bottle shown in Figure 6.19, where the magnetic field strength is B_0. The pitch angle α at some point where the field strength is $B > B_0$ is given by

$$\frac{\sin^2\alpha}{B} = \frac{\sin^2\alpha_0}{B_0}.$$

As the particle travels into the region of increasing field strength, $\sin^2\alpha$ becomes larger, which means that the pitch angle increases. This continues until the particle has a 90° pitch angle and consequently $v_z = 0$. At this point, $\sin\alpha = 1$, so the required field strength is $B = B_0/\sin^2\alpha_0$, and v_z switches sign. The particle is therefore reflected, and travels back towards the region of weaker field strength. The particle will bounce back and forth between the two magnetic mirrors at the ends of the magnetic bottle.

Note that the mirror point is where $B = B_0/\sin^2\alpha_0$, so particles with small pitch angles in the middle of the bottle require a larger field for reflection to occur. In fact, if the field reaches a maximum $B = B_{\max}$ at the ends of the bottle, then particles with pitch angles such that $\sin^2\alpha_0 < B_0/B_{\max}$ see no mirror. Such particles are not reflected and so are not trapped. This means that magnetic bottles always leak. In reality, magnetic bottles leak for a variety of other reasons too, and can contain charged particles for only a limited time.

Exercise 6.12   A magnetic bottle like the one in Figure 6.19 has $B_{\max} = 20B_0$.

(a) What is the minimum value of the pitch angle α_0 at the centre of the bottle for particles that are trapped?

(b) Explain qualitatively why particles that have pitch angles in the middle of the bottle smaller than this minimum value cannot be trapped.

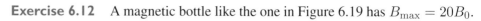

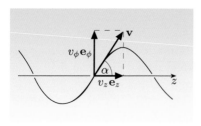

Figure 6.20   Definition of the pitch angle α at a point on a helical trajectory, shown here as a projection onto a plane.

Table 6.1 shows the minimum pitch angle at the centre of a bottle for trapped particles as a function of B_{max}/B_0. It also shows the proportion of particles that leak out of the ends, assuming that the distribution of velocities at the centre is initially isotropic.

Trapping of particles by the Earth's field

The Earth's magnetic field provides an example of a magnetic bottle. You have seen that electrons and protons in the radiation belts spiral around the Earth's magnetic field lines. The field lines intersect the Earth's surface at high latitudes, and without the magnetic mirror effect, the particles would hit the ground after a single passage along a field line. However, the field gets stronger closer to the Earth, as shown by the increased density of field lines close to the Earth in Figure 6.21. This gathering of field lines creates a magnetic mirror. When a charged particle spiralling around a field line approaches the Earth near one of the poles, it encounters an increasingly strong magnetic field. If its pitch angle over the Equator is not too small, the particle will eventually reach its mirror point and be reflected back towards the other pole, where the same process is repeated. Particles are caught in a magnetic trap, and bounce back and forth between the mirror points until liberated by some sort of collision.

Table 6.1 Minimum pitch angle α_{min} of particles trapped by magnetic bottles for various ratios of maximum field B_{max} to central field B_0, and the corresponding percentage of particles leaking.

B_{max}/B_0	α_{min}	Leak
3	35°	18%
10	18°	5%
30	10°	2%
100	6°	0.5%

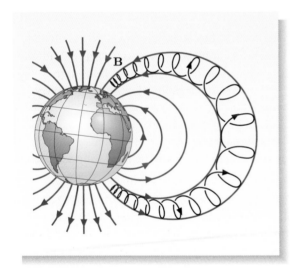

Figure 6.21 Trapping of charged particles between magnetic mirrors formed by bunching of field lines near the magnetic poles.

For particles that cross the Equator at a distance of $4R_E$ from the Earth's centre, the field lines that they follow intersect the Earth's surface about 25° from the magnetic poles. However, at a height of 1000 km above the surface, the field strength along these lines is a factor of almost 100 greater than the field strength over the Equator, so the vast majority of particles will be reflected before they get down to this height. Particles with very small values of the pitch angle α_0 will spiral down into the atmosphere, and can then excite molecules of nitrogen and oxygen in the air. The excited molecules emit light, thus contributing to the beautiful auroral displays (see cover picture) that occur between 80 km and 300 km above the Earth. However, the majority of the particles responsible for auroras come not from the Van Allen belts but from the plasma sheet in the tail of the Earth's magnetosphere. Changes to the magnetic field in this region of the magnetosphere, generated by changes to the solar wind, cause charged particles to follow field lines down into the atmosphere. The unusual view of an aurora in Figure 6.1a shows a ring pattern of auroral illumination, about 5000 km across, around the north magnetic pole. The ring indicates where the field lines around which the charged particles spiral enter the atmosphere, at about $25°$ from the pole.

Summary of Chapter 6

Section 6.1   The Lorentz force on a particle with charge q moving at velocity $\mathbf{v}$ in an electric field $\mathbf{E}$ and a magnetic field $\mathbf{B}$ is given by $\mathbf{F} = q(\mathbf{E} + \mathbf{v} \times \mathbf{B})$. Only the electric field part of the Lorentz force, $q\mathbf{E}$, can change the kinetic energy of a charged particle; the magnetic part, $q\mathbf{v} \times \mathbf{B}$, is perpendicular to the velocity and therefore cannot affect the speed or the kinetic energy of the particle.

Section 6.2   In an electric field, a charged particle with mass m has an acceleration $q\mathbf{E}/m$. In uniform electric fields, a particle's motion can be determined by using the constant acceleration equations. Electric fields are used to accelerate and steer electrons in many important devices, such as the scanning electron microscope.

In a uniform magnetic field, a charged particle has an acceleration perpendicular to the field and to its velocity, and it therefore travels in a circular orbit in a plane perpendicular to the field, or follows a helical path around a field line. The angular frequency and radius of the orbit are known as the cyclotron frequency, $\omega_c = |q|B/m$, and the cyclotron radius, $r_c = mv_\perp/|q|B$. The particle's motion can be described by a velocity component parallel to the magnetic field $v_\parallel$ and a perpendicular speed $v_\perp$, and in a uniform magnetic field both $v_\perp$ and $v_\parallel$ remain constant. Combinations of electric and magnetic fields can be used to focus beams of charged particles.

Section 6.3   Where the direction of a magnetic field changes, a transverse drift is superimposed on the spiralling motion of charged particles. The direction of drift is perpendicular to the field direction and to a vector drawn to the field line from its centre of curvature. When the field strength depends on position, the orbit drifts perpendicular to the field direction and to the direction of the gradient of the field magnitude.

A magnetic bottle is a region of non-uniform field that can be used to trap charged particles. The Earth's magnetic field acts as a magnetic bottle for electrons and protons in the Van Allen belts. Transverse drift of these particles produces the Earth's ring current.

Achievements from Chapter 6

After studying this chapter you should be able to do the following.

6.1 Explain the meanings of the newly defined (emboldened) terms and symbols, and use them appropriately.

6.2 State the Lorentz force law, and use it to calculate forces on charged particles in electric and magnetic fields.

6.3 Use the Lorentz force law to explain why an electric field changes a charged particle's kinetic energy but a magnetic field does not.

6.4 Explain why a particle spirals around a magnetic field line in a uniform magnetic field, derive expressions for the cyclotron frequency and cyclotron radius, and use these expressions to solve problems.

6.5 Use standard results to determine a particle's motion in specified uniform and non-uniform magnetic fields, both with and without electric fields.

6.6 Explain why a particle drifts in a non-uniform magnetic field, explain the direction of drift, and calculate the drift velocity.

6.7 Explain how a magnetic bottle traps charged particles.

Chapter 7   Resistance and inductance

The previous chapter was concerned with ways that electric and magnetic fields affect the motion of charged particles in free space. Examples ranged from beams of electrons in electron microscopes to the motion of the charged particles that cause auroras. In this chapter we consider the motion of charged particles that gives rise to electric currents in conducting materials, and this motion is again caused by electromagnetic fields.

We shall be concerned with two main aspects of the current flow in electrical circuits. The first is the resistance of conducting components, which determines how much current flows in response to an applied field, and we shall present various methods of calculating electrical resistance. The potential differences associated with current flow provide information about the underlying material, and this is the basis of techniques used by archaeologists to search for buried structures. The second half of the chapter looks at another factor that affects current flow in circuits, namely inductance. Mutual inductance gives rise to current in one circuit when the current changes in a second circuit, whereas the self-inductance of a circuit acts to limit the rate of change of current in that circuit. Both forms of inductance are of immense practical importance for electronics and electrical engineering, and both are based on the phenomenon of electromagnetic induction. We therefore preface the discussion of inductance by a brief review of the important aspects of electromagnetic induction.

7.1   Current flow in conducting materials

In most conducting materials, an electric field $\mathbf{E}$ produces a current density $\mathbf{J}$ that is proportional to the field, that is,

$$\mathbf{J} = \sigma\mathbf{E}, \tag{7.1}$$

where the constant of proportionality, σ, is known as the electrical **conductivity** of the material. The SI unit of conductivity is $\mathrm{A\,m^{-2}}/\mathrm{V\,m^{-1}} = \Omega^{-1}\,\mathrm{m^{-1}}$. The reciprocal of the conductivity is known as the **resistivity**, ρ, giving the relation

$$\rho = \frac{1}{\sigma}. \tag{7.2}$$

Table 7.1   The conductivity of various materials at $0\,^{\circ}\mathrm{C}$.

	Conductivity σ /$\Omega^{-1}\,\mathrm{m}^{-1}$
silver	6.8×10^7
copper	6.5×10^7
tungsten	2.0×10^7
iron	1.1×10^7
lead	5.2×10^6
silicon	0.02–10
glass	10^{-12}–10^{-9}
polythene	10^{-18}–10^{-14}
distilled water	10^{-5}–10^{-2}
silicone oil	10^{-12}

We shall use conductivity rather than resistivity in this book in order to avoid confusion with our use of ρ to represent charge density. Table 7.1 shows values of the conductivity of some common materials.

When a conducting material moves with velocity $\mathbf{v}$ in a magnetic field $\mathbf{B}$, there will be a magnetic force $q\mathbf{v} \times \mathbf{B}$ acting on the charge carriers as well as the electric force $q\mathbf{E}$, and Equation 7.1 is extended to the more general expression for the current density:

$$\mathbf{J} = \sigma(\mathbf{E} + \mathbf{v} \times \mathbf{B}). \tag{7.3}$$

In the discussion of conductivity and resistance in the first half of this chapter, we shall be concerned only with stationary conductors, so Equation 7.1 will suffice. However, even for a conductor moving in the Earth's magnetic field ($\sim 10^{-5}\,\mathrm{T}$) at $10^3\,\mathrm{m\,s^{-1}}$ the $(\mathbf{v} \times \mathbf{B})$ term is only about $10^{-2}\,\mathrm{V\,m^{-1}}$, which is small compared with electric field strengths encountered in most applications.

7.1.1 Ohmic materials and Ohm's law

Materials in which Equation 7.1 is obeyed are said to be ohmic, and this equation is often referred to as Ohm's law. This is the *local* form of the law — it relates $\mathbf{J}$ and $\mathbf{E}$ at a point in the material — whereas the form of Ohm's law that we introduced in Book 1 and with which most people are familiar, namely $V = IR$, applies to a discrete object. In the following exercise you can demonstrate the equivalence of the two forms of Ohm's law for a conductor with a simple shape.

Exercise 7.1   The conducting rod in Figure 7.1 has uniform cross-sectional area A and length l, and the current density and field are uniform along its length. By expressing the electric field and current density in terms of the current I and voltage drop V along the rod, show that if $\mathbf{J} = \sigma \mathbf{E}$, then $V = IR$, where the resistance R is a constant, and obtain an expression for R. ∎

Ohm's law is not a fundamental law of physics, in the sense of Gauss's law, and there are materials for which it is not valid. For example, in semiconducting devices, the relationship between V and I is generally highly non-linear. Even for ohmic materials, the conductivity depends on temperature, and this is particularly true for semiconductors. However, when Ohm's law is not valid, the resistance is still *defined* to be V/I, even though the resistance then depends on the voltage drop.

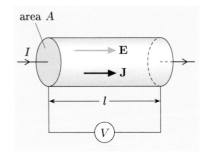

Figure 7.1   Conducting rod in which the electric field $\mathbf{E}$ and current density $\mathbf{J}$ are uniform.

At this point it is worth briefly contrasting the current that flows in a solid with the beam current in an electron microscope. In the microscope, the current is determined by the rate at which electrons are emitted from a heated filament, and this depends on the filament temperature. The anode voltage accelerates the electrons, and all of the electrons in the beam then travel with essentially the same velocity. For example, Exercise 6.1 showed that electrons accelerated through 1.5 keV travelled at a speed of about 2×10^7 m s^{-1} towards the specimen. In contrast, in a metallic conductor , the current is carried by the conduction electrons — those electrons that are free to move throughout the material. In the absence of an electric field, quantum theory indicates that these electrons have typical speeds of 10^6 m s^{-1}, they are travelling in random directions, and they are frequently scattered by thermal vibrations of the lattice and by impurities and defects in the structure. When an electric field is applied, the conduction electrons will accelerate in the opposite direction to the field. However, frequent scattering greatly restricts the velocity change, and the net effect of acceleration and scattering is to add a small drift velocity to the random thermal motion of the electrons. For a current of 1 A flowing in a copper wire with cross-sectional area 1 mm^2, the drift speed is about 10^{-4} m s^{-1}, which is about ten orders of magnitude less than the typical speed of the conduction electrons.

It is the scattering of the conduction electrons that gives rise to electrical resistance and to dissipation of power in a conductor. To determine the power dissipated, consider the electrons contained in a small volume $\delta\tau$ within a conductor, shown in Figure 7.2 overleaf. The electrons are drifting with velocity $\mathbf{v}_d$ in the opposite direction to $\mathbf{E}$ and $\mathbf{J}$, so in time δt they will be displaced through distance $\mathbf{v}_d\,\delta t$. The change in electrostatic potential over this distance is $\delta V = -\mathbf{E} \cdot \mathbf{v}_d\,\delta t = +Ev_d\,\delta t$. Since the charge within the displaced volume is $\delta Q = -en\,\delta\tau$, where n is the number density of conduction electrons, the change

We use τ rather than V to denote volume in this chapter, in order to avoid a clash with the use of V for potential, potential difference and voltage drop.

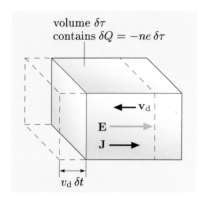

Figure 7.2   In time δt, the electrons in volume $\delta \tau$ move a distance $v_d\,\delta t$, and each loses electrical energy $eEv_d\,\delta t$.

in electric energy is

$$\delta Q\,\delta V = (-en\,\delta \tau)\times(Ev_d\,\delta t) = -nev_d E\,\delta \tau\,\delta t = -JE\,\delta \tau\,\delta t.$$

This energy is converted to thermal energy of the material, and the power δP dissipated is therefore

$$\delta P = JE\,\delta \tau.$$

For a macroscopic object, the total power dissipated is found by integrating over the total volume τ:

$$P = \int_{\tau} JE\,\mathrm{d}\tau. \tag{7.4}$$

● Starting from Equation 7.4, use the geometry of the conductor in Figure 7.1 to derive expressions for power dissipated in terms of I, V and R.

○ Since $J = I/A$ and $E = V/l$, and both are constant in the rod, the power dissipated is $P = (IV/Al) \times$ volume. But in this case, the volume is Al, so $P = IV$, which may be a more familiar expression than $P = \int_{\tau} JE\,\mathrm{d}\tau$. Assuming that Ohm's law, $V = IR$, is valid, we can write this in the equivalent forms

$$P = IV = V^2/R = I^2 R.$$

Electrostatic potential and voltage drop

In Book 1 a careful distinction was drawn between the terms electrostatic potential (and the associated potential differences and potential drops) and voltage drop. So which of these terms is appropriate for the V that appears in the non-local form of Ohm's law? The answer is that it depends on the situation!

We showed above that the general expression for the current density is given by

$$\mathbf{J} = \sigma(\mathbf{E} + \mathbf{v}\times\mathbf{B}). \tag{Eqn 7.3}$$

This expression leads to $V = IR$, where V is the voltage drop along the resistor, given by

$$V = V_{\mathrm{drop}} = \int_{\mathrm{resistor}} (\mathbf{E} + \mathbf{v}\times\mathbf{B})\cdot\mathrm{dl}.$$

Thus it is always correct to refer to a voltage drop V, or V_{drop}, in the context of $V = IR$.

Of course, in many situations the circuit is stationary and/or the magnetic field is zero or negligibly small, and then

$$V = V_{\mathrm{drop}} = \int_{\mathrm{resistor}} \mathbf{E}\cdot\mathrm{dl}. \tag{7.5}$$

So it is still appropriate to use the term voltage drop, though the definition of the term is now slightly simpler. A special case is when we have an electrostatic field, since we can then define an electrostatic potential V at a point $\mathbf{r}$ by

$$V(\mathbf{r}) = -\int_{\mathbf{r_0}}^{\mathbf{r}} \mathbf{E}\cdot\mathrm{dl},$$

where $\mathbf{r}_0$ is a reference point from which the potential is measured, often an infinite distance from the region of interest. The potential drop, or potential difference, across a resistor is then given by the integral in Equation 7.5, and in this situation the terms voltage drop and potential drop mean the same thing. The first half of this chapter is concerned with situations where the electric field is conservative and where the conductors are stationary, so we shall generally refer to electrostatic potentials and potential drops or potential differences. However, you must remember that when dealing with electromagnetic induction, which involves non-conservative electric fields and/or time-dependent magnetic fields, voltage drop is the appropriate term to use.

7.1.2 Resistance of symmetrical conducting objects

When a conducting object has a high degree of symmetry it may be possible to deduce the symmetry of the electric field and the current density, and to use this information to determine the resistance. This was done in Exercise 7.1. The following example shows how the resistance between the centre and surface of a sphere of conducting material can be calculated.

Worked Example 7.1

Determine the electric field and the electrostatic potential within the poorly-conducting sphere shown in Figure 7.3 when a current I flows between a small metallic sphere at the centre, radius r_1, and a metallic coating on the outer surface, radius r_2. Hence determine the resistance of the sphere.

Solution

The spherical symmetry indicates that the current density and electric field must be in the radial direction and can depend only on r, the distance from the centre. In the steady state there is no build up of charge, so the same current I crosses any spherical surface with its centre at the centre of the sphere, and this current is given by

$$I = J_r(r) \times 4\pi r^2.$$

So Ohm's law tells us that

$$E_r = \frac{J_r}{\sigma} = \frac{I}{4\pi \sigma r^2}.$$

Since there are no changing magnetic fields, the electric field is conservative, and an electrostatic potential exists. To find the potential drop ΔV between the centre and the surface of the sphere, we integrate the field along a radial path from r_1 to r_2:

$$\Delta V = V(r_1) - V(r_2)$$

$$= \int_{r_1}^{r_2} E_r(r)\,\mathrm{d}r = \frac{I}{4\pi\sigma} \int_{r_1}^{r_2} \frac{\mathrm{d}r}{r^2} = \frac{I}{4\pi\sigma} \left(-\frac{1}{r_2} + \frac{1}{r_1} \right).$$

The resistance R of the sphere is therefore

$$R = \frac{\Delta V}{I} = \frac{1}{4\pi\sigma} \left(\frac{1}{r_1} - \frac{1}{r_2} \right).$$

Essential skill

Determining the resistance of a symmetrical conductor

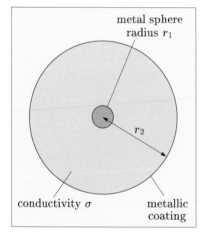

Figure 7.3 Sphere of poorly-conducting material.

Note that as the radius r_2 of the outer sphere tends to infinity, the resistance tends to the limiting value of $1/4\pi\sigma r_1$. Also, the potential in the region around the small sphere becomes $V(r) = I/4\pi\sigma r$ (assuming $V(\infty) = 0$). We shall make use of these important results in the next subsection.

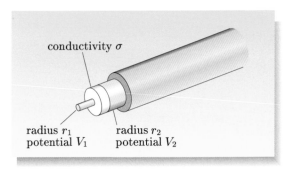

conductivity σ

radius r_1
potential V_1

radius r_2
potential V_2

Figure 7.4   Coaxial cable.

Exercise 7.2   The long coaxial cable shown in Figure 7.4 has an inner conducting wire with radius r_1 and an outer sheath with radius r_2, separated by a dielectric material that is a very poor conductor with conductivity σ. Since both the wire and the sheath have a high conductivity, they are each at a uniform potential, but there is a potential drop ΔV between them. Derive an expression relating the potential drop ΔV to the current I that flows between the wire and sheath in a length l of the cable, and hence calculate the resistance between the inner and outer conductors for this length of cable. (You should ignore any effects of the currents flowing along the wire and along the sheath.)   ■

For a coaxial cable with $r_2/r_1 = 5$ and a polythene dielectric with $\sigma = 10^{-14}\,\Omega^{-1}\,\mathrm{m}^{-1}$, the resistance per metre is over $10^{13}\,\Omega\,\mathrm{m}^{-1}$. So even with $1\,\mathrm{kV}$ between the inner and outer conductors, the current across the dielectric material would be less than $10^{-10}\,\mathrm{A}$ per metre.

It is worth noting that the calculation of the resistance of the coaxial cable in this exercise is very similar to the calculation of the capacitance in Exercise 2.6. In both cases we found an expression for the electrostatic field between the inner and outer conductors, and we integrated this field to determine the potential difference between the conductors. But to find the resistance, we used the local form of Ohm's law, $\mathbf{J} = \sigma\mathbf{E}$, to relate the magnitudes of the field and current density at a cylindrical surface coaxial within the cable. To find the capacitance, we used Gauss's law to relate the magnitude of the field on the surface of a cylinder coaxial with the cable to the charge on the inner conductor. A fixed potential drop ΔV between the two conductors gives rise to charges on them of $\pm Q$ per unit length, where $Q = C\,\Delta V$, and current I per unit length between them, where $I = \Delta V/R$.

7.1.3   Conductivity of the Earth

The electrical conductivities of materials cover a wide range of values, from $\sim 10^8\,\Omega^{-1}\mathrm{m}^{-1}$ for silver to as low as $\sim 10^{-18}\,\Omega^{-1}\mathrm{m}^{-1}$ for a very good insulator (Table 7.1). Even if we restrict ourselves to soils, minerals and rocks, the range is over seven orders of magnitude. A knowledge of the conductivity of the Earth's constituent materials is important for understanding how the Earth interacts with terrestrial and extraterrestrial magnetic and electric fields. For example, the way in which energy is dissipated in a lightning strike depends on the conductivity of the ground in the region of the strike. Also, measurements of conductivity and resistance can be used to provide information about subsurface structures that could be of interest to mineral prospectors, archaeologists or forensic scientists. Understanding these applications requires concepts introduced in this and previous chapters.

A lightning strike

Consider the situation shown in Figure 7.5, where lightning strikes a point on the Earth's surface. A current flows from this point to the thunder clouds above, and the same current must be supplied to the strike point by a current flow through the surrounding ground. We shall model this situation by assuming that the ground in the region of the strike has a uniform conductivity σ, and that away from the path of the lightning strike, the air is an insulator with zero conductivity. We shall also assume that though the current lasts for only a few milliseconds, the time dependence is still slow enough that we can use the results of electrostatics. Our aim is to determine the potential V on the Earth's surface at a distance r from the strike.

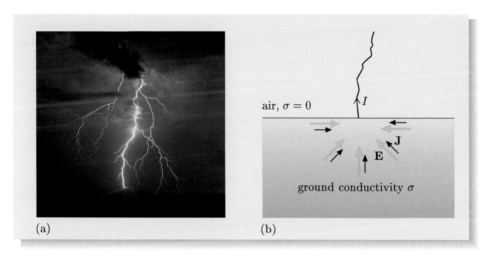

air, $\sigma = 0$

ground conductivity σ

(a) (b)

Figure 7.5 (a) A lightning strike. (b) Current flow and electric field in the region of the strike point.

The symmetry of this problem means that we can use a method similar to that used in Worked Example 7.1. If we use spherical coordinates, with their origin at the strike point, then the symmetry indicates that the current density and the electric field within the ground are radial, and their magnitudes depend on r only:

$$\mathbf{E}(\mathbf{r}) = E_r(r)\mathbf{e}_r = \frac{1}{\sigma}J_r(r)\mathbf{e}_r \quad \text{within the ground.}$$

We are assuming a steady state, so the current I flowing across the surface of a hemisphere of radius r centred on the strike point at the origin is independent of r, and

$$J_r(r) = -\frac{I}{2\pi r^2} = \sigma E_r(r). \tag{7.6}$$

Assuming that the potential is zero at large distances from the strike, the potential at a radius r is given by

$$V(r) = -\int_{\infty}^{r} E_r(r')\,\mathrm{d}r'$$

$$= +\frac{I}{2\pi\sigma}\int_{\infty}^{r} \frac{\mathrm{d}r'}{r'^2} = -\frac{I}{2\pi\sigma}\left[\frac{1}{r'}\right]_{\infty}^{r} = -\frac{I}{2\pi\sigma r}. \tag{7.7}$$

Exercise 7.3   A stroke of lightning carries a charge of $20\,\mathrm{C}$ and lasts $2.0 \times 10^{-3}\,\mathrm{s}$. If the ground where the strike occurs has a conductivity of $0.010\,\Omega^{-1}\mathrm{m}^{-1}$, at what distance from the strike does the field strength within the ground drop to $100\,\mathrm{V\,m}^{-1}$? What is the potential at this point relative to a zero of potential a large distance from the strike? (Make the simplifying assumption that the current is constant for the $2\,\mathrm{ms}$ duration of the strike.) ■

A geophysical survey

Geophysicists and archaeologists use measurements of potential drops associated with currents flowing through the ground to obtain information about subsurface structures, such as mineral deposits or buried building work. However, instead of using a single point source of current as in Figure 7.5, a pair of electrodes is used (Figure 7.6), with current flowing into the ground at point A and flowing back to the power supply through point B. If we assume that the current density is linearly related to the electric field, then the superposition laws for potential and field mean that the current density in the region around the two electrodes is also the superposition of the current densities from a positive point current source at A and a negative point current source — a current sink — at B. The potential at point P, which is at a distance r_A from A and r_B from B, is simply the superposition of the potentials due to these two sources. Each of these potentials is given by an expression like that in Equation 7.7, so

$$V_\mathrm{P} = \frac{I}{2\pi\sigma} \left(\frac{1}{r_\mathrm{A}} - \frac{1}{r_\mathrm{B}} \right).$$

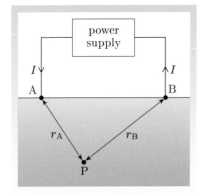

Figure 7.6   Current source at A and current sink at B.

Note that we are assuming initially that the conductivity is uniform in the region through which the current flows.

The potential differences associated with the current flow are measured with two additional electrodes, M and N in Figure 7.7, which are located on a straight line between current electrodes A and B, with equal spacing a between neighbouring electrodes. The use of these additional electrodes means that any high contact resistance between the current probes and the ground does not affect the measured potential difference; a similar four-electrode technique is widely used to measure the conductivity of semiconductors. The potentials at M and N due to the current flow are

$$V_\mathrm{M} = \frac{I}{2\pi\sigma} \left(\frac{1}{a} - \frac{1}{2a} \right) = \frac{I}{4\pi\sigma a} \quad \text{and} \quad V_\mathrm{N} = \frac{I}{2\pi\sigma} \left(\frac{1}{2a} - \frac{1}{a} \right) = -\frac{I}{4\pi\sigma a}.$$

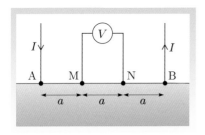

Figure 7.7   An array of four electrodes in a straight line used for geophysical measurements.

The potential difference V_MN is

$$V_\mathrm{MN} = V_\mathrm{M} - V_\mathrm{N} = \frac{I}{2\pi\sigma a},$$

so the conductivity σ is

$$\sigma = \frac{I}{2\pi a V_\mathrm{MN}}. \tag{7.8}$$

This result is based on the assumption that the ground in the path of the current has uniform conductivity.

The current density decreases with the inverse square of the distance from the source, and this means that the path of the current from A to B is mainly confined to depths less than the spacing between the current electrodes. So if archaeologists were looking for building foundations or rubbish pits that might be a few metres below the surface, they would use a spacing of a few metres between the current electrodes, and make measurements with the electrode array located at different positions over the area of interest.

Figure 7.8 shows results from a survey carried out at a former monastic site in Ireland. The figure shows the resistivity (that is, the reciprocal of the conductivity) of the ground for a horizontal section and for a vertical section through the site. The high resistivity regions — shown as red — indicate buried walls and foundations of a small chapel. No evidence for these walls is visible at the surface. The survey was done with neighbouring electrodes spaced by 0.8 m in the y-direction and scanned along a 25 m line in that direction; successive scans were carried out along lines displaced by 1.5 m in the x-direction. Computation of the resistivity as a function of position from the measurements of voltage difference between the electrodes is an example of an inverse problem. In Chapter 5 we discussed a different inverse problem — using measured values of the magnetic field outside a person's head to compute the current sources within the brain responsible for generating those magnetic fields.

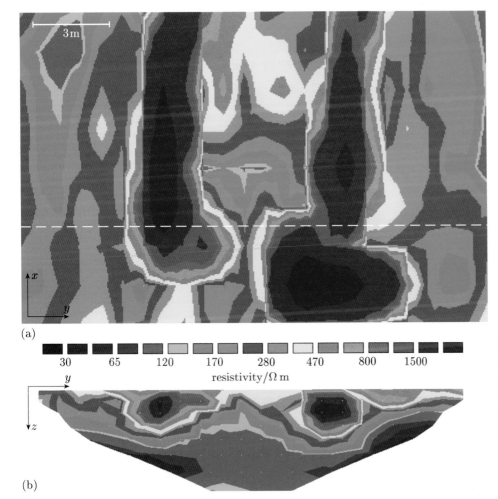

Figure 7.8 Results of a resistivity survey of a monastic site in County Meath, Ireland. (a) Plan view of resistivity computed for a depth range of 0.40–0.86 m. (b) Section showing the resistivity in a vertical plane below the broken line in (a).

Increasing the electrode spacing means that the current passes deeper below the surface, and this may mean that the current traverses several subsurface layers with different conductivities. The value of σ determined from Equation 7.8 is then an effective conductivity for the multiple layers. When the electrodes are close together, with a spacing much less than the depth of the first subsurface boundary, σ is mainly determined by the surface layer. As the spacing of the electrodes is increased, changes in the effective conductivity are recorded when the current penetrates into a deeper layer with a different conductivity. Such changes are particularly apparent where the current starts to flow through a waterlogged lower layer that is overlaid by a dry surface layer, or conversely when the current starts to flow through an impermeable rock layer overlaid by wet soil.

7.1.4 Laplace's equation and current flow

The calculation of resistance of an irregularly shaped conductor is not straightforward, even if the material is homogeneous and obeys the local form of Ohm's law, $\mathbf{J} = \sigma\mathbf{E}$. However, when the electric field is conservative, the electrostatic potential associated with a steady current within such a conducting material obeys Laplace's equation, as we shall now demonstrate. This means that we can use any of the methods for solving this equation that were discussed in Chapter 4.

For a conservative field, $\mathbf{E} = -\operatorname{grad} V$. Consequently, the current density is

$$\mathbf{J} = -\sigma \operatorname{grad} V.$$

If we consider a steady current, then the charge density at any point within the material is independent of time. The equation of continuity, $\operatorname{div}\mathbf{J} = -\partial\rho/\partial t$, therefore indicates that the divergence of $\mathbf{J}$ is zero. For a homogeneous material, σ is independent of position, and this means that

$$\operatorname{div}\mathbf{J} = -\operatorname{div}(\sigma \operatorname{grad} V) = -\sigma \operatorname{div}(\operatorname{grad} V) = 0.$$

But $\operatorname{div}(\operatorname{grad} V) = \nabla^2 V$ — this is one of the standard vector identities listed inside the back cover — so at all points within the conducting material,

$$\nabla^2 V = 0. \tag{7.9}$$

Equation 7.9 is Laplace's equation for the electrostatic potential. You met it in Chapter 4, where you saw that the electrostatic potential in a *dielectric* material obeys this equation if the charge density is zero. Here we have shown that the same equation is obeyed by the electrostatic potential within an ohmic *conducting* material when a steady current flows through it.

Determining resistance by solving Laplace's equation

All of the techniques used to solve Laplace's equation for the electrostatic potential in dielectrics can be used to determine the potential in a conducting material, and hence determine the current flowing and the resistance. Of course, to solve any differential equation we need boundary conditions, and the appropriate boundary conditions for conduction problems involve specification of either the potential V or the current density $\mathbf{J}$ (or equivalently $\mathbf{E}$, since $\mathbf{J} = \sigma\mathbf{E}$) on the boundaries of the material. If we find a solution that satisfies the boundary conditions (by any method — even guesswork) then the *uniqueness theorem* (Section 4.3) tells us that it is the only solution.

So the general technique for determining the resistance R for a homogeneous conductor is as follows.

1. Determine $V(\mathbf{r})$ by solving Laplace's equation with appropriate boundary conditions.

2. Determine the current density using $\mathbf{J} = -\sigma \operatorname{grad} V$.

3. Integrate the current density over an appropriate surface to find the current I.

4. Determine the resistance as the ratio of the potential drop to the current.

In practice, these steps generally require numerical methods, implemented on a computer.

Boundary conditions

Let us consider the appropriate boundary conditions for conducting materials. In Chapter 2 we derived boundary conditions for the interface between two dielectric materials.

- The perpendicular component of $\mathbf{D}$ is continuous at an interface where there is no free charge, that is, $D_{1\perp} = D_{2\perp}$.

- The parallel component of $\mathbf{E}$ is continuous, that is, $E_{1\parallel} = E_{2\parallel}$.

However, for current flow in conducting materials, it is more useful to express the boundary conditions in terms of the current density. One condition can be derived from the equation of continuity, $\operatorname{div} \mathbf{J} = \partial\rho/\partial t$. In a steady state, the charge density ρ must be independent of time, so $\operatorname{div} \mathbf{J} = 0$. Then the divergence theorem indicates that $\int_S \mathbf{J} \cdot \mathrm{d}\mathbf{S} = 0$ for any closed surface S. If we apply this result to a thin pillbox straddling the interface, then we find that the normal component of the current density must be the same either side of the boundary, $J_{1\perp} = J_{2\perp}$. You might like to refer back to Section 2.5, where we derived the boundary condition for the normal component of $\mathbf{D}$ at a dielectric interface using a similar method.

The parallel component of $\mathbf{E}$ is continuous across a boundary, just as with dielectrics. If the local form of Ohm's law is true on both sides of the boundary, then the ratio of the parallel component of current density to conductivity, $J_{\parallel}/\sigma$, must be continuous across the boundary.

In summary:

Boundary conditions for current density in conducting materials

$$J_{1\perp} = J_{2\perp}, \tag{7.10}$$

$$\frac{J_{1\parallel}}{\sigma_1} = \frac{J_{2\parallel}}{\sigma_2}. \tag{7.11}$$

● What can you deduce from these boundary conditions about the directions of the current density and electric field just inside the surface of a good conductor if there is an insulator outside the surface?

○ The current density in an insulator is zero (or negligibly small), so the continuity of the normal component, $J_\perp$, means that $J_\perp = 0$ in the conductor near the surface. The current density must therefore be parallel to the surface. Since $\mathbf{J} = \sigma\mathbf{E}$, the electric field within the conductor must be in the same direction as $\mathbf{J}$; therefore $\mathbf{E}$ is parallel to the surface.

● What can you deduce from these boundary conditions about the directions of the current density and electric field just inside the surface of a poor conductor if there is a material with very high conductivity outside the surface?

○ The boundary condition for $J_\parallel$ indicates that the parallel component of the current density in the poor conductor is smaller by a factor of $\sigma_{\text{poor}}/\sigma_{\text{high}}$ than in the high-conductivity material. This ratio is likely to be much smaller than 10^{-2}, so the parallel component of current density in the poor conductor is negligible. This means that the current density in the poor conductor is essentially perpendicular to the boundary near to the boundary.

Method of images

As an example of how techniques from electrostatics can be applied to current-flow problems, we shall consider how the method of images can be used to calculate the resistance between a point electrode inside a very large block of a poorly-conducting material and a metal coating on one face of the block, as shown in Figure 7.9a. The current flow is difficult to specify, but we can specify some boundary conditions. Close to the point source, the steady current flow will not be influenced by the metallic boundary; it will spread out radially, with $J_r = I/4\pi r^2$, and the equipotential surfaces will be spheres centred on the source. The electric field within the highly-conducting metal layer at the boundary will be small, so the parallel component of the electric field near to the surface of the block is also small, and this means that the field and current density near the surface are perpendicular to the surface, and the equipotentials are parallel to the surface, as shown in Figure 7.9b.

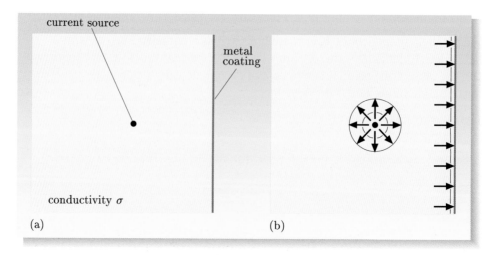

Figure 7.9 (a) A point source of current within a poor conductor with a metal coating on one face. (b) Boundary conditions near the two electrodes; the vectors represent $\mathbf{J}$ and $\mathbf{E}$, and the black lines are equipotentials.

● Can you suggest a configuration of current sources in an infinite conducting medium that would replicate the potential distribution around the point electrode and near the metallic boundary layer shown in Figure 7.9b? (You may wish to refer back to the discussion of the method of images in Subsection 4.3.1.)

○ By analogy with the situation shown in Figures 4.8–4.10, you might expect that two current sources with opposite signs and with separation $2d$ would be appropriate.

The field and potential for the combination of two sources are simply the superpositions of those for the individual sources, as you saw in Subsection 4.3.1. The superposed fields are shown in Figure 7.10; they are identical to the field for two point charges with equal magnitudes but opposite signs, shown in Figure 4.10. Since this field satisfies the boundary conditions for the original problem, the uniqueness theorem tells us that the solution of this new problem will be a solution of the original problem in the region of the block. Now we can write down an expression for the electrostatic potential at any point along the line between the real and image sources in terms of the distance z from the real source:

$$V(z) = \frac{I}{4\pi\sigma z} - \frac{I}{4\pi\sigma(2d - z)}.$$

By integrating this expression between the real source and the metal boundary, we could obtain an expression for the potential drop ΔV, and dividing this by the current would give the resistance.

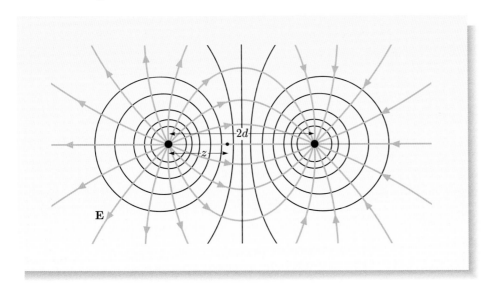

Figure 7.10   Electric field **E** and equipotentials for two current sources with opposite signs in a poorly-conducting material of infinite extent.

The number of problems that are soluble using the method of images is very small, and the other analytic methods of calculating resistance are also limited to a small number of situations with reasonably high symmetry. But once again the power of computers comes to the rescue. The numerical techniques described in Chapter 4 for solving Laplace's equation in dielectrics can equally well be used to determine the potential, field, current and hence resistance for a conducting object.

7.2   Electromagnetic induction and inductance

Resistance in electrical circuits leads to the dissipation of energy, so a source of energy is required to maintain a steady current flow. Electric batteries (Book 1, Chapter 6) are one such source of energy, and electrical power supplies that convert mains electricity (240 V, 50 Hz) to a steady voltage are another. These sources each provide an *emf* that drives current through a circuit, and in Book 1 you saw that the emf in a circuit is defined as the energy input per unit charge transferred around the circuit. Alternatively, the emf, V_{emf}, can be expressed as

$$V_{\text{emf}} = \frac{1}{q} \oint_C \mathbf{F} \cdot d\mathbf{l},$$

where $\mathbf{F}$ is the force acting on a charge q that drives it round the circuit, and the path C is a complete loop around the circuit.

In the remainder of this chapter we shall be concerned with emfs that arise from electromagnetic induction, another topic that was introduced in Book 1. We shall briefly review the two main types of induction, but the main focus will be on the emfs induced in circuits due to changing currents.

7.2.1   Emfs produced by induction

Faraday's induction experiments in the early 19th century were of revolutionary significance for their time because they generated currents in closed circuits that did not contain a battery. His results can be encapsulated in the following relationship, known as the generalized Faraday law, which was derived in Book 1:

$$V_{\text{emf}} = \oint_C (\mathbf{E} + \mathbf{v} \times \mathbf{B}) \cdot d\mathbf{l} = -\frac{d}{dt} \int_S \mathbf{B} \cdot d\mathbf{S}, \tag{7.12}$$

Remember that the positive sense of progression around C and the orientation of S are related by the right-hand grip rule.

where $\mathbf{v}$ is the velocity of an element $d\mathbf{l}$ of a circuit defined by path C, and S is any open surface bounded by this path.

This indicates that the induced emf V_{emf} in a circuit that follows a path C is equal to the path integral around this circuit of the Lorentz force per unit charge, $(\mathbf{E} + \mathbf{v} \times \mathbf{B})$, and it is also equal to the rate of change of the magnetic flux through the circuit, $\int_S \mathbf{B} \cdot d\mathbf{S}$. This result is valid for all types of electromagnetic induction, whether due to time-dependent magnetic fields, or due to motion of circuits in steady magnetic fields, or due to a combination of both of these effects.

Magnetic flux plays an important role in the rest of this chapter, and for convenience it will be denoted by the symbol Φ, the Greek capital letter phi (pronounced 'fie', as in pie). Thus

$$\Phi = \int_S \mathbf{B} \cdot d\mathbf{S}$$

is the flux through a surface S, and the *induced* emf is

$$V_{\text{emf}} = -\frac{d\Phi}{dt}. \tag{7.13}$$

Induction in a circuit moving through a steady non-uniform field

This type of induction involves a conducting circuit moving through a steady magnetic field that varies with position. An example of this situation is shown in Figure 7.11: a coil connected to a current meter moves towards a stationary magnet. The magnetic field does not depend on time, so from the differential version of Faraday's law ($\mathrm{curl}\,\mathbf{E} = -\partial\mathbf{B}/\partial t$) we deduce that $\mathrm{curl}\,\mathbf{E} = \mathbf{0}$. This means that any electric field present is conservative, $\oint_C \mathbf{E} \cdot \mathrm{d}\mathbf{l} = 0$, and so cannot make a contribution to the emf in the circuit. In this situation, where the conducting circuit is moving in the magnetic field, the emf is generated by the *magnetic* forces on the conduction electrons, and Equation 7.12 becomes

Induced emf in a moving circuit

$$V_{\mathrm{emf}} = \oint_C (\mathbf{v} \times \mathbf{B}) \cdot \mathrm{d}\mathbf{l} = -\frac{\mathrm{d}\Phi}{\mathrm{d}t}. \qquad (7.14)$$

Note that Φ is the flux through the surface defined by all the turns of the coil, *not* the flux through a single turn. For a coil with N turns, each of area A, in a uniform field $\mathbf{B}$ that is normal to the plane of the coil, the magnitude of the flux through a single turn is BA, but the magnitude of the total flux through the coil is NBA.

In the following worked example and exercise we shall consider induction in a simple ac-generator, and demonstrate that the two approaches implicit in Equation 7.14 for determining the emf lead to the same result.

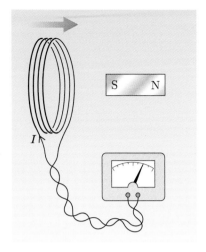

Figure 7.11 Induction in a moving coil.

Worked Example 7.2

The small rectangular loop shown in Figure 7.12 is an alternating current generator. It rotates about a vertical axis through its centre at angular frequency ω in a uniform horizontal magnetic field. The rings at the top allow contact to be maintained between the two leads from the rotating coil and the external circuit. By considering the magnetic forces on the electrons in the loop, derive an expression for the emf induced in the circuit containing the rotating loop.

Solution

We have already established that $\oint_C \mathbf{E} \cdot \mathrm{d}\mathbf{l} = 0$ in this case, so the emf is the path integral of the magnetic force per unit charge around the circuit containing the loop. Since the external circuit is stationary we need only integrate around the rotating loop. From the right-hand rule, the magnetic forces, $-e(\mathbf{v} \times \mathbf{B})$, on electrons in the top and bottom sections of the loop are perpendicular to the conductor, and so perpendicular to $\mathrm{d}\mathbf{l}$, and therefore make no contribution to the path integral around the loop used to determine the emf. However, the right-hand rule indicates that the forces on electrons in the two side sections are parallel to the conductor — downwards for the side on the left, and upwards for the side on the right. When the normal to the plane of the coil is at an angle α to the magnetic field direction, the magnitude of the force on each electron in the side sections is

$$F = evB\sin\alpha = e(\omega a/2)B\sin\alpha.$$

Essential skill

Deriving an expression for an emf

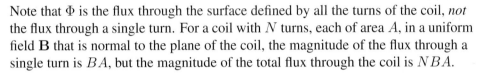

Figure 7.12 A simple ac-generator.

Integrating the force per unit charge around the loop gives

$$V_{\text{emf}} = 2b \times (\omega a/2)B \sin\alpha,$$

and if we set $\alpha = 0$ at $t = 0$, so that $\alpha = \omega t$, then

$$V_{\text{emf}} = ab\omega B \sin\omega t.$$

The emf varies sinusoidally, and its amplitude is the product of the area of the loop, ab, the angular frequency and the field strength.

Exercise 7.4   Verify that the rate of change of flux through the loop in Figure 7.12 is equal in magnitude but opposite in sign to the emf calculated in Worked Example 7.2.

Exercise 7.5   Figure 7.13 shows a homopolar generator, which is a metal disc, radius a, rotating at angular speed ω in a uniform magnetic field **B**, which is perpendicular to the plane of the disc. A resistive load R is connected between the axle and the rim of the disc. By considering the Lorentz force on the electrons along a path that includes a line between the axle and the rim of the disc, derive an expression for the emf of this generator.   ∎

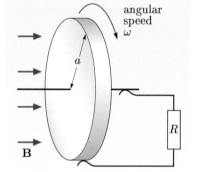

Figure 7.13   A homopolar generator.

The generators in power stations are unlike either of the systems shown in Figures 7.12 and 7.13. Instead, they use a rotating electromagnet, driven by a steam turbine, to produce a time-dependent magnetic field in coils that surround the rotating magnet. This avoids the problems associated with passing huge currents through rotating contacts. The electromagnetic induction responsible for generating the emf in this case is associated not with a moving conductor, but with a time-dependent magnetic field.

Induction by time-dependent field

A second type of induction involves stationary circuits and magnetic fields that are time dependent. As an example, consider the simple circuit shown in Figure 7.14, which consists of a coil and a meter with which to detect current. If the magnetic field in the region where the coil is located varies with time, for example because the magnet moves towards the coil, then an electric field is generated that satisfies Faraday's law, $\text{curl}\,\mathbf{E} = -\partial\mathbf{B}/\partial t$. This is a non-conservative electric field (that is, $\text{curl}\,\mathbf{E} \neq 0$), and it exists at all points where the magnetic field is changing, including points within the conducting material from which the coil is made. The induced emf is again given by Equation 7.12, but this time there is no contribution to the emf from magnetic forces. This is because the circuit is stationary, so the drift velocity of the charge carriers associated with any current flow must be parallel or antiparallel to the integration path. The vector product $\mathbf{v} \times \mathbf{B}$ is therefore perpendicular to the integration path, so $\int_C (\mathbf{v} \times \mathbf{B}) \cdot \mathrm{d}\mathbf{l} = 0$. Therefore in a stationary circuit, the induced emf is given by

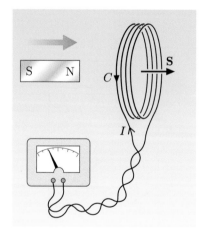

Figure 7.14   The moving magnet induces an emf in the circuit, and an induced current is indicated by the meter.

Induced emf in a stationary circuit

$$V_{\text{emf}} = \oint_C \mathbf{E} \cdot \mathrm{d}\mathbf{l} = -\frac{\mathrm{d}\Phi}{\mathrm{d}t}, \tag{7.15}$$

where the path C is taken around the circuit containing the coil, and Φ is the flux through any surface bounded by this path.

The emf produces an induced current $I = V_{\text{emf}}/R$, where R is the total resistance in the circuit. A positive value for the current means that it circulates in the same sense as the path C in Figure 7.14. The minus sign that accompanies the $\mathrm{d}\Phi/\mathrm{d}t$ term is consistent with Lenz's law, which states that the direction of the induced emf is such that any induced current would produce a magnetic flux that opposes the original change of flux.

● Verify that the prediction of Equation 7.15 for the situation shown in Figure 7.14 is consistent with Lenz's law.

○ The directions of path C and the vector $\mathbf{S}$ representing the oriented area enclosed by C are related by a right-hand grip rule. Positive emfs and positive currents are in the direction of path C, and positive flux is in the direction of the vector $\mathbf{S}$. So when the north pole of the magnet approaches the coil, the flux linking the coil increases, so $\mathrm{d}\Phi/\mathrm{d}t$ is positive. From Equation 7.15, the induced emf and the induced current are therefore negative, which means the current flows in the opposite direction to path C. This current will generate a magnetic field towards the left, in the opposite direction to the field of the magnet. So the flux due to the induced current is in the opposite direction to the change of flux due to the movement of the magnet, as required by Lenz's law.

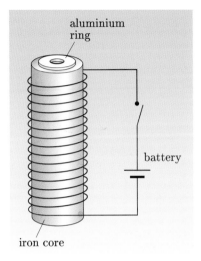

Exercise 7.6 The iron-cored solenoid in Figure 7.15 has an aluminium ring on the top face. When the switch is closed, the aluminium ring jumps upwards. Explain why. ■

Figure 7.15 Why does the aluminium ring fly upwards when the switch is closed?

You can reinforce your understanding of induction by a time-dependent field by using the software simulation *Faraday's law* on the course DVD.

Potentials for conservative and non-conservative electric fields

Many electrostatics problems are solved most easily by first calculating the electrostatic potential field V, and then determining the electric field using the relationship $\mathbf{E} = -\operatorname{grad} V$. However, this relationship is valid only for conservative electric fields. For time-dependent fields, Faraday's law indicates that $\operatorname{curl} \mathbf{E} = -\partial\mathbf{B}/\partial t$, and the electric field is not conservative. In this situation it is not possible to define an electrostatic potential field. The question that can be asked is whether there is an alternative expression for a potential, from which the non-conservative electric field can be determined. The answer to this question is 'yes', and the appropriate expression involves the magnetic vector potential $\mathbf{A}$ that was introduced briefly in Subsection 5.2.4.

To derive the appropriate expression, we start from the definition of the vector potential,

$$\mathbf{B} = \operatorname{curl} \mathbf{A}.$$

We can use this to rewrite Faraday's law:

$$\operatorname{curl} \mathbf{E} = -\frac{\partial\mathbf{B}}{\partial t} = -\frac{\partial(\operatorname{curl}\mathbf{A})}{\partial t} = -\operatorname{curl}\left(\frac{\partial\mathbf{A}}{\partial t}\right),$$

so

$$\operatorname{curl}\left(\mathbf{E} + \frac{\partial \mathbf{A}}{\partial t}\right) = \mathbf{0}. \tag{7.16}$$

This shows that the field $(\mathbf{E} + \partial \mathbf{A}/\partial t)$ is irrotational. It follows that this field can be written as

$$\mathbf{E} + \frac{\partial \mathbf{A}}{\partial t} = -\operatorname{grad} V,$$

or

$$\mathbf{E} = -\operatorname{grad} V - \frac{\partial \mathbf{A}}{\partial t}, \tag{7.17}$$

where V is a scalar potential field. This equation is a general expression that applies to both conservative and non-conservative electric fields. Clearly, for static fields, this expression reduces to the familiar relationship $\mathbf{E} = -\operatorname{grad} V$, and the potential in this expression is then the electrostatic potential. Also, when there is no conservative component to the electric field, such as the situation in Figure 7.14, it reduces to

$$\mathbf{E} = -\frac{\partial \mathbf{A}}{\partial t}. \tag{7.18}$$

This is an alternative way of expressing Faraday's law, as can easily be demonstrated. If we take the line integral of Equation 7.18 around a loop, then

$$\oint_C \mathbf{E} \cdot \mathrm{d}\mathbf{l} = -\oint_C \left(\frac{\partial \mathbf{A}}{\partial t}\right) \cdot \mathrm{d}\mathbf{l} = -\frac{\mathrm{d}}{\mathrm{d}t}\oint_C \mathbf{A} \cdot \mathrm{d}\mathbf{l}$$

$$= -\frac{\mathrm{d}}{\mathrm{d}t}\oint_C \operatorname{curl}\mathbf{A} \cdot \mathrm{d}\mathbf{S} = -\frac{\mathrm{d}}{\mathrm{d}t}\int_S \mathbf{B} \cdot \mathrm{d}\mathbf{S},$$

which is the integral version of Faraday's law. It is interesting to note that Maxwell himself expressed Faraday's law in the alternative form shown in Equation 7.18. In some respects, this is the simplest way of representing Faraday's law, because the relationship between $\mathbf{E}$ and $\partial \mathbf{A}/\partial t$ is a *local* relationship. Where $\partial \mathbf{A}/\partial t = \mathbf{0}$, there can be no induced electric field. The same cannot be said about the relationship between $\mathbf{E}$ and $\partial \mathbf{B}/\partial t$; for example, the induced electric field *outside* a long solenoid can be non-zero, even though the magnetic field is constant there.

In Subsection 5.2.4 we noted that the magnetic vector potential $\mathbf{A}$ was not particularly useful for calculating magnetostatic fields because of its vector nature. For the same reason, $\mathbf{A}$ is rarely used for determining induced electric fields, so we shall not discuss it further in this book. However, the vector potential is helpful in situations involving rapid changes of currents and charge distributions.

7.2.2   Mutual inductance

In the previous subsection we discussed emfs induced by changing magnetic fields, and we shall now look more closely at the induced emfs generated in a circuit when the changing magnetic field is caused by a changing current in a second circuit that is in proximity to the first. This type of induced emf is the basis of the operation of transformers that are widely used to step up or step down the voltage of the 50 Hz mains electricity supply. Such transformers are wound on ferromagnetic cores, like that shown in Figure 7.16, and the high-permeability material ensures very effective coupling of the flux between the two coils. In the absence of such a core, the coupling of two circuits would be much weaker. This coupling between different circuits is known as *mutual inductance*.

Figure 7.17 shows two circuits, labelled 1 and 2. Changes in the current I_1 in coil 1 cause changes to the magnetic field $\mathbf{B}_1$, and Faraday's law, $\mathrm{curl}\,\mathbf{E}_1 = -\partial\mathbf{B}_1/\partial t$, indicates that the changing magnetic field generates an electric field in the region of circuit 2. This electric field gives rise to an emf in circuit 2:

$$V_{\mathrm{emf2}} = \oint_{C_2} \mathbf{E}_1 \cdot \mathrm{d}\mathbf{l}_2$$

$$= \int_{S_2} \mathrm{curl}\,\mathbf{E}_1 \cdot \mathrm{d}\mathbf{S}_2 = \int_{S_2} \left(-\frac{\partial\mathbf{B}_1}{\partial t}\right) \cdot \mathrm{d}\mathbf{S}_2 = -\frac{\mathrm{d}\Phi_{21}}{\mathrm{d}t}, \qquad (7.19)$$

where Φ_{21} is the total flux through circuit 2 due to the field $\mathbf{B}_1$ produced by a current in circuit 1. Note that if the path C_2 is in the direction shown, then the flux Φ_{21} through surface S_2 is positive. Thus if this flux is increasing, i.e. $\mathrm{d}\Phi_{21}/\mathrm{d}t > 0$, then the induced emf V_{emf2} is negative, which means that it generates a current in the opposite direction to C_2. This current gives rise to a magnetic field directed upwards in Figure 7.17, and the flux of this through C_2 is negative — it opposes the increase in flux through C_2 due to the current in coil 1, as expected from Lenz's law.

Now, since the flux Φ_{21} is generated by the current I_1 in coil 1, we can express the rate of change of flux as

$$\frac{\mathrm{d}\Phi_{21}}{\mathrm{d}t} = \frac{\mathrm{d}\Phi_{21}}{\mathrm{d}I_1}\frac{\mathrm{d}I_1}{\mathrm{d}t}.$$

Equation 7.19 can therefore be written in the form

$$V_{\mathrm{emf2}} = -\frac{\mathrm{d}\Phi_{21}}{\mathrm{d}I_1}\frac{\mathrm{d}I_1}{\mathrm{d}t} = -M_{21}\frac{\mathrm{d}I_1}{\mathrm{d}t},$$

where

$$M_{21} = \frac{\mathrm{d}\Phi_{21}}{\mathrm{d}I_1}. \qquad (7.20)$$

The quantity M_{21} is known as the **mutual inductance** between the two circuits. Its SI unit is $\mathrm{T\,m^2\,A^{-1}}$, but this unit is sufficiently important to be given the name **henry** and the symbol H.

This general definition of mutual inductance in Equation 7.20 is always valid, and in particular it is valid even when non-linear magnetic materials are present, so that the relationship between current and flux is not linear. However, in the absence of ferromagnetic materials, magnetic field strength, and therefore magnetic flux, is proportional to the current generating it, so

$$M_{21} = \frac{\Phi_{21}}{I_1}. \qquad (7.21)$$

The magnitude of M_{21} clearly depends on the geometry of the two coils in Figure 7.17. It could be increased by locating the coils concentrically in a

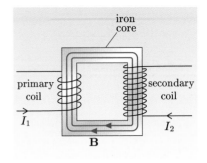

Figure 7.16 A transformer. An alternating current in the primary coil generates an induced emf in the secondary coil.

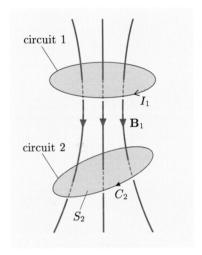

Figure 7.17 Current I_1 in circuit 1 produces a magnetic field $\mathbf{B}_1$, which intersects circuit 2.

common plane, since this would maximize the flux passing through coil 2. A much larger increase would be obtained by inserting a ferromagnetic cylinder through the two coils. For the same current in coil 1, the field $\mathbf{H}_1$ would be unchanged by the ferromagnetic material (since it depends only on the free current in the coil), but the field $\mathbf{B}_1$, which generates the flux Φ_{21}, would be enhanced by a factor equal to the relative permeability μ. The mutual inductance would therefore be increased by the same factor. Use of a ferromagnetic core has another advantage: the two coils can be on different parts of the core, as shown in Figure 7.16. The magnetic flux is confined within the high-permeability core, so the coupling between the primary and secondary coils of this transformer is very good in spite of their physical separation.

Note that there is ambiguity in the sign of M_{12} because there is no convention that links the directions of positive circulation in two separate circuits. For each circuit, the right-hand grip rule relates the direction of positive circulation to the direction of positive flux, but positive current in circuit 1 could produce either positive or negative flux in circuit 2, depending on our choice of the direction of positive circulation in circuit 2.

Essential skill

Calculating mutual inductance

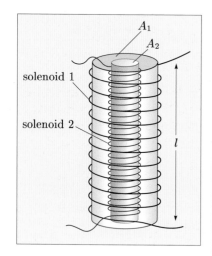

Figure 7.18   Two coaxial solenoids.

Worked Example 7.3

Two long thin coaxial solenoids, each of length l and with cross-sectional areas A_1 and A_2, are shown in Figure 7.18. The number of turns per unit length of the solenoids are n_1 and n_2. Derive expressions for the flux Φ_{21} in solenoid 2 due to a current I_1 in solenoid 1, and for the flux Φ_{12} in solenoid 1 due to a current I_2 in solenoid 2. Hence write down expressions for M_{21} and M_{12}, and compare them. Assume $\mu = 1$ in the solenoids.

Solution

The magnitude of the magnetic field within solenoid 1 due to a current I_1 in this solenoid is $B_1 = \mu_0 n_1 I_1$. Consequently, the total flux through solenoid 2 is

$$\Phi_{21} = n_2 l A_2 B_1 = \mu_0 n_1 n_2 l A_2 I_1,$$

and

$$M_{21} = \Phi_{21}/I_1 = \mu_0 n_1 n_2 l A_2.$$

The field within solenoid 2 due to a current I_2 in this solenoid is $B_2 = \mu_0 n_2 I_2$, but the field between the windings of the two solenoids is zero. So the flux Φ_{12} through solenoid 1 is restricted to the region inside solenoid 2:

$$\Phi_{12} = n_1 l A_2 B_2 = \mu_0 n_1 n_2 l A_2 I_2,$$

and

$$M_{12} = \Phi_{12}/I_2 = \mu_0 n_1 n_2 l A_2.$$

So $M_{21} = M_{12}$.

You can see from Worked Example 7.3 that $M_{12} = M_{21}$, and this is the reason it is called 'mutual' inductance. This symmetry is a general property for any pair of conducting circuits, so it is convenient to set

$$M = M_{12} = M_{21}.$$

Worked Example 7.4

Derive an expression for the mutual inductance of the two circular coils shown in Figure 7.19, which have radii r_1 and r_2 (with $r_1 \gg r_2$), numbers of turns N_1 and N_2, and are separated by distance d.

Solution

We know that $M_{12} = M_{21} = M$, where M_{12} is the flux through coil 1 per unit current in coil 2, and M_{21} is the flux through coil 2 per unit current in coil 1. So there are two ways that we could determine M. However, it is far easier to determine the flux through the small coil due to the current in the large coil, because the field will be approximately uniform over the area of the small coil.

In Book 1 we derived an expression for the field on the axis of a single-turn coil:

$$B_z = \frac{\mu_0 I r^2}{2(r^2 + d^2)^{3/2}},$$

where r is the coil radius, and d is the distance from its centre to the field point. So the flux through the small coil (2) when current I_1 flows in the N_1 turns of the large coil, producing a field strength B_1 at coil 2, is given by

$$\Phi_{21} = N_2 A_2 B_1 = N_2 \times \pi r_2^2 \times \frac{\mu_0 N_1 I_1 r_1^2}{2(r_1^2 + d^2)^{3/2}} = \frac{\pi \mu_0 N_1 N_2 I_1 r_1^2 r_2^2}{2(r_1^2 + d^2)^{3/2}}.$$

So the mutual inductance is

$$M = M_{21} = \frac{\Phi_{21}}{I_1} = \frac{\pi \mu_0 N_1 N_2 r_1^2 r_2^2}{2(r_1^2 + d^2)^{3/2}}.$$

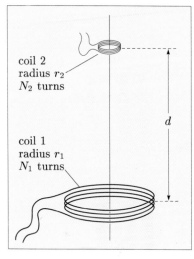

Figure 7.19 Two coaxial coils.

The device shown in Figure 7.20a overleaf uses mutual inductance between a rectangular loop and a straight wire to measure radio-frequency currents. A 13.5 MHz current, used for exciting a plasma discharge, flows in the straight wire, and it induces an emf in the small rectangular loop, which is proportional to the current. The cylinder to the right of the loop forms the outer plate of a coaxial capacitor, and the rf-voltage of this plate indicates the voltage on the central wire. In the following exercise you can estimate the magnitude of the emf induced in the rectangular loop.

We often abbreviate radio frequency to rf.

Exercise 7.7 Figure 7.20b is an idealized diagram of the current measuring device in Figure 7.20a. Derive an expression for the mutual inductance between the long straight wire and the rectangular loop, and hence calculate the amplitude of the emf induced in the loop when current $I = I_0 \sin(2\pi f t)$ flows in the wire. Take $r_1 = 1.0$ mm, $r_2 = 10$ mm, $l = 15$ mm, current amplitude $I_0 = 1.0$ A and $f = 13.5$ MHz. ■

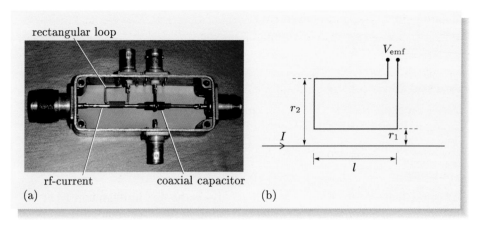

Figure 7.20   (a) A device used to measure the rf-current exciting a plasma discharge. (b) A simplified diagram of the circuit in (a).

7.2.3   Self-inductance

When the current in the circuit shown in Figure 7.21 changes, the changing magnetic field produced by the current has an associated electric field, which generates an induced emf in the same circuit. We can rewrite Equation 7.19 to describe this situation by dropping the subscripts 1 and 2, so that all quantities are related to a single circuit:

$$
\begin{aligned}
V_{\text{emf}} &= \oint_C \mathbf{E} \cdot d\mathbf{l} \\
&= \int_S \text{curl}\,\mathbf{E} \cdot d\mathbf{S} \\
&= \int_S \left(-\frac{\partial \mathbf{B}}{\partial t}\right) \cdot d\mathbf{S} = -\frac{d}{dt}\int_S \mathbf{B} \cdot d\mathbf{S} = -\frac{d\Phi}{dt}.
\end{aligned}
\tag{7.22}
$$

Note that if the current flow is in the direction of path C in Figure 7.21, then the flux Φ that it generates through surface S will be positive. Thus if the flux is increasing, i.e. $d\Phi/dt > 0$, then the induced emf V_{emf} is negative, which means that it acts to oppose the increasing current, as expected from Lenz's law.

Now, since the flux Φ is generated by the current I in the circuit, we can express the rate of change of flux as

$$
\frac{d\Phi}{dt} = \frac{d\Phi}{dI}\frac{dI}{dt}.
$$

Equation 7.22 can therefore be written in the form

$$
V_{\text{emf}} = -\frac{d\Phi}{dI}\frac{dI}{dt} = -L\frac{dI}{dt},
\tag{7.23}
$$

where

$$
L = \frac{d\Phi}{dI}.
\tag{7.24}
$$

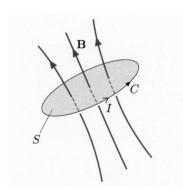

Figure 7.21   An emf is induced in this circuit when the current changes.

The quantity L is known as the **self-inductance**, or often simply the **inductance** of the circuit. The SI unit of self-inductance is the same as that for mutual inductance, the henry, symbol H.

This definition of self-inductance in Equation 7.24 is always valid, and in particular it is valid even when non-linear magnetic materials are present, so that the relationship between current and flux is not linear. However, in the absence of ferromagnetic materials, magnetic field strength, and therefore magnetic flux, is proportional to the current generating it, so

$$L = \frac{\Phi}{I}. \qquad (7.25)$$

L depends only on the geometry of the circuit in Figure 7.21.

Because of the minus sign in Equation 7.23, the induced emf opposes the change in current, and it is sometimes described as a **back-emf**. Although strictly the source of this induced back-emf is non-localized, it is convenient to regard the circuit as the source of an emf $-L\,dI/dt$.

A coil that is used in an electrical circuit because of its self-inductance is known as an **inductor**. From the viewpoint of a circuit designer, an inductor is a component that obeys the relationship $V(t) = L\,dI/dt$, where $V(t)$ is the voltage drop across the inductor in the direction of the current I. In practice, inductors also have some resistance, although this is usually made as small as possible. Figure 7.22 shows a circuit containing an inductor, with the inductor viewed as a source of emf and viewed as a circuit component with a voltage drop related to the rate of change of current. These two viewpoints are equivalent.

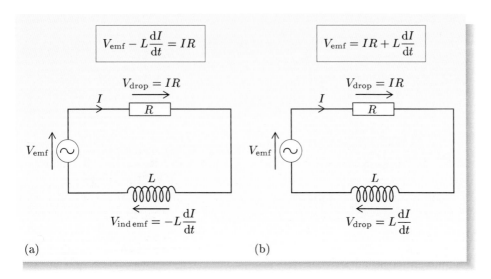

Figure 7.22 A source of emf connected to a resistor and an inductor. (a) The inductor viewed as a source of emf, $-L\,dI/dt$, in the direction of the current flow I. (b) The inductor viewed as a circuit element with a voltage drop, $L\,dI/dt$, in the direction of current flow.

Figure 7.23 overleaf shows the emfs induced in inductors in two different situations. In both of them, the induced back-emf is proportional to the rate of change of current. For a sinusoidal current (Figure 7.23a), the amplitude of the induced emf is proportional to the inductance and to the frequency of the alternating current. Thus for a given inductor the induced emf is larger by a factor of 2×10^6 for a 100 MHz current than for a 50 Hz current of the same amplitude. An inductor in a circuit therefore acts as an effective block for high-frequency signals, providing 'inertia' that inhibits rapid changes to the current. A common use for inductors is to prevent radio-frequency signals from interfering with sensitive electronic equipment. An equally important use is to prevent sudden surges in the mains power supply, perhaps due to lightning, from damaging electronic circuits. Inductors in series with the mains electricity supply will produce a large back-emf in response to a very rapid voltage change, and this helps suppress potentially-damaging voltage spikes.

Figure 7.23b highlights the need for care when a current is flowing in a coil that has a large inductance, such as an electromagnet. Opening a switch to stop the current leads to a very large back-emf, and this can cause dangerous sparking at the switch or electrocution for somebody touching the switch contacts. The current in such coils should always be reduced to zero before opening the switch.

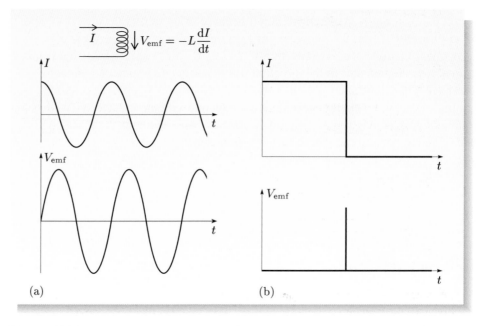

Figure 7.23   (a) A sinusoidal current I through a coil with inductance L generates an induced emf $V_{\text{emf}} = -L\,dI/dt$. Note that when dI/dt has its maximum positive value, V_{emf} has its maximum negative value. (b) At time T, the steady current I through a coil is interrupted by opening a switch; the abrupt decrease of the current generates a very large induced emf, which can cause sparking at the switch.

Essential skill

Calculating self-inductance

Worked Example 7.5

Derive an expression for the self-inductance of a long thin solenoid, length l, number of turns per unit length n, closely wound on a rod with relative permeability μ and cross-sectional area A. Hence calculate the self-inductance of a solenoid with 100 turns, length 2.0 cm, radius 2.5 mm, wound on material with $\mu = 500$. (Assume that the rod is made from an LIH magnetic material.)

Solution

Since self-inductance is defined by $L = \Phi/I$ for linear materials, and $\Phi = \int \mathbf{B} \cdot d\mathbf{S}$, we need to determine the field $\mathbf{B}$ produced by a current in the solenoid, and integrate this over the area of the coil.

Since magnetic material is present, the field $\mathbf{B}$ will depend on both the free current in the solenoid and the bound current density in the material. So we first determine $\mathbf{H}$, which depends only on the free current in the solenoid. The field $\mathbf{H}$ within a long thin solenoid is uniform and parallel to its axis, and the field outside can be neglected. Using the integral version of Ampère's law, with the rectangular path shown in Figure 7.24, the magnitude of $\mathbf{H}$ inside the solenoid is given by

$$H \Delta l = n \Delta l I,$$

so

$$H = nI.$$

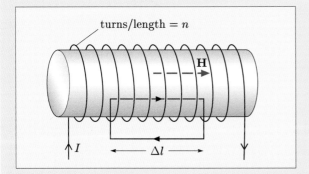

Figure 7.24 Using Ampère's law to determine H inside a solenoid.

The material inside the solenoid is linear, so $\mathbf{B} = \mu\mu_0\mathbf{H}$, which means that $\mathbf{B}$ is also uniform and parallel to the axis of the solenoid. The magnetic flux through a single turn of the solenoid is the product BA, and, since the solenoid has nl turns, the total flux Φ is

$$\Phi = nl \times BA = nl \times \mu\mu_0 nI \times A = \mu\mu_0 n^2 lAI.$$

Hence

$$L = \Phi/I = \mu\mu_0 n^2 lA. \tag{7.26}$$

For a solenoid with $n = 100/(0.020\,\text{m})$, $l = 0.020\,\text{m}$ and $A = \pi(2.5 \times 10^{-3}\,\text{m})^2$,

$$L = 500 \times 4\pi \times 10^{-7}(100/0.020)^2 \times 0.020 \times \pi(2.5 \times 10^{-3})^2\,\text{H}$$
$$= 6.2 \times 10^{-3}\,\text{H}.$$

Comment: Because this solenoid is wound around a high-permeability rod, the value of L is a factor 500 larger than for a similar solenoid with an air core.

In Subsection 7.1.2, we calculated the resistance between the inner and outer conductors of a coaxial cable, and in Exercise 2.6 we calculated its capacitance. In the following exercise you can calculate the self-inductance per unit length of a coaxial cable.

Exercise 7.8   Derive an expression for the inductance per unit length of the coaxial cable shown in Figure 7.25. Note that a coaxial cable carries currents of equal magnitude in the inner and outer conductors, but the currents flow in opposite directions. Ignore the magnetic flux within the central wire itself and within the conducting sheath, and assume that the relative permeability of the dielectric material between the conductors is unity.

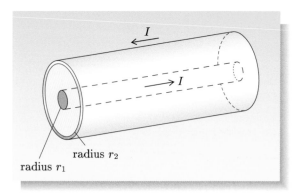

Figure 7.25   Coaxial cable.

Exercise 7.9   A long metal tube has conductivity σ, radius a, wall thickness t and length d, where $d \gg a \gg t$. Obtain expressions for the resistance and self-inductance of the tube for a uniform current density in the azimuthal direction, that is, around the wall of the tube.   ■

Summary of Chapter 7

Section 7.1   For many materials, current density $\mathbf{J}$ is proportional to electric field, so $\mathbf{J} = \sigma \mathbf{E}$, where σ is the electrical conductivity. This local relationship leads to the result $V = IR$ for the voltage drop V across a conducting object when current I flows through it. R is the resistance of the object. Both of these relationships are known as Ohm's law. More generally, in the presence of magnetic fields, $\mathbf{J} = \sigma(\mathbf{E} + \mathbf{v} \times \mathbf{B})$.

Measurements of the resistance of the ground can be used to deduce information about underlying structure.

For steady currents, the potential V within a conducting material obeys Laplace's equation, $\nabla^2 V = 0$. If this equation is solved, with appropriate boundary conditions, the current density and electric field can be calculated using $\mathbf{E} = -\operatorname{grad} V = \mathbf{J}/\sigma$. The current flowing can then be determined by integrating the current density, $I = \int_S \mathbf{J} \cdot d\mathbf{S}$, and the resistance calculated using $R = \Delta V/I$.

Section 7.2   Emfs can be induced in a circuit either by moving the circuit with respect to a stationary magnetic field, or by a time-dependent magnetic field, with no movement of the circuit, or by a combination of both. In all cases, the emf is given by

$$V_{\text{emf}} = \oint_C (\mathbf{E} + \mathbf{v} \times \mathbf{B}) \cdot d\mathbf{l} = -\frac{d\Phi}{dt},$$

where $\mathbf{v}$ is the velocity of an element $d\mathbf{l}$ of the circuit defined by the path C, and Φ is the flux through a surface S bounded by the path C.

The mutual inductance M between two circuits, 1 and 2, is defined by $M = d\Phi_{21}/dI_1$, where Φ_{21} is the flux in circuit 2 due to a current I_1 in circuit 1. The self-inductance L for a circuit in which current I produces flux Φ is defined by $L = d\Phi/dI$. In the absence of ferromagnetic media, these relationships simplify to $M = \Phi_{21}/I_1$ and $L = \Phi/I$. The unit of inductance is the henry (symbol H). The emf induced in an inductance is given by $V_{\text{emf}} = -d\Phi/dt = -L\,dI/dt$.

Achievements from Chapter 7

After studying this chapter you should be able to do the following.

7.1 Explain the meanings of the newly defined (emboldened) terms and symbols, and use them appropriately.

7.2 State Ohm's law in both the local form $\mathbf{J} = \sigma\mathbf{E}$, or $\mathbf{J} = \sigma(\mathbf{E} + \mathbf{v} \times \mathbf{B})$, and the non-local form $V = IR$, and show how one follows from the other for a simple geometry.

7.3 Calculate the resistance of conducting objects by using information about symmetry and boundary conditions.

7.4 Explain how measurements of electrostatic potentials at the surface of the Earth due to current flows can be used to provide information about underlying structure.

7.5 Derive Laplace's equation for the potential within a homogeneous conductor carrying a constant current, and use it to calculate the resistance of conducting objects with simple symmetries.

7.6 Explain how emfs are induced by motion in a magnetic field or by a time-dependent magnetic field, and solve problems involving electromagnetic induction.

7.7 Explain the meaning of mutual inductance, and calculate mutual inductance for two circuits.

7.8 Explain the meaning of self-inductance, and calculate self-inductance for circuits with simple symmetries.

Chapter 8   Electromagnetic energy

This chapter is concerned with energy in electromagnetism. A system of charges possesses potential energy, and we can understand this because work has to be done to push charges of the same sign closer together, or to separate charges of opposite sign, as is done when capacitors become charged. Similarly, a system of currents possesses potential energy; work must be done against induced emfs to set up a current in an inductor.

The energy associated with charged capacitors and current-carrying inductors can be regarded as being located within electric and magnetic fields. It may seem merely a matter of taste and convenience whether we choose to associate the energy with the fields rather than with the charges and currents that are their sources. However, associating the energy with the fields has advantages when we consider electromagnetic waves, which can exist in free space effectively detached from any charges or currents.

Steady currents and fixed charge distributions have to be set up and do not exist indefinitely. Neither growth nor decay of these distributions can be accomplished instantaneously. We shall investigate the factors that govern the time scale of the changes, together with the energy flows that take place when charges move and currents change their magnitudes.

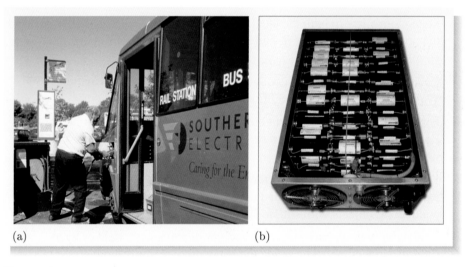

(a)   (b)

Figure 8.1 (a) An electric bus being connected to an electricity supply to recharge its batteries. (b) A large bank of capacitors developed for use in electric vehicles (Subsection 8.1.5). Its dimensions are $1\,m \times 0.6\,m \times 0.3\,m$ and its mass is $100\,kg$.

There are many applications of energy-storage capacitors, and a lot of research and development activity has gone into developing capacitors that can pack lots of energy into a small volume. We shall discuss a number of these applications, including heart defibrillators, electric vehicles (Figure 8.1) and power supplies for pulsed electromagnets. Inductors can also be used for energy storage. The superconducting magnetic energy storage system shown in Figure 8.2 can store about 2 MJ and release it over about 10 s, corresponding to a power of 200 kW.

In the final section we shall discuss the transfer of energy between an inductor and a capacitor in a circuit. This has important applications in shaping the current pulses produced by a defibrillator and in oscillatory circuits.

8.1 Charges, electric fields and energy

8.1.1 Potential energy of charge distributions

Systems of point charges

We first consider the energy of systems of point charges in a vacuum. We know that the electric field $\mathbf{E}$ of an isolated point charge q_1 held stationary at the origin of spherical coordinates is

$$\mathbf{E} = \frac{q_1}{4\pi\varepsilon_0 r^2}\,\mathbf{e}_r.$$

When we bring a second charge q_2 from infinity to a distance r_{21} from the first charge, then a force must be applied that just overcomes the Coulomb force. This means that $\mathbf{F}_{\text{applied}} = -\mathbf{F} = -q\mathbf{E}$, and the work W done by the applied force is

$$W = -\int_\infty^{r_{21}} q_2 \mathbf{E} \cdot d\mathbf{l}$$

$$= -\frac{q_1 q_2}{4\pi\varepsilon_0}\int_\infty^{r_{21}} \frac{dr}{r^2} = \left[\frac{q_1 q_2}{4\pi\varepsilon_0 r}\right]_\infty^{r_{21}} = \frac{q_1 q_2}{4\pi\varepsilon_0 r_{21}}, \tag{8.1}$$

where the zero of potential has been placed at infinity.

Since electrostatic fields are conservative, the work done is independent of the path followed by the second charge. If we now introduce a third charge q_3 (see Figure 8.3), the work done in bringing this charge from infinity to a distance r_{31} from charge q_1 and r_{32} from q_2 is the sum of the work done against the forces on q_3 due to each of the other two charges. Each of these contributions to the work done has the same form as Equation 8.1, so the total work done to bring together the three charges is

$$W = \frac{q_1 q_2}{4\pi\varepsilon_0 r_{21}} + \frac{q_1 q_3}{4\pi\varepsilon_0 r_{31}} + \frac{q_2 q_3}{4\pi\varepsilon_0 r_{32}}. \tag{8.2}$$

Notice that the three charges in this equation appear symmetrically, so the work done does not depend on the order in which we assemble the charges. Also, it depends only on the final distances between the charges, not on the routes taken by the charges. This uniqueness allows us to define the **electrostatic potential energy** U of this arrangement as the work done in assembling the arrangement of charges, that is, $U = W$.

We can continue this process indefinitely, and for n charges we obtain

$$U = \tfrac{1}{2}\sum_{i=1}^{n}\sum_{j=1,\,j\neq i}^{n} \frac{q_i q_j}{4\pi\varepsilon_0 r_{ij}},$$

where the factor $\tfrac{1}{2}$ compensates for the fact that each pair of charges (such as $q_1 q_2$) occurs twice in this summation. We can rewrite U as

$$U = \tfrac{1}{2}\sum_{i=1}^{n} q_i \sum_{j=1,\,j\neq i}^{n} \frac{q_j}{4\pi\varepsilon_0 r_{ij}}, \tag{8.3}$$

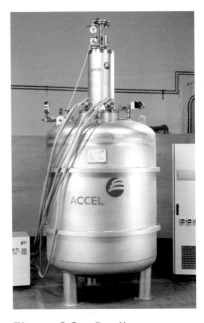

Figure 8.2 Small superconducting magnetic energy storage unit, which can store 2 MJ of energy.

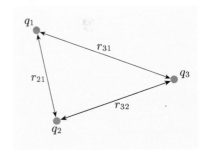

Figure 8.3 Three point charges.

or

$$U = \tfrac{1}{2} \sum_{i=1}^{n} q_i V_i, \quad \text{where} \quad V_i = \sum_{j=1, \, j \neq i}^{n} \frac{q_j}{4\pi\varepsilon_0 r_{ij}}. \tag{8.4}$$

The quantity V_i is the electrostatic potential at the position of the ith charge due to the Coulomb potentials of the other $(n-1)$ charges. Notice the crucial distinction between the electrostatic potential at a point and the electrostatic potential energy of a system of charges; the electrostatic potential V is the work done to bring a unit positive test charge to a point in the field, whereas the electrostatic potential energy U is the energy of all of the charges that are present.

Exercise 8.1   Show that Equation 8.4 reduces to Equation 8.2 for three charges.   ■

Volume and surface charge distributions

The expression for U in Equation 8.4 can be generalized to continuous charge distributions by replacing the sum with an integral. For a surface charge distribution with charge per unit area $\sigma(\mathbf{r})$, the potential energy U is

$$U = \tfrac{1}{2} \int_S \sigma(\mathbf{r}) V(\mathbf{r}) \, \mathrm{d}S. \tag{8.5}$$

For a volume charge distribution with charge density $\rho(\mathbf{r})$, the potential energy is

$$U = \tfrac{1}{2} \int_\tau \rho(\mathbf{r}) V(\mathbf{r}) \, \mathrm{d}\tau, \tag{8.6}$$

where τ denotes the volume containing the charge, and $\mathrm{d}\tau$ is a small volume element within that region. Both of these expressions apply to finite distributions of charge only, since the integrals may not converge for infinite distributions.

Essential skill

Determining the electric potential energy of distributed charges

Worked Example 8.1

A sphere of radius R containing a uniform charge density ρ is located in air ($\varepsilon = 1$) in a region remote from other sources of charge. What is the potential energy of this charge distribution?

Solution

The spherical symmetry of the charge distribution indicates that we should use spherical coordinates with their origin at the centre of the charge distribution, and the field must then have the form $\mathbf{E}(\mathbf{r}) = E_r(r)\mathbf{e}_r$. The potential energy is given by Equation 8.6, so we need to determine $V(\mathbf{r})$ within the sphere. This can be done by using Gauss's law to determine $E_r(r)$ both inside and outside the sphere, then using the relationship

$$V(r) = -\int_\infty^r E_r(r) \, \mathrm{d}r,$$

where we assume that the potential is zero at an infinite distance from the sphere.

To evaluate $E_r(r)$, we use a Gaussian surface that is a sphere with radius s, concentric with the charge distribution (Figure 8.4). The charge Q that lies within the Gaussian surface is

$$Q = \tfrac{4}{3}\pi s^3 \rho \quad \text{for } s \leq R, \quad \text{and} \quad Q = \tfrac{4}{3}\pi R^3 \rho \quad \text{for } s \geq R.$$

Then, using the integral version of Gauss's law, we find that for $s \leq R$,

$$\varepsilon_0 E_r(s)4\pi s^2 = \tfrac{4}{3}\pi s^3 \rho, \quad \text{so} \quad E_r(s) = \frac{\rho s}{3\varepsilon_0} \quad (s \leq R).$$

For $s \geq R$,

$$\varepsilon_0 E_r(s)4\pi s^2 = \tfrac{4}{3}\pi R^3 \rho, \quad \text{so} \quad E_r(s) = \frac{\rho R^3}{3\varepsilon_0 s^2} \quad (s \geq R).$$

The potential at radius $r < R$ is then

$$V(r) = -\int_\infty^r E_r(s)\,\mathrm{d}s$$

$$= -\int_\infty^R \frac{\rho R^3}{3\varepsilon_0 s^2}\,\mathrm{d}s - \int_R^r \frac{\rho s}{3\varepsilon_0}\,\mathrm{d}s$$

$$= -\frac{\rho R^3}{3\varepsilon_0}\left[-\frac{1}{s}\right]_\infty^R - \frac{\rho}{3\varepsilon_0}\left[\frac{s^2}{2}\right]_R^r$$

$$= \frac{\rho}{2\varepsilon_0}\left(R^2 - \frac{r^2}{3}\right).$$

The potential energy is $U = \tfrac{1}{2}\int \rho V\,\mathrm{d}\tau$. Because of the radial symmetry, we choose a volume element $\delta\tau$ that is a thin spherical shell, so $\delta\tau = 4\pi r^2 \delta r$. Then

$$U = \tfrac{1}{2}\int_0^R \rho \frac{\rho}{2\varepsilon_0}\left(R^2 - \frac{r^2}{3}\right)4\pi r^2\,\mathrm{d}r$$

$$= \frac{\pi\rho^2}{\varepsilon_0}\int_0^R \left(R^2 r^2 - \frac{r^4}{3}\right)\,\mathrm{d}r$$

$$= \frac{\pi\rho^2}{\varepsilon_0}\left(\frac{R^5}{3} - \frac{R^5}{15}\right) = \frac{4\pi\rho^2 R^5}{15\varepsilon_0}.$$

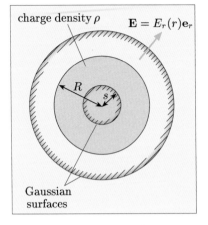

Figure 8.4 Spherical Gaussian surfaces within and around a spherical charge distribution.

This example illustrates the general principles of how the potential energy can be calculated for a distribution of charge. However, even with a highly symmetrical, uniform charge distribution, the calculation is rather laborious. For more complex distributions of charge, the maths soon becomes painful, but fortunately such problems can be easily handled by a computer, working through the same generic processes used in this example.

Exercise 8.2 Use a method similar to that used in Worked Example 8.1 to obtain an expression for the electric potential energy of a conducting sphere, radius R, with a surface charge density σ, in a region remote from other charges. (There are short-cuts to the solution, but it is instructive to work through the generic steps, since they can be applied to many problems with high symmetry.)

8.1.2 Energy stored in a capacitor

A capacitor consists of a pair of conductors separated by an insulating medium. The two conductors generally have charges $+Q$ and $-Q$, so the net charge on the pair is zero. The potential within each conductor must be uniform in a steady state, irrespective of their sizes and shapes, and we shall denote these potentials as V_+ and V_-. Note that the free charge will all be on the surfaces of the conductors, but the charge densities on the surfaces need not be uniform. From Equation 8.5, we deduce that the potential energy U of the capacitor is

$$U = \tfrac{1}{2}QV_+ + \tfrac{1}{2}(-Q)V_- = \tfrac{1}{2}Q(V_+ - V_-) = \tfrac{1}{2}QV, \tag{8.7}$$

where $Q = \int_{S_+} \sigma(\mathbf{r})\,dS$ is the charge on the positively-charged conductor, and V is the difference between the potentials of the two conductors.

Now, the capacitance C of a capacitor is defined as the ratio of the charge Q on the positively-charged conductor to the magnitude of the potential difference V between the two conductors, that is, $C = Q/V$. This allows us to write Equation 8.7 for a capacitor's energy in two other equivalent forms:

$$U = \tfrac{1}{2}QV = \tfrac{1}{2}CV^2 = \frac{Q^2}{2C}. \tag{8.8}$$

In Book 1 we derived an expression for the energy stored in a charged capacitor by considering the work done when transferring charge from one of the conducting surfaces to the other. Transferring charge δq from the negatively-charged conductor to the positive conductor requires work $V\,\delta q$ to be done, and this is the increase in energy stored in the capacitor. So the total energy stored in a capacitor when the charges on the conductors are $\pm Q$ is

$$U = \int_0^Q V\,dq = \int_0^Q \frac{q}{C}\,dq = \frac{Q^2}{2C}, \tag{8.9}$$

which is one of the three equivalent expressions in Equation 8.8.

Exercise 8.3   How much electrical energy is stored in a $16\,\mu\text{F}$ capacitor when the potential difference between the plates is $240\,\text{V}$? Compare your answer with the kinetic energy of a $1\,\text{kg}$ object moving at $1\,\text{m}\,\text{s}^{-1}$, and the gravitational energy increase of a $1\,\text{kg}$ object when you lift it $5\,\text{cm}$ above your desk. ■

8.1.3 Energy stored in an electric field

The discussion of electrical energy so far has focused on charges and on the work done in bringing them together. But there is another way of determining electrical energy, focusing on the fields produced by the charges rather than the charges themselves. This alternative viewpoint is the subject of this subsection.

Energy stored in the field of a parallel plate capacitor

Let's first consider the parallel plate capacitor shown in Figure 8.5, with plate area A, plate separation d, filled with a dielectric material with relative permittivity ε. We assume that the plate dimensions are very large compared with their separation, so that the electric field between the plates is uniform, and the

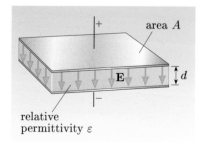

Figure 8.5   A parallel plate capacitor. The field **E** is concentrated between the plates, and the fringing fields around the edges can be neglected.

voltage difference V and the field strength E are related by $V = Ed$. The electrical energy stored is

$$U = \tfrac{1}{2}CV^2 = \tfrac{1}{2}CE^2d^2.$$

For a parallel plate capacitor, $C = \varepsilon\varepsilon_0 A/d$ (Equation 2.15), and substituting this into the expression for the energy stored, we obtain

$$U = \tfrac{1}{2}\varepsilon\varepsilon_0 E^2 Ad. \tag{8.10}$$

Since Ad is the volume between the plates, this expression suggests an alternative way of thinking about the energy stored by the capacitor: we can think of it as being associated with the electric field between the plates. The energy per unit volume in this region — usually referred to as the **energy density** u of the electric field — is then given by

$$u = \tfrac{1}{2}\varepsilon\varepsilon_0 E^2. \tag{8.11}$$

Now, we are assuming large plates with a small separation, so $\mathbf{E} = 0$ outside the capacitor. This means that if we integrate this expression for the energy density over *all* space, we obtain the total energy stored in the capacitor, as given by Equation 8.10:

$$U = \int_{\text{all space}} u \, d\tau = \int_{\text{all space}} \tfrac{1}{2}\varepsilon\varepsilon_0 E^2 \, d\tau = \tfrac{1}{2}\varepsilon\varepsilon_0 E^2 Ad. \tag{8.12}$$

We derived these results for a particularly simple situation, but they are generally valid when we are dealing with LIH materials. A more general expression for the energy density associated with an electric field is

$$u = \tfrac{1}{2}\mathbf{D} \cdot \mathbf{E}, \tag{8.13}$$

and this reduces to Equation 8.11 when $\mathbf{D} = \varepsilon\varepsilon_0\mathbf{E}$.

Worked Example 8.2

A long coaxial cable consists of a solid inner cylinder with radius r_1 and a coaxial outer cylindrical tube with internal radius r_2 (Figure 8.6). The space between the cylinders is filled by an LIH dielectric of relative permittivity ε. If the charge per unit length of the inner cylinder is λ, and that on the outer cylinder is $-\lambda$, calculate the electrostatic field energy stored in a length l of the cable. Then verify that the expression $U = Q^2/2C$ (Equation 8.8), together with the expression for the capacitance of coaxial cable obtained in Exercise 2.6 ($C = 2\pi\varepsilon\varepsilon_0 l/\ln(r_2/r_1)$), gives the same result for the stored energy.

Essential skill

Calculating energy stored in an electric field

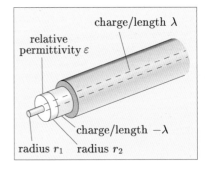

Figure 8.6 Coaxial cable.

Solution

The cylindrical symmetry suggests that we should choose a cylindrical coordinate system with its z-axis coincident with the axis of the cable. Then $\mathbf{D} = D_r(r)\mathbf{e}_r$. To find the field $\mathbf{D}$ within the dielectric, we choose a cylindrical Gaussian surface with radius r, such that $r_1 \leq r \leq r_2$, and length l, with its axis along the z-axis. Applying Gauss's law to this surface,

$$D(r) \times 2\pi rl = \lambda l, \quad \text{so} \quad D(r) = \frac{\lambda}{2\pi r}.$$

For a linear isotropic dielectric, $\mathbf{D} = \varepsilon\varepsilon_0\mathbf{E}$, and the energy density is

$$u = \tfrac{1}{2}\mathbf{D}\cdot\mathbf{E} = \tfrac{1}{2}\varepsilon\varepsilon_0 E^2.$$

The total energy within a volume τ of the dielectric is $\int_\tau u\,d\tau$. Because of the cylindrical symmetry, we choose a volume element $\delta\tau$ that is a cylindrical shell of radius r, thickness δr, and length l. Consequently, $\delta\tau = 2\pi r l\,\delta r$, and the total energy U is given by

$$U = \tfrac{1}{2}\varepsilon\varepsilon_0 \int_{r_1}^{r_2} \left(\frac{\lambda}{2\pi\varepsilon\varepsilon_0 r}\right)^2 2\pi r l\,dr$$

$$= \frac{\lambda^2 l}{4\pi\varepsilon\varepsilon_0} \int_{r_1}^{r_2} \frac{dr}{r} = \frac{\lambda^2 l}{4\pi\varepsilon\varepsilon_0}\ln\left(\frac{r_2}{r_1}\right).$$

We now verify this result by using an alternative method that involves calculating the energy in terms of the capacitance and the stored charge. The charge on a length l of the inner conductor is $Q = \lambda l$, and U can be written as $U = Q^2/2C$, so using the expression $C = 2\pi\varepsilon\varepsilon_0 l/\ln(r_2/r_1)$, the stored energy is

$$U = \frac{(\lambda l)^2}{2\times 2\pi\varepsilon\varepsilon_0 l/\ln(r_2/r_1)} = \frac{\lambda^2 l}{4\pi\varepsilon\varepsilon_0}\ln\left(\frac{r_2}{r_1}\right),$$

which is the same result as obtained above from consideration of the energy density of the field.

Exercise 8.4   A capacitor is constructed from two concentric conducting spherical shells of radii r_1 and r_2, with $r_2 > r_1$, and the space between the shells is filled with air. The inner sphere has charge $+Q$, and the outer sphere has charge $-Q$. Derive an expression for the energy stored in the capacitor in terms of r_1, r_2 and Q. ∎

Energy of a point charge

In this subsection we discuss the energy associated with a point charge. We shall consider an isolated point charge, in a vacuum, placed at the origin of a spherical coordinate system. The direction of the electric field is radial, and its magnitude is given by $E = q/4\pi\varepsilon_0 r^2$. The total energy is

$$U = \tfrac{1}{2}\int \mathbf{D}\cdot\mathbf{E}\,d\tau = \frac{\varepsilon_0}{2}\int E^2\,d\tau.$$

This has similarities with the problem we considered in Exercise 8.4. Because of the spherical symmetry, we choose the volume element $\delta\tau$ to be a spherical shell, of radius r and thickness δr, so that $\delta\tau = 4\pi r^2\,\delta r$, and therefore

$$U = \frac{\varepsilon_0}{2}\int_0^\infty \left(\frac{q}{4\pi\varepsilon_0 r^2}\right)^2 4\pi r^2 dr = \frac{q^2}{8\pi\varepsilon_0}\int_0^\infty \frac{dr}{r^2} = \frac{q^2}{8\pi\varepsilon_0}\left[-\frac{1}{r}\right]_0^\infty.$$

At this stage we hit a problem, since substituting $r = 0$ for the lower limit leads to infinity — the energy stored in the electric field of a point charge appears to be infinite! We could attempt to overcome this problem by assuming that the particle has a non-zero radius, R, in which case we obtain

$$U = \frac{q^2}{8\pi\varepsilon_0 R}.$$

However, this only gives rise to more problems. For instance, the charge could not be rigid, otherwise information could travel instantaneously from one side of the charge to the other, which would contradict special relativity. Consequently, a charge with non-zero radius would need to have some elasticity and some structure (like a rubber ball), and would therefore be made of something. Since this 'something' would have to be charged, this only moves the problem down to a lower level. Furthermore, there is no evidence of elementary particles, such as electrons, having any structure. Of course, at this level you might think that it is necessary to invoke quantum mechanics, and you would be absolutely right. In the resulting theory (known as quantum electrodynamics), the situation is slightly better in that the infinity appears as $\ln R$ rather than $1/R$ as $R \to 0$, but this is still a problem. Up to now, physicists have not found a satisfactory way to calculate the so-called self-energy of a particle like an electron. This remains an area of theoretical physics research, but this unsolved problem in no way invalidates any of the results that we have derived in this book when considering macroscopic fields.

Exercise 8.5   Suppose that the electron has a radius R. Calculate the value of R such that the entire rest energy mc^2 of the electron is stored as energy in the electric field outside the electron.   ∎

8.1.4   Energy transfers charging and discharging a capacitor

You have seen that a capacitor can store energy, and that the amount of stored energy can be quantified in terms of the charges on the plates and the potential difference between the plates, or in terms of the fields in the region of the plates. We shall now investigate the energy transfers that occur when a capacitor is charged or discharged.

Charging a capacitor

Consider the circuit in Figure 8.7, which shows a resistor R, capacitor C, and switch S, in series with a source of constant emf V_s. Suppose that the switch is open for $t < 0$, but it is then closed at $t = 0$ to complete the circuit. The sum of the voltage drops across the resistor, V_R, and the capacitor, V_C, must be equal to the emf V_s at all times $t \geq 0$, so

$$V_s = IR + \frac{Q}{C}, \tag{8.14}$$

where I is the current in the circuit and Q is the charge on the positive plate of the capacitor.

If we differentiate Equation 8.14 with respect to time, and use the relation $I = dQ/dt$, we obtain

$$R\frac{dI}{dt} + \frac{I}{C} = 0, \quad \text{or} \quad \frac{dI}{dt} = -\frac{I}{RC}. \tag{8.15}$$

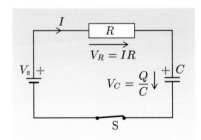

Figure 8.7   A capacitor C and a resistor R in series with a constant source of emf V_s.

This linear, first-order differential equation indicates that the rate of change of the current is proportional to the current, and the standard solution to this equation is

$$I = I_0 \exp\left(-\frac{t}{RC}\right), \tag{8.16}$$

where the constant I_0 is the current at $t = 0$. There is no charge on the capacitor at $t = 0$, so from Equation 8.14, $I_0 = V_s/R$. Therefore

$$I = \frac{V_s}{R} \exp\left(-\frac{t}{RC}\right). \tag{8.17}$$

This equation shows that the current decays exponentially from its initial value V_s/R. At time $t = RC$, the current has decayed to e^{-1} ($\simeq 0.37$) of its initial value, and this characteristic time is called the **time constant**. Thus for a circuit with resistance R and capacitance C,

$$\text{time constant} = RC. \tag{8.18}$$

From Equation 8.14, the voltage drop across the capacitor, V_C, is

$$V_C = \frac{Q}{C} = V_s - IR = V_s\left[1 - \exp\left(-\frac{t}{RC}\right)\right]. \tag{8.19}$$

Therefore V_C approaches the value of the source emf V_s exponentially, with time constant RC. The time dependences of the current, and of the voltage drops across the resistor and capacitor, are shown in Figure 8.8.

Figure 8.8   The exponential time dependence of (a) the current I and (b) the voltage drops V_R ($= IR$) and V_C ($= Q/C$) after a constant emf V_s is connected in series with resistance R and capacitance C at $t = 0$.

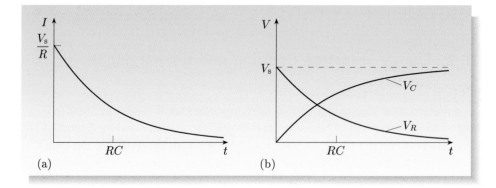

Energy transfers during charging

We now consider the energy transferred during this charging process. The total energy transferred by the source of emf is simply the time integral of the instantaneous power, IV_s:

$$U_s = \int_0^\infty IV_s \, dt = V_s \int_0^\infty \frac{dq}{dt} \, dt = V_s \int_0^Q dq = V_s Q = CV_s^2,$$

where $q = Q = CV_s$ is the steady-state charge on the positive plate as $t \to \infty$. Compare this with the energy that is stored in the capacitor, which we showed in Subsection 8.1.2 is $\frac{1}{2}CV_s^2$. Only half of the energy from the source of emf has been stored in the capacitor, so the other half must have been dissipated in the resistor. We can confirm this by calculating the dissipated energy:

$$U_R = \int_0^\infty IV_R \, dt = \int_0^\infty I^2 R \, dt.$$

Using Equation 8.17 to substitute for I in this equation, we obtain

$$U_R = \frac{V_s^2}{R} \int_0^\infty \exp\left(-\frac{2t}{RC}\right) dt$$
$$= \frac{V_s^2}{R} \left[-\frac{RC}{2} \exp\left(-\frac{2t}{RC}\right)\right]_0^\infty = \tfrac{1}{2}CV_s^2.$$

As we would expect, energy is conserved in the charging process:

$$U_C + U_R = \tfrac{1}{2}CV_s^2 + \tfrac{1}{2}CV_s^2 = CV_s^2 = U_s.$$

However, you may be surprised that exactly one half of the energy extracted from the source ends up stored in the capacitor, while the other half is dissipated in the resistor, whatever the value of R. For example, you might expect that if the resistance were very small, very little heat could be dissipated. However, as R become very small, the current becomes very large but the time constant becomes very small. This happens in such a way that the charge transferred remains the same, and the energy stored in the capacitor — and the energy dissipated in the resistor — remains the same.

Discharge of a capacitor

Now consider the changes in current, voltage and energy stored when a capacitor is discharged. Suppose that the capacitor in Figure 8.9 is initially charged so that there is a potential difference V_0 across its terminals, and at time $t = 0$ the switch S is closed. There is now no source of emf in the circuit, so the voltage drops V_C and V_R shown in Figure 8.9 must cancel, that is,

$$V_C = V_R, \quad \text{so} \quad \frac{Q}{C} = IR.$$

Differentiating with respect to time, and recognizing that in this case $I = -dQ/dt$ (since Q decreases when the current is in the direction indicated in Figure 8.9), we obtain the same differential equation as for charging the capacitor:

$$\frac{dI}{dt} = -\frac{I}{RC}. \tag{Eqn 8.15}$$

The general solution for the current must also be the same,

$$I = I_0 \exp\left(-\frac{t}{RC}\right), \tag{Eqn 8.16}$$

with the same time constant, RC, but with I_0 determined by different initial conditions in the two cases.

For the discharging case, $I = V_C/R$, and at $t = 0$ we obtain $I_0 = V_0/R$, so

$$I = \frac{V_0}{R} \exp\left(-\frac{t}{RC}\right). \tag{8.20}$$

The voltage drops across the capacitor and the resistor are

$$V_C = V_R = IR = V_0 \exp\left(-\frac{t}{RC}\right). \tag{8.21}$$

The stored energy released by the capacitor as it discharges is dissipated in the resistor. The amount of energy dissipated is again $\tfrac{1}{2}CV_0^2$. However, in this case

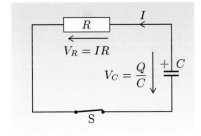

Figure 8.9 Capacitance C discharging through resistance R.

the energy comes from the release of the capacitor's stored energy and not from a battery.

Exercise 8.6   Use Equations 8.20 and 8.21 to confirm that the energy dissipated during discharge of the capacitor is equal to the energy $\frac{1}{2}CV_0^2$ that was stored in the capacitor.   ■

8.1.5   Energy storage applications of capacitors

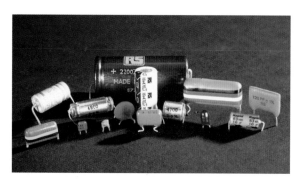

Figure 8.10   A range of capacitors.

Capacitors come in a rich variety of shapes and sizes, some of which are shown in Figure 8.10. This variety reflects the wide range of dielectric materials that can be employed and the wide spectrum of uses to which capacitors are put. Capacitors are readily available with capacitance from a fraction of a picofarad to thousands of farads.

For energy storage applications, capacitors can be connected together in series or in parallel to provide the required current, voltage and energy. An application that is likely to become much more common is the use of capacitors in electric vehicles. A bank of capacitors can provide high power for a short period while the vehicle accelerates; batteries then provide the power while the vehicle is cruising, and the capacitors are recharged by a generator that is part of the braking system. Using capacitors to meet the peak power requirement means that a much smaller battery can provide the required performance. For example, the capacitor bank shown in Figure 8.1b consists of 144 capacitors, each of which has a capacitance of 2600 F and a maximum voltage rating of 2.5 V. When fully charged they store 1.2 MJ. During acceleration, the power output of the capacitor bank is up to 150 kW, so the capacitors discharge in about ten seconds, and they can then be recharged at a similar rate during braking. Although batteries have much greater energy densities than capacitors, capacitors have much greater maximum power densities — that is, their maximum power output per unit volume is greater — and they can be charged and discharged rapidly without affecting their performance.

Figure 8.11   A bank of capacitors used for producing large pulsed magnetic fields.

Capacitor banks are also used to provide emergency power for computer systems, life-support systems in hospitals, air traffic control systems, and so on, during very short power cuts. For longer power cuts, capacitor banks can keep critical equipment running for the 10 seconds or so it takes for diesel generators to start up.

An application that demonstrates the huge power output possible from capacitor banks is the production of large pulsed magnetic fields in research laboratories. A facility in Dresden (Figure 8.11) charges 12×1.7 mF capacitors to 10 kV, thus storing 1 MJ. This is then rapidly discharged through the coil of an electromagnet, providing a peak current of about 10 kA, which generates a peak field of 50 T. The peak power is about 100 MW, though the pulse lasts only about 20 ms.

A final example is the cardiac **defibrillator** (Figure 8.12a), a device used to pass a short pulse of current from a capacitor through the human chest to restore normal function of the heart when it is undergoing uncoordinated contractions, known as fibrillations. Figure 8.12b shows the basic elements of the circuit. With switch S_1 closed and switch S_2 open, the source of emf V_s charges a large capacitor C through a resistor R_s. Switch S_1 is then opened, the paddles P are placed on either side of the chest, and S_2 is closed, allowing the capacitor to discharge through the chest, which has an effective resistance R_{chest}. Exercise 8.7 allows you to calculate typical parameters for these current pulses.

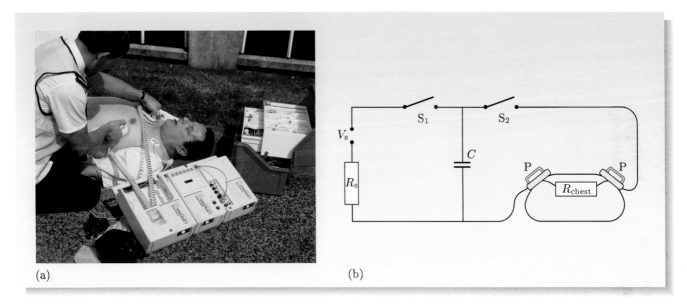

(a) (b)

Figure 8.12 (a) A cardiac defibrillator in use. (b) The essential components in the charging and discharging circuits of a defibrillator.

Exercise 8.7 Suppose the defibrillator circuit in Figure 8.12b has the following parameters: $V_s = 5\,\text{kV}$, $C = 32\,\mu\text{F}$, $R_s = 100\,\Omega$ and $R_{chest} = 75\,\Omega$. Calculate:

(a) the time taken to charge the capacitor to 99% of its maximum charge;

(b) the peak current delivered to the patient;

(c) the time taken for the current to fall to 10% of its peak value;

(d) the energy delivered to the patient.

Exercise 8.8 A cylindrical $1000\,\mu\text{F}$ capacitor has a maximum working voltage of 63 V; its length is 40 mm and its diameter is 16 mm. Calculate the maximum energy that can be stored in the capacitor, and also the maximum energy density. ∎

As was shown in the previous exercise, even with a potential difference of 63 V across the capacitor, it stores only 2 J, a tiny amount of energy. In terms of gross energy storage, capacitors are much less effective than the batteries used in portable consumer devices. For example, the commonly used AA-size alkaline battery, which has similar dimensions to the capacitor in Exercise 8.8, delivers 2.7 A h (ampere-hour) of charge at 1.5 V — almost 15 kJ. With a volume of $7.4\,\text{cm}^3$, the energy density is about $2 \times 10^9\,\text{J}\,\text{m}^{-3}$, a factor of 10^4 greater than the capacitor. This is because the chemical processes that take place in a battery typically release about 1 eV per molecule, whereas energy stored per molecule of dielectric is much smaller because the field has to be kept well below the value at which the dielectric breaks down.

8.2   Currents, magnetic fields and energy

The concept of inductance was introduced in the previous chapter, and our aim here is to examine the energy stored in an inductor when a current is flowing through it. When considering electrostatic energy, we started by considering the energy required to set up an arbitrary system of charges, then considered the energy stored by a capacitor both in terms of the charge on (or potential difference between) the plates and in terms of the electric field around the plates, and finally calculated the energy transferred to or from a capacitor as it was charged or discharged. We shall approach the discussion of the energy stored in an inductor from the opposite direction, starting by working out the energy stored by a single inductor in a circuit, and then expressing the stored energy in terms of the magnetic field.

8.2.1   Changing the current in an inductor

We want to calculate the energy required to establish a constant current in an inductor that has inductance L. Real inductors have a non-zero resistance, so we shall consider the circuit shown in Figure 8.13, where the resistance R represents the sum of the resistance of the inductor together with any other resistance in the circuit.

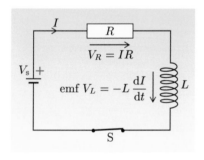

The emf V_L induced across an inductor by a changing current is

$$V_L = -L \frac{\mathrm{d}I}{\mathrm{d}t},$$

and is in the direction that opposes changes in the current. Thus when the current is in the direction shown and is increasing, V_L will be negative, which means that it opposes V_s and acts to decrease the current. We shall consider only situations where any magnetic material present is linear, so that L is constant.

Figure 8.13   Inductance L and resistance R in series with a source of constant emf.

Now let's assume that the switch S is initially open, and is closed at time $t = 0$. Then for $t \geq 0$, we can equate the net emf in the circuit with the voltage drop across the resistor, that is,

$$V_s - L \frac{\mathrm{d}I}{\mathrm{d}t} = IR. \tag{8.22}$$

Separating the variables, and integrating, we obtain

$$\int \frac{\mathrm{d}I}{(V_s/R) - I} = \int \frac{R}{L} \, \mathrm{d}t,$$

and hence

$$-\ln\left(\frac{V_s}{R} - I\right) + K = \frac{R}{L}t.$$

The integration constant K is determined from the initial conditions. Since the current is zero for $t < 0$, we know that it must also be zero at time $t = 0$. If this were not the case, then dI/dt would be infinite at $t = 0$, which would be inconsistent with Equation 8.22. This initial condition means that $K = \ln(V_s/R)$, so

$$\ln\left(\frac{V_s}{R} - I\right) - \ln\left(\frac{V_s}{R}\right) = -\frac{R}{L}t.$$

Hence, using the mathematical identities $\ln x - \ln y = \ln(x/y)$ and $\exp(\ln x) = x$, we obtain

$$I = \frac{V_s}{R}\left[1 - \exp\left(-\frac{Rt}{L}\right)\right]. \tag{8.23}$$

Notice that as $t \to \infty$, the current approaches the steady-state value $I_{max} = V_s/R$, as shown in Figure 8.14a.

The voltage drop $V_{L,\mathrm{drop}}$ across the inductor has the same magnitude as the induced emf V_L, but it has the opposite sign, so

$$V_{L,\mathrm{drop}} = -V_L = L\frac{dI}{dt} = V_s \exp\left(-\frac{Rt}{L}\right),$$

and this decays exponentially with time. In the limit as $t \to \infty$, $V_{L,\mathrm{drop}}$ tends to zero, and the voltage drop V_R across the resistance R becomes equal to the source emf V_s (Figure 8.14b).

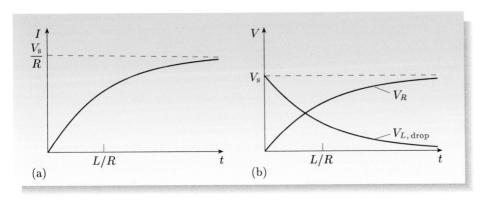

Figure 8.14 Exponential time dependences of (a) the current I and (b) the voltage drops V_R and $V_{L,\mathrm{drop}}$ across resistance R and inductance L in the circuit shown in Figure 8.13.

You can see from Equation 8.23 that L/R has the dimensions of time and plays the same role as played by the product RC for the charge or discharge of a capacitor. Thus for a circuit containing inductance L and resistance R,

$$\text{time constant} = L/R. \tag{8.24}$$

In time $t = L/R$, the current grows to $(1 - e^{-1})$ (about 63%) of its final, steady-state value, and the voltage drop across the inductance falls to e^{-1} (about 37%) of its initial value (Figure 8.14b).

Figure 8.15 shows the growth of the current in a circuit in which $V_s = 1.5\,\mathrm{V}$, $R = 10\,\Omega$ and $L = 1.0\,\mathrm{mH}$. The time constant L/R is 0.1 ms, and in this time the current grows to $0.63V_s/R = 95\,\mathrm{mA}$. Notice that in a time of about $5L/R = 0.5\,\mathrm{ms}$, the current has essentially reached its steady value; on the time scale of human perception, this growth phase would appear instantaneous.

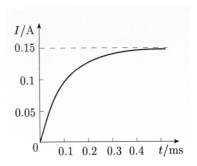

Figure 8.15 Growth of current in a circuit with $L = 1.0\,\mathrm{mH}$, $R = 10\,\Omega$ and $V_s = 1.5\,\mathrm{V}$.

8.2.2   Energy stored in an inductor

The energy stored when a current is set up in an inductor can be calculated in a similar way to the calculation of energy stored when a capacitor is charged (Subsection 8.1.4). The energy transferred to the inductor is

$$U_L = \int_0^\infty I V_{L,\,\mathrm{drop}}\,\mathrm{d}t = \int_0^\infty I \left(L\,\frac{\mathrm{d}I}{\mathrm{d}t} \right)\mathrm{d}t = \int_0^{V_s/R} LI\,\mathrm{d}I = \frac{LV_{\mathrm{s}}^2}{2R^2},$$

where we made use of the fact that the steady-state current is V_{s}/R when setting the upper limit of the current integral. If we now denote this steady-state current as I, then the energy transferred to the inductor can be written as

$$U_L = \tfrac{1}{2}LI^2. \tag{8.25}$$

During the build-up of the current, energy is dissipated in the resistor, and this dissipation continues in the steady state, with power I^2R transferred to the resistor.

Recovering the energy stored in an inductor

We have shown that energy $\frac{1}{2}LI^2$ is transferred to an inductor as the current builds up. This energy must be rapidly dissipated when the switch in the circuit in Figure 8.13 is opened. The current rapidly drops to zero, but this induces a large emf, $V_L = -L\,\mathrm{d}I/\mathrm{d}t$, in the circuit. The consequence is that the air in the vicinity of the switch may become ionized, resulting in arcing between the contacts. In most cases such arcing is unwanted and is suppressed by putting a suitable capacitor in parallel with the switch. An alternative (though not very practical) way of recovering the stored energy can be investigated in the next exercise.

Exercise 8.9   A resistor R and inductor L are connected in series with a source of emf, and the steady-state current flowing through the circuit is I_0. At time $t = 0$, the emf is replaced by a short-circuit.

(a) Derive an expression for the current flowing in the circuit for $t \geq 0$.

(b) By explicit integration, find the total energy dissipated in the resistor.   ■

8.2.3   Energy stored in a magnetic field

You have seen that the energy stored in a current-carrying inductor can be specified in terms of the current and the self-inductance of the circuit through which the current flows. But the stored energy can also be quantified in terms of the magnetic field generated by the current, as we shall now show.

Energy stored in the field of a toroidal solenoid

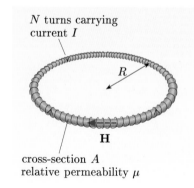

N turns carrying current I

R

H

cross-section A
relative permeability μ

Figure 8.16   What is the energy stored in a toroidal solenoid?

As a specific example, consider the toroidal solenoid shown in Figure 8.16, which has N turns carrying current I wound on a former of radius R, cross-sectional area A. The former is made from an LIH material with magnetic permeability μ, and the value of μ is large so that the magnetic field lines are confined within the material. To simplify the calculation, we assume that the radius of the cross-section is very much smaller than the radius R of the toroid.

From the symmetry it is clear that the field $\mathbf{H}$ within the solenoid must be in the azimuthal direction and have a strength that is independent of the azimuthal angle, and it can therefore be determined from the integral version of Ampère's law, using a path of radius R around the inside of the solenoid:

$$H \times 2\pi R = NI, \quad \text{or} \quad H = \frac{NI}{2\pi R},$$

hence

$$B = \frac{\mu\mu_0 NI}{2\pi R}.$$

Because of the small cross-section, we can assume that the field has constant strength inside the solenoid.

The inductance of the solenoid is the magnetic flux passing through it per unit current (Equation 7.25), so

$$L = \frac{\Phi}{I} = \frac{NAB}{I}.$$

Combining this with Equation 8.25 and the expression for B above, we obtain

$$U = \tfrac{1}{2}LI^2 = \tfrac{1}{2}\frac{NAB}{I}I^2 = \tfrac{1}{2}NAB \times \frac{2\pi RB}{\mu\mu_0 N} = \tfrac{1}{2}\frac{B^2}{\mu\mu_0}2\pi RA.$$

Now, $2\pi RA$ is the volume of the toroid, within which there is a magnetic field of constant strength B, and outside which the field strength is zero. So this expression for the energy suggests that there is a magnetic energy density u associated with the magnetic field B — a magnetic energy per unit volume — given by

$$u = \frac{B^2}{2\mu\mu_0}, \tag{8.26}$$

and that the total magnetic energy is the integral over all space of the magnetic energy density:

$$U = \int_{\text{all space}} u\,\mathrm{d}\tau = \int_{\text{all space}} \frac{B^2}{2\mu\mu_0}\,\mathrm{d}\tau. \tag{8.27}$$

Although we have obtained these results for a particularly simple situation, they are generally valid when we are dealing with LIH materials. A more general expression for the energy density associated with a magnetic field is

$$u = \tfrac{1}{2}\mathbf{B} \cdot \mathbf{H}, \tag{8.28}$$

which reduces to Equation 8.26 when $\mathbf{B} = \mu\mu_0\mathbf{H}$.

Exercise 8.10   The coaxial cable shown in Figure 8.17 consists of two long thin-walled conducting tubes of radii r_1 and r_2 (with $r_2 > r_1$). The volume between the tubes is filled with an insulator, which is a linear magnetic material of relative permeability μ. A current I flows along the length of the inner tube and returns through the outer tube. Derive an expression for the energy density of the magnetic field between the two tubes, and hence find the total energy stored in a length l of the magnetic material.

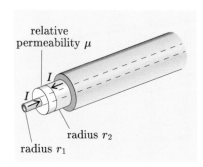

Figure 8.17   A coaxial cable with material of relative permeability μ between the conducting tubes.

Exercise 8.11   Estimate the stored magnetic energy for a superconducting solenoid that produces a field of 20 T in an air-filled region 5 cm in diameter and 20 cm long.   ■

Research and development is currently underway, chiefly in Japan, Germany and the USA, into the use of magnetic energy storage. The small system shown in Figure 8.2 can be used to compensate for sudden voltage fluctuations in the distribution grid. It can respond on a time scale of milliseconds, and provide hundreds of kilowatts of power for periods of about ten seconds. But design studies have also been carried out on diurnal storage systems that would store much larger amounts of energy during the night or periods of low demand, and then release it to cope with sudden demands from industry or from domestic consumers at the end of popular television programmes. Such systems could store 1000 MWh and would be of the order of 1 km in diameter. Magnetic energy storage can have a very high efficiency, with over 90 per cent of the energy supplied to the system being released to the distribution network. This is possible only because the coils are made from superconducting materials, which we shall discuss in the next chapter.

8.3   Energy exchange in LCR circuits

Many circuits include resistance, capacitance and inductance, and by selecting appropriate values of these components, the response of the circuit can be tailored for specific applications. In such circuits — often referred to as LCR circuits — there is often an interchange between the energy stored in the capacitor and that in the inductor. We shall discuss briefly two contrasting applications: adding an inductor to the defibrillator discharge circuit to shape the current pulse, and producing circuits that oscillate at a desired frequency.

8.3.1   Modifying the defibrillator

When a capacitor is discharged through a resistive load, the current has the simple exponential time dependence shown in Figure 8.18a. However, a pulse with the shape shown in Figure 8.18b has been found to be more effective for defibrillation.

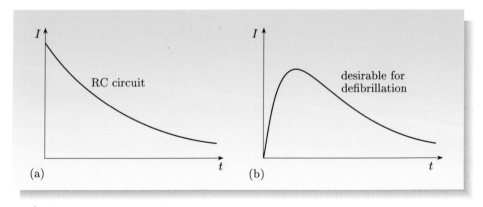

Figure 8.18   (a) Current from a capacitor discharging through a resistor. (b) Current variation required from a defibrillator.

● Suggest a way that the simple RC circuit could be modified so that a pulse with a slower rise than in Figure 8.18a is produced.

○ An inductor limits the rate of growth of current in a circuit, as shown in Figure 8.15, so inserting an inductor in series with the capacitor and resistor seems a good possibility.

Let's consider the circuit shown in Figure 8.19. We assume that the capacitor is charged by applying a voltage difference V_0, and then at time $t = 0$ the switch S is closed. Equating the voltage drop across the capacitor to the sum of the voltage drops across the resistor and the inductor, we obtain

$$\frac{Q}{C} = IR + L\frac{dI}{dt}. \tag{8.29}$$

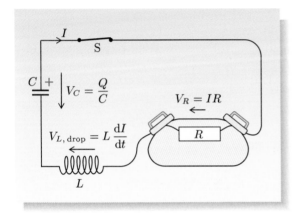

Figure 8.19   LCR circuit for a defibrillator.

Differentiating this equation with respect to time, and noting that for the sense of current shown $I = -dQ/dt$, we obtain

$$\frac{I}{C} + R\frac{dI}{dt} + L\frac{d^2I}{dt^2} = 0. \tag{8.30}$$

The transient responses of the RC and RL circuits that we have considered so far have involved simple exponential time dependences, so we shall look for a solution to Equation 8.30 of the form $I = A\exp\alpha t$. Substituting this into the differential equation leads to

$$(1/C + R\alpha + L\alpha^2) = 0.$$

This quadratic equation for α has two solutions,

$$\alpha_1 = -\frac{R}{2L} + \frac{R}{2L}\sqrt{1 - \frac{4L}{R^2C}} \quad \text{and} \quad \alpha_2 = -\frac{R}{2L} - \frac{R}{2L}\sqrt{1 - \frac{4L}{R^2C}},$$

and a general solution is therefore

$$I = A_1\exp\alpha_1 t + A_2\exp\alpha_2 t.$$

The constants A_1 and A_2 are determined by the initial conditions. At $t = 0$, the current I must be zero, since the inductance prevents any instantaneous change of current, and this means that $A_2 = -A_1$. Also, since $I = 0$ at $t = 0$, there is no voltage difference across the resistor, so Equation 8.29 reduces to

$$L\,dI/dt = Q/C = V_0,$$

which means that

$$L(\alpha_1 A_1 + \alpha_2 A_2) = L A_1 (\alpha_1 - \alpha_2) = V_0,$$

or

$$A_1 = \frac{V_0}{L(\alpha_1 - \alpha_2)}.$$

So the current is

$$I = \frac{V_0 (\exp \alpha_1 t - \exp \alpha_2 t)}{L(\alpha_1 - \alpha_2)}.$$

Now, the shaped current pulse we require from the defibrillator has an initial rise time much less than the decay time (Figure 8.18b). The former is determined by the inductive time constant, L/R, and the latter by the capacitative time constant, RC, so for the defibrillator circuit we require $L/R \ll RC$, or $L/R^2 C \ll 1$. In this limit,

$$\alpha_1 \simeq -\frac{R}{2L} + \frac{R}{2L}\left(1 - \frac{2L}{R^2 C}\right) = -\frac{1}{RC},$$

$$\alpha_2 \simeq -\frac{R}{2L} - \frac{R}{2L}\left(1 - \frac{2L}{R^2 C}\right) = -\frac{R}{L} + \frac{1}{RC} \simeq -\frac{R}{L},$$

$$L(\alpha_1 - \alpha_2) \simeq -\frac{L}{RC} + \frac{LR}{L} \simeq R,$$

so the approximate form of the current pulse is given by

$$I \simeq \frac{V_0}{R}\left[\exp\left(-\frac{t}{RC}\right) - \exp\left(-\frac{Rt}{L}\right)\right].$$

Note that in the limit of very small inductance, this expression tends to the result for the discharge of a capacitor in Equation 8.16, and in the limit of very large capacitance, it tends to the result for build up of current in an inductor in Equation 8.23, as you might have anticipated. Figure 8.20 shows the effect of different values of inductance on the shape of the defibrillator current pulse for the circuit parameters used in Exercise 8.7, namely $V_s = 5\,\text{kV}$, $C = 32\,\mu\text{F}$ and $R_{\text{chest}} = 75\,\Omega$. The inductor is storing some of the energy supplied by the capacitor immediately after the switch is closed, and feeding this back to the resistive load at later times.

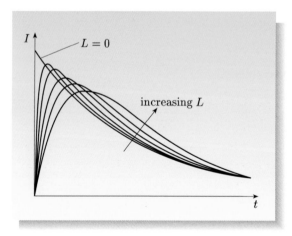

Figure 8.20   The effect of changing the series inductance on defibrillator pulse shape.

8.3.2 Oscillatory circuits

The values of L, C and R used in the defibrillator circuit satisfied the condition $R^2 \gg L/C$. We now consider situations where $R^2 \ll L/C$, starting with the limiting case, $R = 0$. Equation 8.30 then reduces to

$$L\frac{\mathrm{d}^2 I}{\mathrm{d}t^2} + \frac{I}{C} = 0.$$

This is the well-known equation for simple harmonic motion, and has the general solution

$$I = I_0 \sin(\omega_n t + \phi_0),$$

where $\omega_n = 1/\sqrt{LC}$ is the **natural angular frequency** of oscillation of the circuit, and I_0 and ϕ_0 are constants determined by the initial conditions. The sinusoidal time dependence of the current is shown in Figure 8.21a, where for simplicity we have chosen the time origin so that $\phi_0 = 0$. The natural angular frequency ω_n can be tuned to a required value by choosing appropriate values for L and C.

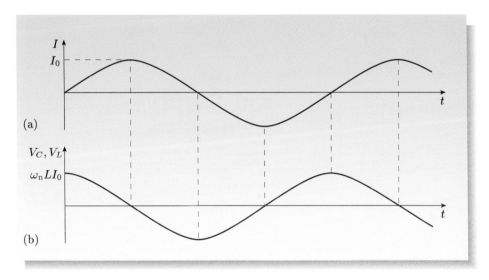

Figure 8.21   (a) Current and (b) voltage drops, V_C and V_L, across the capacitor and inductor in an LC circuit.

The voltage drop across the inductor, V_L, which must be equal in magnitude to the voltage drop across the capacitor, V_C, is

$$V_L = L\frac{\mathrm{d}I}{\mathrm{d}t} = \omega_n L I_0 \cos \omega_n t = V_C,$$

and the time dependence of the voltage drop is shown in Figure 8.21b.

● By considering the current through the inductor and the voltage across the capacitor, indicate on Figure 8.21 the times at which the energy stored in the inductor, U_L, has maximum values, and the times at which the energy stored in the capacitor, U_C, has maximum values.

○ Since $U_L = \frac{1}{2}LI^2$, the energy stored in the inductor has maximum values at the maxima and minima of the current in Figure 8.21a. Since $U_C = \frac{1}{2}CV_C^2$, the energy stored in the capacitor has maximum values when V_C has maximum and minimum values in Figure 8.21b, and these occur each time the current is zero.

The energy stored in the capacitor is given by

$$\tfrac{1}{2}CV_C^2 = \tfrac{1}{2}CV_L^2 = \tfrac{1}{2}C\left(L\,\frac{\mathrm{d}I}{\mathrm{d}t}\right)^2 = \tfrac{1}{2}CL^2 \times \omega_n^2 I_0^2 \cos^2\omega_n t$$

$$= \tfrac{1}{2}LI_0^2 \cos^2\omega_n t,$$

which has a maximum value of $\tfrac{1}{2}LI_0^2$. The energy stored in the inductor is

$$\tfrac{1}{2}LI^2 = \tfrac{1}{2}LI_0^2 \sin^2\omega_n t,$$

which has a maximum value of $\tfrac{1}{2}LI_0^2$, equal to the maximum energy stored in the capacitor. The energy is shuttled back and forth between capacitor and inductor, with the total energy stored in the circuit constant, as shown in Figure 8.22.

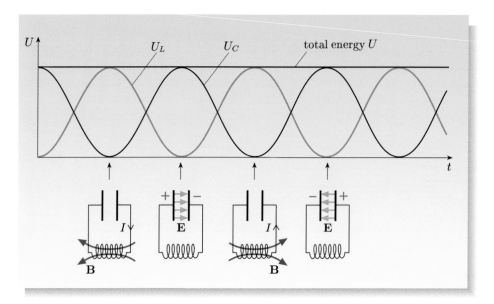

Figure 8.22   Energy stored in an inductor, U_L, and in a capacitor, U_C, and the total energy stored, U, for an LC circuit with negligible resistance.

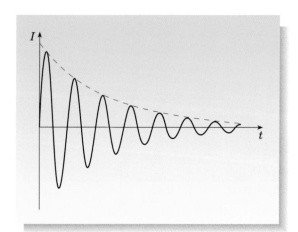

Figure 8.23   Exponentially decaying amplitude of the oscillations in an LCR circuit. The dashed line shows the exponential decay.

In practice, all circuits have some resistance. When this is included in the analysis, the simple sinusoidal solution for the current is modified by an exponential decay factor,

$$I = I_0 \exp\left(-\frac{Rt}{2L}\right)\sin\omega t,$$

as shown in Figure 8.23, with $\omega \simeq \omega_n$ if R is small. To maintain the oscillations, the circuit must be driven by applying an external signal at the natural angular frequency ω_n, as for example is done in the tuning circuit of a radio or television receiver. When the driving signal matches the natural angular frequency of the tuning circuit in the receiver, it maintains large resonant oscillations in the circuit, and for this reason ω_n is often referred to as the resonant angular frequency.

Exercise 8.12   An LCR circuit has component values $L = 5.0\,\text{mH}$, $C = 2.0\,\text{pF}$ and $R = 0.20\,\Omega$. What is the natural angular frequency ω_n of the circuit, and what is the maximum energy stored in the capacitor when the amplitude of current oscillations is $2.5\,\text{mA}$? ∎

Summary of Chapter 8

Section 8.1   The potential energy of a system of point charges can be expressed in terms of the values of the charges and the potentials at the positions where they are located:

$$U = \tfrac{1}{2} \sum_{i=1}^{n} Q_i V_i.$$

For charge distributed over surfaces and throughout a volume, the potential energy is given by

$$U = \tfrac{1}{2} \int_S \sigma(\mathbf{r})\, V(\mathbf{r})\, \mathrm{d}S + \tfrac{1}{2} \int_\tau \rho(\mathbf{r})\, V(\mathbf{r})\, \mathrm{d}\tau.$$

The energy stored in a capacitor is

$$U = \tfrac{1}{2} C V^2 = \frac{Q^2}{2C} = \tfrac{1}{2} Q V.$$

Alternatively, the electric potential energy can be associated with the electric field. The energy density associated with an electric field is

$$u = \tfrac{1}{2}\mathbf{D} \cdot \mathbf{E}.$$

This is valid for linear dielectric materials. The total potential energy is

$$U = \int_\tau \mathbf{D} \cdot \mathbf{E}\, \mathrm{d}\tau.$$

When a capacitor is connected in series with a resistor and a source of constant emf, the voltage across the capacitor increases exponentially, with time constant RC, and the current decreases exponentially:

$$V_C = V_\text{s}\left(1 - \exp\left(-\frac{t}{RC}\right)\right); \quad I = \frac{V_\text{s}}{R}\exp\left(-\frac{t}{RC}\right).$$

Capacitors are widely used for energy storage.

Section 8.2   When an inductor is connected in series with a resistor and a source of emf, the voltage across the inductance and the current in the circuit change exponentially, with time constant L/R:

$$V_L = V_\text{s}\exp\left(-\frac{Rt}{L}\right); \quad I = \frac{V_\text{s}}{R}\left[1 - \exp\left(-\frac{Rt}{L}\right)\right].$$

The potential energy stored in an isolated inductance is $U = \tfrac{1}{2}LI^2$.

Alternatively, the magnetic potential energy can be associated with the magnetic field. The energy density associated with a magnetic field is

$$u = \tfrac{1}{2}\mathbf{B} \cdot \mathbf{H}.$$

The total magnetic potential energy is

$$U = \int_\tau \mathbf{B} \cdot \mathbf{H}\,d\tau.$$

This is valid for linear magnetic materials. Magnetic fields produced by large currents in coils can be used for energy storage.

Section 8.3   In circuits that contain both an inductor and a capacitor, there can be an interchange of energy between the two components. Such circuits are used for pulse shaping and as oscillators, where the natural angular frequency is $\omega_n = 1/\sqrt{LC}$.

Achievements from Chapter 8

After studying this chapter you should be able to do the following.

8.1   Explain the meanings of the newly-defined (emboldened) terms and symbols, and use them appropriately.

8.2   Recall expressions for the potential energy of point and distributed charges, and use them to calculate the electrostatic energy associated with simple distributions of point charges and with highly-symmetric surface and volume charge distributions.

8.3   Recall and apply expressions for the energy stored by capacitors and inductors.

8.4   Recall expressions for the energy density associated with electric and magnetic fields, and use them to calculate the potential energy of systems with simple symmetry.

8.5   Write down and solve differential equations describing the transient behaviour of series circuits involving a capacitor and a resistor, or an inductor and a resistor, and use the solutions to determine power and energy transfers in these circuits.

8.6   Describe the interchange of energy between an inductor and a capacitor in a circuit, and discuss how this interchange is used for pulse shaping and for oscillators.

Chapter 9 Superconductivity

The fascinating phenomenon of superconductivity — which most notably includes the disappearance of any resistance to electric current flow at sufficiently low temperature — and its potential applications have attracted the attention of scientists, engineers and businessmen. Intense research has taken place to discover new superconductors, to understand the physics that underlies the properties of superconductors, and to develop new applications for these materials. The range of applications is already extensive. Superconducting electromagnets produce the large magnetic fields required in the world's largest particle accelerators (see Figure 6 in the Introduction to this book), in MRI machines used for diagnostic imaging of the human body (Figure 5 in the Introduction), in magnetically levitated trains (Figure 9.8) and in superconducting magnetic energy storage systems (Figure 8.2). But at the other extreme they are used in SQUID (superconducting quantum interference device) magnetometers, which can measure the tiny magnetic fields ($\sim 10^{-13}$ T) associated with electrical activity in the brain (Subsection 5.3.3), and there is great interest in their potential as extremely fast switches for a new generation of very powerful computers.

In this chapter, we shall focus on the macroscopic electrodynamic properties of superconductors, and particularly on some of the properties that can be explained in terms of electromagnetism concepts with which you should be familiar. A full understanding of superconductivity requires knowledge of materials science and quantum theory, and discussion of these aspects is beyond the scope of this book. We begin with a review of some of the main developments over the last hundred years, then describe in more detail some of the key electromagnetic properties. These can be modelled in a simple way without using quantum mechanics, and we shall show how this can be done. Finally, we distinguish between the type of superconductivity shown by most of the elemental superconductors, known as *type-I superconductivity*, and that shown by superconducting alloys that have commercial applications, known as *type-II superconductivity*.

Figure 9.1 Heike Kamerlingh Onnes (left) and Johannes Van der Waals beside a helium liquefier (1908).

9.1 A century of superconductivity

Superconductivity was discovered in 1911 by Heike Kamerlingh Onnes (Figure 9.1) as he studied the properties of metals at low temperatures. A few years earlier he had become the first person to liquefy helium, which has a boiling point of 4.2 K at atmospheric pressure, and this had opened up a new range of temperature to experimental investigation. On measuring the resistance of a small tube filled with mercury, he was astonished to observe that its resistance fell from $\sim 0.1 \, \Omega$ at a temperature of 4.3 K to less than $3 \times 10^{-6} \, \Omega$ at 4.1 K. His results are reproduced in Figure 9.2. Below 4.1 K, mercury is said to be a **superconductor**, and no experiment has yet detected any resistance to steady current flow in a superconducting material. The temperature below which the mercury becomes superconducting is known as its **critical temperature** T_c. Kamerlingh Onnes was awarded the Nobel Prize for Physics in 1913 'for his investigations on the properties of matter at low temperatures which led, *inter alia*, to the production of liquid helium' (Nobel Prize citation).

Since this initial discovery, many more elements have been discovered to be

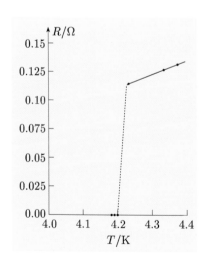

Figure 9.2 Graph showing the resistance of a specimen of mercury versus absolute temperature.

superconductors. Indeed, superconductivity is by no means a rare phenomenon, as the Periodic Table in Figure 9.3 demonstrates. The dark pink cells indicate elements that become superconducting at atmospheric pressure, and the numbers at the bottoms of the cells are their critical temperatures, which range from 9.3 K for niobium (Nb, $Z = 41$) down to 3×10^{-4} K for rhodium (Rh, $Z = 45$). The orange cells are elements that become superconductors only under high pressures. The four pale pink cells are elements that are superconducting in particular forms: carbon (C, $Z = 6$) in the form of nanotubes, chromium (Cr, $Z = 24$) as thin films, palladium (Pd, $Z = 46$) after irradiation with alpha particles, and platinum (Pt, $Z = 78$) as a compacted powder. It is worth noting that copper (Cu, $Z = 29$), silver (Ag, $Z = 47$) and gold (Au, $Z = 79$), three elements that are excellent conductors at room temperature, do not become superconductors even at the lowest temperatures that are attainable.

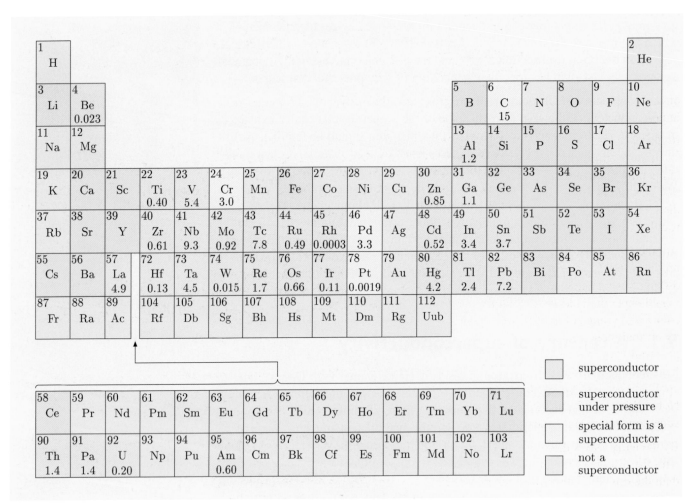

Figure 9.3 The Periodic Table showing all known elemental superconductors and their critical temperatures.

A major advance in the understanding of superconductivity came in 1933, when Walter Meissner and Robert Ochsenfeld discovered that superconductors are more than perfect conductors of electricity. They also have the important property of excluding a magnetic field from their interior. However, the field is excluded only if it is below a certain critical field strength, which depends on the material, the temperature and the geometry of the specimen. Above this critical field strength the superconductivity disappears. Brothers Fritz and Heinz London proposed a model that described the exclusion of the field in 1935, but it was another 20 years before a microscopic explanation was developed.

The long awaited quantum theory of superconductivity was published in 1957 by three US physicists, John Bardeen, Leon Cooper and John Schrieffer, and they were awarded the Nobel Prize for Physics in 1972 'for their jointly developed theory of superconductivity, usually called the BCS theory' (Nobel Prize citation). According to their theory, in the superconducting state there is an attractive interaction between electrons that is mediated by the vibrations of the ion lattice. A consequence of this interaction is that pairs of electrons are coupled together, and all of the pairs of electrons condense into a macroscopic quantum state, called the **condensate**, that extends through the superconductor. Not all of the free electrons in a superconductor are in the condensate; those that are in this state are called **superconducting electrons**, and the others are referred to as **normal electrons**. At temperatures very much lower than the critical temperature, there are very few normal electrons, but the proportion of normal electrons increases as the temperature increases, until at the critical temperature all of the electrons are normal. Because the superconducting electrons are linked in a macroscopic state, they behave coherently, and a consequence of this is that there is a characteristic distance over which their number density can change, known as the **coherence length** ξ (the Greek lower-case xi, pronounced 'ksye').

It takes a significant amount of energy to scatter an electron from the condensate — more than the thermal energy available to an electron below the critical temperature — so the superconducting electrons can flow without being scattered, that is, without any resistance. The BCS theory successfully explained many of the known properties of superconductors, but it predicted an upper bound of roughly 30 K for the critical temperature.

Another important theoretical discovery was made in 1957. Alexei Abrikosov predicted the existence of a second type of superconductor that behaved in a different way from elements like lead and tin. This new type of superconductor would expel the field from its interior when the applied field strength was low, but over a wide range of applied field strengths the superconductor would be threaded by normal metal regions through which the magnetic field could pass. The penetration of the field meant that superconductivity could exist in magnetic field strengths up to 10 T or more, which opened up the possibility of many applications. For this work, and subsequent research, Abrikosov received a Nobel Prize for Physics in 2003 'for pioneering contributions to the theory of superconductors and superfluids' (Nobel Prize citation).

By the early 1960s there had been major advances in superconductor technology, with the discovery of alloys that were superconducting at temperatures higher than the critical temperatures of the elemental superconductors. In particular, alloys of niobium and titanium (NbTi, $T_c = 9.8$ K) and niobium and tin (Nb$_3$Sn, $T_c = 18.1$ K) were becoming widely used to produce high-field magnets, and a major impetus for this development was the requirement for powerful magnets for particle accelerators, like the Tevatron at Fermilab in the USA. At about the same time, Brian Josephson made an important theoretical prediction that was to have major consequences for the application of superconductivity on a very small scale. He predicted that a current could flow between two superconductors that were separated by a very thin insulating layer. The so-called Josephson tunnelling effect has been widely used for making various sensitive measurements, including the determination of fundamental physical constants and the measurement of magnetic fields that are a billion (10^9) times weaker than the Earth's field. The significance of his work was recognized when he was awarded a Nobel Prize for Physics in 1973 'for his theoretical predictions of the properties of a supercurrent through a tunnel barrier, in particular those phenomena which are generally known as the Josephson effects' (Nobel Prize citation).

The hunt for superconductors with higher critical temperatures continued in the decades following publication of the BCS theory, in spite of its prediction that the upper limit for T_c was less than 30 K. The holy grail for scientists working in this area was a material that was superconducting at the temperature of liquid nitrogen (77 K), or, even better, at room temperature. This would mean that all of the technology and costs associated with use of liquid helium for cooling could be dispensed with, and applications of superconductivity would immediately become far more economically worthwhile. The breakthrough came in 1986, when Georg Bednorz and Alex Muller discovered that ceramics made of barium, lanthanum, copper and oxygen became superconducting at 30 K, the highest known critical temperature at that time. The discovery was particularly surprising because this material is an insulator at room temperature. The following year they received the Nobel Prize for Physics 'for their important breakthrough in the discovery of superconductivity in ceramic materials' (Nobel Prize citation), and the unprecedented rapidity with which the prize followed publication of their results reflects the importance attached to their work.

As a result of this breakthrough, a scientific bandwagon started to roll and many other scientists began to examine similar materials. In 1987, Paul Chu produced a new ceramic material by replacing lanthanum by yttrium, and found that it had a critical temperature of 90 K. This great jump in the critical temperature made it possible to use liquid nitrogen as a coolant, and with the promise of commercial viability for the new materials, a scramble ensued to find new high-temperature superconductors and to explain why they superconduct at such high temperatures. At the time of writing (2005), the highest critical temperature was 138 K, for a thallium-doped mercuric-cuprate, $Hg_{0.8}Tl_{0.2}Ba_2Ca_2Cu_3O_{8.33}$. Figure 9.4 shows the progress of the highest known superconducting critical temperature over the last century.

In recent years, no materials with significantly higher critical temperatures have been found, but other discoveries of equal importance have been made. These include the discovery that, against conventional wisdom, several materials exhibit the coexistence of ferromagnetism and superconductivity. We have also seen the discovery of the first high-temperature superconductors that do not contain copper. Startling discoveries like these are demanding that scientists continually re-examine long-standing theories on superconductivity and consider novel combinations of elements.

Unfortunately, no superconductors have yet been found with critical temperatures above room temperature, so cryogenic cooling is still a vital part of any superconducting application. Difficulties with fabricating ceramic materials into conducting wires or strips have also slowed down the development of new applications of high-temperature superconductors. However, despite these drawbacks, the commercial use of superconductors continues to rise.

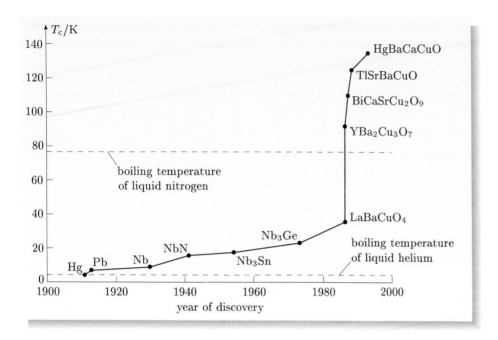

Figure 9.4 The critical temperature T_c of various superconductors plotted against their discovery date.

9.2 Properties of superconductors

In this section we shall discuss some of the most important electrical and magnetic properties of superconductors.

9.2.1 Zero electrical resistance

The most obvious characteristic of a superconductor is the complete disappearance of its electrical resistance below a temperature that is known as its critical temperature. Experiments have been carried out to attempt to detect whether there is any small residual resistance in the superconducting state. A sensitive test is to start a current flowing round a superconducting ring and observe whether the current decays. The current flowing in the superconducting loop clearly cannot be measured by inserting an ammeter into the loop, since this would introduce a resistance and the current would rapidly decay.

● Suggest a method of monitoring the current that does not involve interfering with the superconducting loop.

○ The magnetic field generated by the current in the loop could be monitored.

The magnitude of the magnetic field is directly proportional to the current circulating in the loop, and the field can be measured without drawing energy from the circuit. Experiments of this type have been carried out over periods of years, and the magnetic field — and hence the superconducting current — has always remained constant within the precision of the measuring equipment. Such a **persistent current** is characteristic of the superconducting state. From the lack of any decay of the current it has been deduced that the resistivity ρ of a superconductor is less than $10^{-26}\,\Omega\,\mathrm{m}$. This is about 18 orders of magnitude smaller than the resistivity of copper at room temperature ($\simeq 10^{-8}\,\Omega\,\mathrm{m}$).

Resistivity is the reciprocal of conductivity, that is, $\rho = \sigma^{-1}$. We prefer to describe a superconductor by $\rho = 0$, rather than by $\sigma = \infty$.

In the following exercise you can apply what you learned in the previous chapter about decay of currents in RL circuits to estimate an upper limit for the resistivity of a superconductor.

Exercise 9.1   (a) A circuit, with self-inductance L, has a current I_0 flowing in it at time $t = 0$. Assuming that the circuit has a small residual resistance R but contains no source of emf, what will be the current in the circuit after a time T has elapsed?

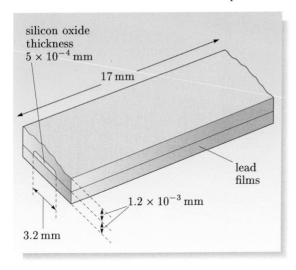

silicon oxide
thickness
5×10^{-4} mm

17 mm

lead
films

1.2×10^{-3} mm

3.2 mm

Figure 9.5   A lead 'tube' used in a persistent current experiment.

(b) In a classic experiment performed by Quinn and Ittner in 1962, a current was set up around the 'squashed tube', shown in Figure 9.5, which was made from two thin films of superconducting lead separated by a thin layer of insulating silicon oxide. The inductance L of the tube was estimated to be 1.4×10^{-13} H. No change in the magnetic moment due to the current could be detected after 7 hours, to within the 2 per cent precision of their measurement, so the current was at least 98 per cent of its initial value. Estimate the maximum possible resistance of the tube for circulating currents.

(c) The dimensions of the tube used in the experiment are shown in Figure 9.5. Estimate the maximum possible resistivity ρ_{max} of the lead films. Compare your answer with the resistivity of pure lead at $0\,^\circ$C, which you can deduce from Table 7.1. ■

9.2.2   Persistent currents lead to constant magnetic flux

An important consequence of the persistent currents that flow in materials with zero resistance is that the magnetic flux that passes through a continuous loop of such a material remains constant. To see how this comes about, consider a ring of metal, enclosing a fixed area A, as shown in Figure 9.6a. An initial magnetic field $\mathbf{B}_0$ is applied perpendicular to the plane of the ring when the temperature is above the critical temperature of the material from which the ring is made. The magnetic flux Φ through the ring is $B_0 A$, and if the ring is cooled below its critical temperature while in this applied field, then the flux passing through it is unchanged. If we now change the applied field, then a current will be induced in the ring (see Subsection 7.2.1), and according to Lenz's law the direction of this current will be such that the magnetic flux it generates compensates for the flux change due to the change in the applied field. From Faraday's law, the induced emf in the ring is $-\mathrm{d}\Phi/\mathrm{d}t = -A\,\mathrm{d}(B - B_0)/\mathrm{d}t$, and this generates an induced current I given by

$$L\frac{\mathrm{d}I}{\mathrm{d}t} = -A\frac{\mathrm{d}B}{\mathrm{d}t},$$

where L is the self-inductance of the ring. Note that there is no ohmic term, IR, on the left-hand side of this equation, because we are assuming that $R = 0$. Integrating this equation, we obtain

$$LI + BA = \text{constant}.$$

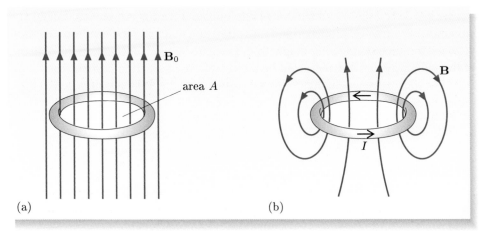

(a) (b)

Figure 9.6 (a) A ring cooled below its critical temperature in an applied field $\mathbf{B}_0$. (b) When the applied field is removed, a superconducting current maintains the flux through the ring at the same value.

But LI is the amount of flux passing through the ring generated by the current I flowing in the ring — this is just the definition of self-inductance L (Equation 7.25) — so $(LI + BA)$ is the total magnetic flux through the ring. The total flux threading a circuit with zero resistance must therefore remain constant — it cannot change. If the applied magnetic field is changed, an induced current is set up that creates a flux to compensate exactly for the change in the flux from the applied magnetic field. Because the circuit has no resistance, the induced current can flow indefinitely, and the original amount of flux through the ring can be maintained indefinitely. This is true even if the external field is removed altogether; the flux through the ring is maintained by a persistent induced current, as in Figure 9.6b. However, note that constant flux through the ring does not mean that the magnetic field is unchanged. In Figure 9.6a there is a uniform field within the ring, whereas in Figure 9.6b the field is produced by a current flowing in the ring and will be much larger close to the ring than at its centre.

An important application of the constant flux through a superconducting circuit is shown in Figure 9.7. A superconducting solenoid, used to produce large magnetic fields, is connected to a power supply that can be adjusted to provide the appropriate current to generate the required field. For some applications it is important for the field to remain constant to a higher precision than the stability of the power supply would allow. A stable field is achieved by including a superconducting switch in parallel with the solenoid. This is not a mechanical switch, but a length of superconducting wire that is heated to above its critical temperature to 'open' the switch, and cooled below the critical temperature to 'close' it. With the switch open, the current from the power supply is set to give the required field strength. The switch is then closed to produce a completely superconducting circuit that includes the solenoid, the switch and the leads connecting them. The flux through this circuit must remain constant in time, so the field inside the solenoid will also remain constant in time. An added bonus is that the power supply can now be disconnected, which means that no energy is being dissipated while maintaining the field.

Superconducting coils with persistent currents can be used in high-speed magnetically-levitated trains. In the system used on the Yamanashi Maglev Test Line in Japan (Figure 9.8 overleaf), superconducting coils mounted on the sides of the train induce currents in coils mounted in the walls of a guideway, and the attractive and repulsive forces between the superconducting

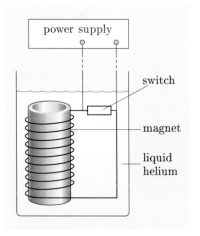

Figure 9.7 A superconducting solenoid with a superconducting switch that allows it to operate in a persistent current mode.

magnets and the track-mounted coils both levitate the train and provide lateral guidance. The train is propelled forwards by attractive and repulsive forces between the superconducting magnets and propulsion coils located on the walls of the guideway that are energized by a three-phase alternating current that creates a shifting magnetic field along the guideway. In 2003, a train reached the record-breaking speed of $581 \, \mathrm{km \, h^{-1}}$ on this track.

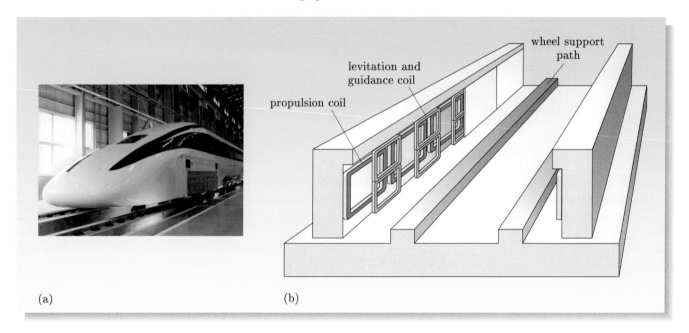

(a)   (b)

Figure 9.8   (a) A train that uses superconducting coils for magnetic levitation. (b) The guideway for the train, showing the coils used for levitation, guidance and propulsion.

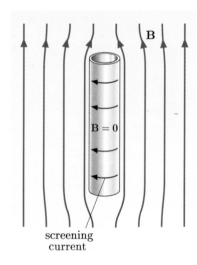

Figure 9.9   A long superconducting tube screens the region inside from externally applied magnetic fields.

A second application is the use of a superconducting tube to screen sensitive components from magnetic fields, as shown in Figure 9.9. The tube is cooled below its critical temperature in a very small magnetic field. If a magnetic field is subsequently applied in the region of the tube, screening currents will be induced that generate fields which cancel out the applied field within the tube. However, note that effective screening requires a long tube, because only this geometry will generate a uniform magnetic field in the middle of the tube.

9.2.3   The Meissner effect

The second defining characteristic of a superconducting material is much less obvious than its zero electrical resistance. It was over 20 years after the discovery of superconductivity that Meissner and Ochsenfeld published a paper describing this second characteristic. They discovered that when a magnetic field is applied to a sample of tin, say, in the superconducting state, the applied field is excluded, so that $B = 0$ throughout its interior. This property of the superconducting state is known as the **Meissner effect**.

The exclusion of the magnetic field from a superconductor takes place regardless of whether the sample becomes superconducting before or after the external magnetic field is applied. In the steady state, the external magnetic field is cancelled in the interior of the superconductor by opposing magnetic fields produced by a steady screening current that flows on the surface of the superconductor.

It is important to recognize that the exclusion of the magnetic field from inside a superconductor cannot be predicted by applying Maxwell's equations to a material that has zero electrical resistance. We shall refer to a material that has zero resistance but does not exhibit the Meissner effect as a **perfect conductor**, and we shall show that a superconductor has additional properties besides those that can be predicted from its zero resistance.

Consider first the behaviour of a perfect conductor. We showed in the previous subsection that the flux enclosed by a continuous path through zero resistance material — a perfect conductor — remains constant, and this must be true for *any* path within the material, whatever its size or orientation. This means that the magnetic field throughout the material must remain constant, that is, $\partial \mathbf{B}/\partial t = 0$. The consequences of this are shown in Figure 9.10 parts (a) and (b).

Figure 9.10 A comparison of the response of a perfect conductor, (a) and (b), and a superconductor, (c) and (d), to an applied magnetic field.

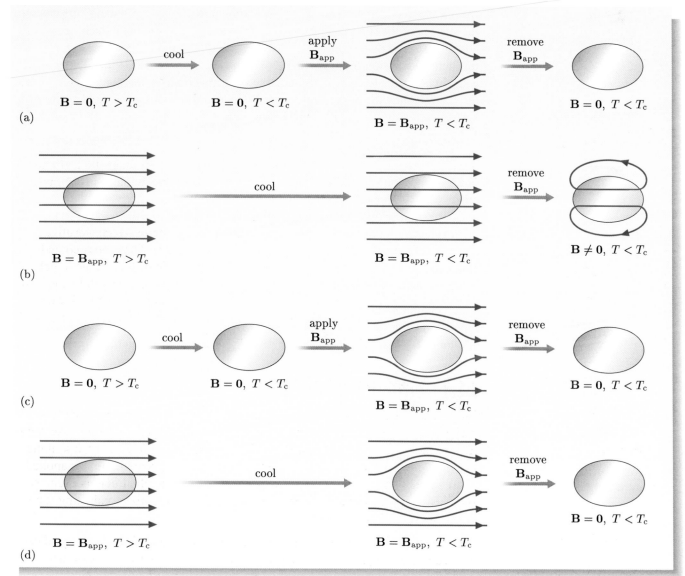

In part (a) of this figure, a perfect conductor is cooled in zero magnetic field to below the temperature at which its resistance becomes zero. When a magnetic field is applied, screening currents are induced in the surface to maintain the field at zero within the material, and when the field is removed, the field within the material stays at zero. In contrast, part (b) shows that cooling a perfect conductor to below its critical temperature in a uniform magnetic field leads to a situation where the uniform field is maintained within the material. If the applied field is then removed, the field within the conductor remains uniform, and continuity of magnetic field lines means there is a field in the region around the perfect conductor. Clearly, the magnetization state of the perfect conductor depends not just on temperature and magnetic field, but also on the previous history of the material.

Contrast this with the behaviour of a superconductor, shown in Figure 9.10 parts (c) and (d). Whether a material is cooled below its superconducting critical temperature in zero field, (c), or in a finite field, (d), the magnetic field within a superconducting material is always zero. The magnetic field is always expelled from a superconductor. This is achieved spontaneously by producing currents on the surface of the superconductor. The direction of the currents is such as to create a magnetic field that exactly cancels the applied field in the superconductor. It is this active exclusion of magnetic field — the Meissner effect — that distinguishes a superconductor from a perfect conductor, a material that merely has zero resistance. Thus we can regard zero resistance and zero magnetic field as the two key characteristics of superconductivity.

Perfect diamagnetism

In Chapter 3 you saw that diamagnetism is due to currents induced in atomic orbitals by an applied magnetic field. The induced currents produce a magnetization within the diamagnetic material that opposes the applied field, and the magnetization disappears when the applied field is removed. However, this effect is very small: the magnetization generally reduces the applied field by less than one part in 10^5 within the material. In diamagnetic material, $\mathbf{B} = \mu\mu_0\mathbf{H}$, with the relative permeability μ slightly less than unity.

Superconductors take the diamagnetic effect to the extreme, since in a superconductor the field $\mathbf{B}$ is zero — the field is completely screened from the interior of the material. Thus the relative permeability of a superconductor is zero.

9.2.4   Critical magnetic field

An important characteristic of a superconductor is that its normal resistance is restored if a sufficiently large magnetic field is applied. The nature of this transition to the normal state depends on the shape of the superconductor and the orientation of the magnetic field, and it is also different for pure elements and for alloys. In this subsection we describe the behaviour in the simplest situation; we shall discuss other more complex behaviour in Section 9.4.

If an increasing magnetic field is applied parallel to a long thin cylinder of tin at a constant temperature below the critical temperature, then the cylinder will make a transition from the superconducting state to the normal state when the field reaches a well-defined strength. This field at which the superconductivity is destroyed is known as the **critical magnetic field strength**, B_c. If the field is reduced, with the temperature held constant, the tin cylinder returns to the superconducting state at the same critical field strength B_c.

Experiments indicate that the critical magnetic field strength depends on temperature, and the form of this temperature dependence is shown in Figure 9.11 for several elements. At very low temperatures, the critical field strength is essentially independent of temperature, but as the temperature increases, the critical field strength drops, and becomes zero at the critical temperature. At temperatures just below the critical temperature it requires only a very small magnetic field to destroy the superconductivity.

The temperature dependence of the critical field strength is approximately parabolic:

$$B_c(T) = B_c(0) \left[1 - \left(\frac{T}{T_c} \right)^2 \right], \tag{9.1}$$

where $B_c(0)$ is the extrapolated value of the critical field strength at absolute zero and T_c is the critical temperature. The curves in Figure 9.11 indicate that a superconductor with a high critical temperature T_c has a high critical field strength B_c at $T = 0$ K, and Table 9.1 confirms this correlation for a larger number of superconducting elements.

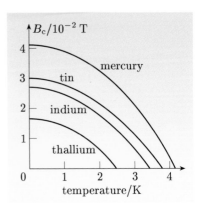

Figure 9.11 The temperature dependences of the critical magnetic field strengths of mercury, tin, indium and thallium.

Table 9.1 The critical temperatures T_c and critical magnetic field strengths $B_c(0)$ for various superconducting elements.

	T_c/K	$B_c(0)/\mathrm{mT}$
aluminium	1.2	10
cadmium	0.52	2.8
indium	3.4	28
lead	7.2	80
mercury	4.2	41
tantalum	4.5	83
thallium	2.4	18
tin	3.7	31
titanium	0.40	5.6
zinc	0.85	5.4

Exercise 9.2 Estimate the magnetic field strength necessary to destroy superconductivity in a sample of lead at 4.2 K. ∎

It is interesting to compare the magnetic behaviour of a superconducting element with typical curves for diamagnetic, paramagnetic and ferromagnetic materials. When discussing ferromagnetic materials in Chapter 3, we showed how their magnetic behaviour could be represented by B versus H graphs (Figure 3.12). Figure 9.12a shows the behaviour of typical diamagnetic and paramagnetic materials. Note that we have plotted $\mu_0 H$ on the horizontal axis rather than H, so that both axes use the same unit (tesla). The straight lines plotted correspond to the relationship $B = \mu\mu_0 H$, with μ slightly smaller than unity for the diamagnetic material and slightly greater than unity for the paramagnetic material. The behaviour of a ferromagnet, shown in Figure 9.12b, is quite different, with $B \gg \mu_0 H$, and a highly non-linear and irreversible curve until the magnetization saturates, after which B increases linearly with H.

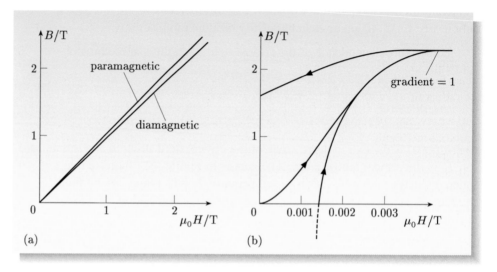

Figure 9.12   Graphs showing B versus $\mu_0 H$ for (a) diamagnetic and paramagnetic materials, and (b) a ferromagnetic material. Note the different scales for the $\mu_0 H$-axes in the two graphs.

Compare these graphs with Figure 9.13, which shows the B-H curve for a superconducting cylinder of tin, with the field parallel to its axis. The field strength B within the superconductor is zero when $\mu_0 H$ is less than the critical field strength B_c; the superconductor behaves like a perfect diamagnetic material and completely excludes the field from its interior. But then B jumps abruptly to a value B_c, and at higher fields the tin cylinder obeys the relationship $B \simeq \mu_0 H$, since the material is weakly diamagnetic in its normal state, with $\mu = 0.9998$. The linear graphs in Figure 9.12a are similar to those for a superconductor above the critical field strength.

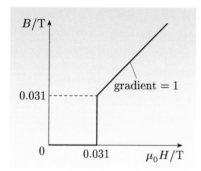

Figure 9.13   Graph showing B versus $\mu_0 H$ for a tin cylinder, aligned parallel to the field.

9.2.5   Critical current

The current density for a steady current flowing along a wire in its normal state is essentially uniform over its cross-section. A consequence of this is that the magnetic field strength B within a wire of radius a, carrying current I, increases linearly with distance from the centre of the wire, and reaches a maximum value of $\mu_0 I/2\pi a$ at the surface of the wire (see Exercise 3.6). Within a superconductor, however, the magnetic field $\mathbf{B}$ is zero.

● What can you deduce about the current flow in a superconducting wire from the fact that $\mathbf{B} = 0$ within a superconductor?

○ The current density within the bulk of the wire must be zero, since Ampère's law ($\mathrm{curl}\,\mathbf{B} = \mu_0\mathbf{J}$) indicates that a non-zero current density would produce a magnetic field. The current must therefore flow in the surface of the wire.

● How does the magnetic field just outside the surface of a superconducting wire, radius a, carrying current I, compare with the field just outside the surface of a normal wire with the same radius, carrying the same current?

○ The fields just outside the surface are identical. The currents in both wires are axially symmetric, so the integral version of Ampère's law indicates that the fields just outside the surfaces of the wires are the same.

The magnetic field strength B just outside the surface of the wire is $\mu_0 I/2\pi a$. It follows that if the current flowing in a superconducting wire is increased, eventually the field strength at the surface of the wire will exceed B_c and the sample will revert to its normal state. The maximum current that a wire can carry with zero resistance is known as its **critical current**, and for a long straight wire the critical current I_c is given by $I_c = 2\pi a B_c/\mu_0$. A current greater than I_c will cause the wire to revert to its normal state. This critical current is proportional to the radius of the wire.

In the previous subsection you saw that the critical field strength is dependent on temperature, decreasing to zero as the temperature is increased to the critical temperature. This means that the superconducting current that a wire can carry will also decrease as the temperature gets closer to the critical temperature. Because of this, in real applications superconductors generally operate at temperatures less than half of the critical temperature, where the critical field strength, and therefore the critical current, is greater than 75 per cent of the maximum value.

Now, the current carried by a superconducting wire actually flows in a thin layer at the surface; it cannot be restricted to an infinitesimal layer, because that would lead to an infinite current density. As you will see in Section 9.3, this means that the magnetic field penetrates into this thin layer, and we derive there relationships between the field and the current density. But in the present context, the point to note is that the transition to the normal state takes place when the magnetic field strength at the surface corresponds to the critical field strength, and this occurs when the current density at the surface reaches a critical current density. This critical current density is much greater than $I_c/\pi a^2$ because the current flows only in a thin surface layer.

The magnetic field at the surface of a superconductor may have a contribution from an external source of magnetic field, as well as from the field produced by the current in the wire. This external field will set up screening currents in the surface layer of the material. The transition to the normal state then occurs when the vector sum of the current densities at the surface due to the current in the wire and due to the screening current exceeds the critical current density, or, equivalently, when the magnitude of the vector sum of the magnetic fields that are present at the surface of the wire exceeds the critical field strength.

Exercise 9.3 Tin has $T_c = 3.7\,\mathrm{K}$ and $B_c = 31\,\mathrm{mT}$ at $T = 0\,\mathrm{K}$. What is the minimum radius required for tin wire if it is to carry a current of 200 A at $T = 2.0\,\mathrm{K}$? ■

9.3   Modelling properties of superconductors

As was mentioned earlier, a substantial dose of quantum mechanics would be required to provide a full explanation of the properties of superconductors. This would take us too far away from electromagnetism, and we shall therefore restrict our discussion to aspects that can be discussed using classical concepts of electromagnetism that you have already encountered.

9.3.1   A two-fluid model

We shall model the free electrons within a superconductor as two fluids. According to this **two-fluid model**, one fluid consists of 'normal' electrons, number density n_n, and these behave in exactly the same way as the free electrons in a normal metal. As we mentioned in Subsection 7.1.1, they are accelerated by an electric field $\mathbf{E}$, but are frequently scattered by impurities and defects in the ion lattice and by thermal vibrations of the lattice. The scattering limits the speed of the electrons, and they attain a mean drift velocity $\langle \mathbf{v}_n \rangle = -e\tau \mathbf{E}/m$, where τ is the mean time between scattering events for the electrons and m is the electron mass. The current density $\mathbf{J}_n$ due to flow of these electrons is

$$\mathbf{J}_n = -n_n e \langle \mathbf{v}_n \rangle = \frac{n_n e^2 \tau}{m} \mathbf{E}. \tag{9.2}$$

Interspersed with the normal electrons are what we shall call the superconducting electrons, or superelectrons, which form a fluid with number density n_s. The superconducting electrons are not scattered by impurities, defects or thermal vibrations, so they are freely accelerated by an electric field. If the velocity of a superconducting electron is $\mathbf{v}_s$, then its equation of motion is

$$m \frac{d\mathbf{v}_s}{dt} = -e\mathbf{E}.$$

Combining this with the expression for the current density, $\mathbf{J}_s = -n_s e \mathbf{v}_s$, we find that

$$\frac{\partial \mathbf{J}_s}{\partial t} = -n_s e \frac{\partial \mathbf{v}_s}{\partial t} = \frac{n_s e^2}{m} \mathbf{E}. \tag{9.3}$$

Compare this with Equation 9.2, which relates current density and electric field in a normal conductor. Scattering of the normal electrons leads to a constant current in a constant electric field, whereas the absence of scattering of the electrons in a superconductor means that the current density would increase steadily in a constant electric field. However, if we consider a constant current flowing in the superconductor, then $\partial \mathbf{J}_s/\partial t = \mathbf{0}$, so $\mathbf{E} = \mathbf{0}$. Therefore the normal current density must be zero — all of the steady current in a superconductor is carried by the superconducting electrons. Of course, with no electric field within the superconductor, there will be no potential difference across it, and so it has zero resistance.

9.3.2   Magnetic field in a perfect conductor

When discussing the Meissner effect in Subsection 9.2.3, we argued qualitatively that a material that just had the property of zero resistance — a perfect conductor rather than a superconductor — would maintain a constant magnetic field in its interior, and would not expel any field that was present when the material became superconducting. We shall now show how that conclusion follows from an application of Maxwell's equations to a perfect conductor. We can then see what additional assumptions are needed to account for the Meissner effect in a superconductor.

We assume that the electrons in a perfect conductor (or a proportion of them) are not scattered, and therefore the current density is governed by Equation 9.3. However, we shall use the subscript 'pc' (for perfect conductor) here to indicate that we are not dealing with a superconductor. We are interested in the magnetic field in a perfect conductor, so we shall apply Maxwell's equations to this situation. Faraday's law is valid in all situations,

$$\mathrm{curl}\,\mathbf{E} = -\frac{\partial \mathbf{B}}{\partial t},$$

and if we substitute for $\mathbf{E}$ using Equation 9.3, we obtain

$$\mathrm{curl}\,\frac{\partial \mathbf{J}_{\mathrm{pc}}}{\partial t} = -\frac{n_{\mathrm{pc}}e^2}{m}\frac{\partial \mathbf{B}}{\partial t}. \tag{9.4}$$

Looking now at the Ampère–Maxwell law, $\mathrm{curl}\,\mathbf{H} = \mathbf{J}_{\mathrm{f}} + \partial \mathbf{D}/\partial t$, we shall assume that our perfect conductor is either weakly diamagnetic or weakly paramagnetic, so that $\mu \simeq 1$ and $\mathbf{H} \simeq \mathbf{B}/\mu_0$ are very good approximations. We shall also omit the Maxwell term, $\partial \mathbf{D}/\partial t$, since this is negligible for the static, or slowly-varying, fields that we shall be considering. With these approximations, the Ampère–Maxwell law simplifies to Ampère's law,

$$\mathrm{curl}\,\mathbf{B} = \mu_0 \mathbf{J}_{\mathrm{pc}}, \tag{9.5}$$

where use of the subscript pc for the current density reminds us that the free current $\mathbf{J}_{\mathrm{f}}$ is carried by the perfectly-conducting electrons. We now use this expression to eliminate $\mathbf{J}_{\mathrm{pc}}$ from Equation 9.4:

$$\mathrm{curl}\left(\mathrm{curl}\,\frac{\partial \mathbf{B}}{\partial t}\right) = -\frac{\mu_0 n_{\mathrm{pc}}e^2}{m}\frac{\partial \mathbf{B}}{\partial t}. \tag{9.6}$$

We can use a standard vector identity from inside the back cover to rewrite the left-hand side of this equation:

$$\mathrm{curl}\left(\mathrm{curl}\,\frac{\partial \mathbf{B}}{\partial t}\right) = \mathrm{grad}\left(\mathrm{div}\,\frac{\partial \mathbf{B}}{\partial t}\right) - \nabla^2\left(\frac{\partial \mathbf{B}}{\partial t}\right).$$

The no-monopole law, $\mathrm{div}\,\mathbf{B} = 0$, means that the first term on the right-hand side of this equation is zero, so Equation 9.6 can be rewritten as

$$\nabla^2\left(\frac{\partial \mathbf{B}}{\partial t}\right) = \frac{\mu_0 n_{\mathrm{pc}}e^2}{m}\frac{\partial \mathbf{B}}{\partial t}. \tag{9.7}$$

This equation determines how $\partial \mathbf{B}/\partial t$ varies in a perfect conductor.

We shall look for the solution to Equation 9.7 for the simple geometry shown in Figure 9.14; a conductor has a boundary corresponding to the plane $z = 0$, and occupies the region $z > 0$, with a uniform field outside the conductor given by $\mathbf{B}_0 = B_0 \mathbf{e}_x$.

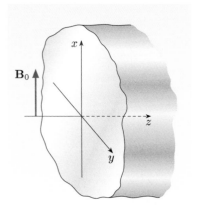

Figure 9.14 A plane boundary between a conductor and air.

The uniform external field in the x-direction means that the field inside the conductor will also be in the x-direction, and its strength will depend only on z. So Equation 9.7 reduces to the one-dimensional form

$$\frac{\partial^2}{\partial z^2}\left(\frac{\partial B_x(z,t)}{\partial t}\right) = \frac{1}{\lambda_{\mathrm{pc}}^2}\frac{\partial B_x(z,t)}{\partial t},$$

where we have simplified the equation, for reasons that will soon become clear, by writing $\mu_0 n_{\mathrm{pc}} e^2/m = 1/\lambda_{\mathrm{pc}}^2$. The general solution of this equation is

$$\frac{\partial B_x(z,t)}{\partial t} = a(t)\mathrm{e}^{-z/\lambda_{\mathrm{pc}}} + b(t)\mathrm{e}^{+z/\lambda_{\mathrm{pc}}},$$

where a and b are independent of position. The second term on the right-hand side corresponds to a rate of change of field strength that continues to increase exponentially with distance from the boundary; since this is unphysical, we set $b = 0$. The boundary condition for the field parallel to the boundary is that $H_\parallel$ is continuous (Equation 3.15), and since we are assuming that $\mu \simeq 1$ in both the air and the conductor, this is equivalent to $B_\parallel$ being the same on either side of the boundary at all times. This means that $\partial B_x/\partial t$ is the same on either side of the boundary, so $a = \partial B_0/\partial t$, and the field within the perfect conductor satisfies the equation

$$\frac{\partial B_x(z,t)}{\partial t} = \frac{\partial B_0(t)}{\partial t}\,\mathrm{e}^{-z/\lambda_{\mathrm{pc}}}. \tag{9.8}$$

This indicates that any *changes* in the external magnetic field are attenuated exponentially with distance below the surface of the perfect conductor. If the distance λ_{pc} is very small, then the field will not change within the bulk of the perfect conductor, and this is the behaviour that we described qualitatively in Subsection 9.2.3. Note that this does not mean the magnetic field *must* be expelled: flux expulsion *requires* $B = 0$, rather than just $\partial B/\partial t = 0$. So how do we modify the description that we have given of a perfect conductor so that it describes a superconductor and leads to a prediction that $B = 0$?

9.3.3 The London equations

A simple but useful description of the electrodynamics of superconductivity was put forward by the brothers Fritz and Heinz London in 1935, shortly after the discovery that magnetic fields are expelled from superconductors. Their proposed equations are consistent with the Meissner effect and can be used with Maxwell's equations to predict how the magnetic field and surface current vary with distance from the surface of a superconductor.

In order to account for the Meissner effect, the London brothers proposed that in a superconductor, Equation 9.4 is replaced by the more restrictive relationship

$$\operatorname{curl}\mathbf{J}_{\mathrm{s}} = -\frac{n_{\mathrm{s}}e^2}{m}\mathbf{B}.$$

This equation, and Equation 9.3 which relates the rate of change of current to the electric field, are now known as the **London equations**.

London equations

$$\operatorname{curl} \mathbf{J}_s = -\frac{n_s e^2}{m}\mathbf{B}, \tag{9.9}$$

$$\frac{\partial \mathbf{J}_s}{\partial t} = \frac{n_s e^2}{m}\mathbf{E}. \tag{Eqn 9.3}$$

It is important to note that these equations are not an explanation of superconductivity. They were introduced as a restriction on Maxwell's equations so that the behaviour of superconductors deduced from the equations was consistent with experimental observations, and in particular with the Meissner effect. Their status is somewhat similar to Ohm's law, which is a useful description of the behaviour of many normal metals, but which does not provide any explanation for the conduction process at the microscopic level.

To demonstrate how the London equations lead to the Meissner effect, we proceed in the same way as for the perfect conductor. First we use Ampère's law, $\operatorname{curl}\mathbf{B} = \mu_0\mathbf{J}_s$, to substitute for $\mathbf{J}_s$ in Equation 9.9, and we obtain

$$\operatorname{curl}(\operatorname{curl}\mathbf{B}) = -\frac{\mu_0 n_s e^2}{m}\mathbf{B} = -\frac{1}{\lambda^2}\mathbf{B},$$

where

$$\lambda = \left(\frac{m}{\mu_0 n_s e^2}\right)^{1/2}. \tag{9.10}$$

But $\operatorname{curl}(\operatorname{curl}\mathbf{B}) = \operatorname{grad}(\operatorname{div}\mathbf{B}) - \nabla^2\mathbf{B} = -\nabla^2\mathbf{B}$, since $\operatorname{div}\mathbf{B} = 0$. So

$$\nabla^2\mathbf{B} = \frac{1}{\lambda^2}\mathbf{B}. \tag{9.11}$$

This equation is similar to Equation 9.7, but $\partial\mathbf{B}/\partial t$ has been replaced by $\mathbf{B}$. The important point to note about this equation is that the only solution that corresponds to a spatially uniform field (for which $\nabla^2\mathbf{B} = \mathbf{0}$) is the field that is identically zero everywhere. If $\mathbf{B}$ were not equal to zero, then $\nabla^2\mathbf{B}$ would not be zero, so $\mathbf{B}$ would depend on position. Thus, a uniform magnetic field like that shown in Figure 9.10b cannot exist in a superconductor.

If we consider again the simple one-dimensional geometry shown in Figure 9.14, then we obtain the solution to Equation 9.11 by simply replacing the partial time derivatives of the fields in the solution for the perfect conductor (Equation 9.8) by the fields themselves, that is,

$$B_x(z) = B_0 e^{-z/\lambda}. \tag{9.12}$$

Therefore, the London equations lead to the prediction of an exponential decay of the magnetic field within the superconductor, as shown in Figure 9.15.

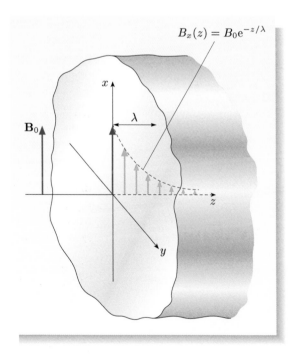

Figure 9.15 The penetration of a magnetic field into a superconducting material, showing the penetration depth, λ.

9.3.4   Penetration depth

The characteristic length, λ, associated with the decay of the magnetic field at the surface of a superconductor is known as the **penetration depth**, and it depends on the number density n_{s} of superconducting electrons.

We can estimate a value for λ by assuming that all of the free electrons are superconducting. If we set $n_{\mathrm{s}} = 10^{29}\,\mathrm{m}^{-3}$, a typical free electron density in a metal, then we find that

$$\lambda = \left(\frac{m}{\mu_0 n_{\mathrm{s}} e^2}\right)^{1/2} = 1.7 \times 10^{-8}\,\mathrm{m} \simeq 20\,\mathrm{nm}.$$

The small size of λ indicates that the magnetic field is effectively excluded from the interior of macroscopic specimens of superconductors, in agreement with the experimentally observed Meissner effect.

The small scale of the field penetration means that carefully-designed experiments are needed to measure the value of λ. Many experiments have been done with samples that have a large surface to volume ratio to make the penetration effect of the field appreciable. Thin films, thin wires and colloidal particles of superconductors have all been used for this purpose. But it is also possible to use large specimens if the measurement is sensitive to the amount of magnetic flux passing through the superconductor's surface, and not to the ratio of flux excluded by the superconductor to flux through the normal material, which is close to unity.

In a classic experiment performed in the 1950s, Schawlow and Devlin measured the self-inductance of a solenoid within which they inserted a long single-crystal cylinder of superconducting tin, 7.4 mm in diameter. They minimized the space between the coil and the tin cylinder, and since no magnetic flux passed through the bulk of the superconductor, the flux was essentially restricted to a thin cylindrical shell of thickness λ at the surface of the cylinder. The inductance of the solenoid was therefore determined mainly by the magnitude of the penetration depth. To measure the inductance, a capacitor was connected in parallel with the solenoid, and the natural angular frequency, $\omega_{\mathrm{n}} = 1/\sqrt{LC}$ (see Subsection 8.3.2), of the LC circuit was measured. The precision of the frequency measurement was about one part in 10^6, which corresponded to a precision of 0.4 nm in the value of the penetration depth. The result that they obtained for the penetration depth of tin for temperatures much lower than the critical temperature was 52 nm.

The number density of superconducting electrons depends on temperature, so the penetration depth is temperature dependent. For $T \ll T_{\mathrm{c}}$, all of the free electrons are superconducting, but the number density falls steadily with increasing temperature until it reaches zero at the critical temperature. Since $\lambda \propto n_{\mathrm{s}}^{-1/2}$ according to the London model, the penetration depth increases as the temperature approaches the critical temperature, becoming effectively infinite — corresponding to a uniform field in the material — at and above the critical temperature. Figure 9.16 shows this temperature dependence for tin, which is well represented by the expression

$$\lambda(T) = \frac{\lambda(0)}{[1 - (T/T_{\mathrm{c}})^4]^{1/2}},$$

where $\lambda(0)$ is the value of the penetration depth at $T = 0\,\mathrm{K}$.

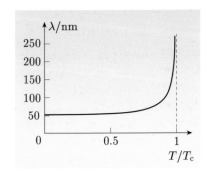

Figure 9.16   The penetration depth λ as a function of temperature for tin.

9.3.5 The screening current

The London equations relate the magnetic field in a superconductor to the superconducting current density, and we derived the dependence of field on position by eliminating the current density. However, if we eliminate the magnetic field instead, we can derive the following equation for the current density:

$$\nabla^2 \mathbf{J}_s = \frac{1}{\lambda^2} \mathbf{J}_s. \tag{9.13}$$

Exercise 9.4 Derive Equation 9.13 by taking the curl of both sides of Equation 9.9 and then using Ampère's law to eliminate curl $\mathbf{B}$. Assume that the currents are steady. ∎

Equation 9.13 has exactly the same form as Equation 9.11. So for the planar symmetry that we discussed earlier — superconducting material occupying the region $z > 0$ (Figure 9.14) — the solution for the current density will have the same form as Equation 9.12, that is,

$$J_s(z) = J_0 e^{-z/\lambda}. \tag{9.14}$$

This equation gives no indication of the absolute magnitude or direction of current flow, but we can deduce this by using Ampère's law, $\operatorname{curl} \mathbf{B} = \mu_0 \mathbf{J}_s$. In the planar situation that we are considering, $\mathbf{B} = B_x(z)\, \mathbf{e}_x$, so

$$\operatorname{curl} \mathbf{B} = \frac{\partial B_x(z)}{\partial z}\, \mathbf{e}_y.$$

Then

$$\mathbf{J}_s = \frac{1}{\mu_0} \operatorname{curl} \mathbf{B} = \frac{1}{\mu_0} \frac{\partial B_x(z)}{\partial z}\, \mathbf{e}_y = J_{sy}(z)\, \mathbf{e}_y,$$

where

$$J_{sy}(z) = \frac{1}{\mu_0} \frac{\partial B_x(z)}{\partial z}.$$

But we know that $B_x(z) = B_0 e^{-z/\lambda}$ (Equation 9.12), so

$$J_{sy}(z) = -\frac{B_0}{\mu_0 \lambda}\, e^{-z/\lambda}.$$

Thus the current that screens the interior of the superconductor from an applied field flows within a thin surface layer, which has a thickness characterized by the penetration depth λ, and the current flows parallel to the surface and in a direction perpendicular to the magnetic field, as shown in Figure 9.17.

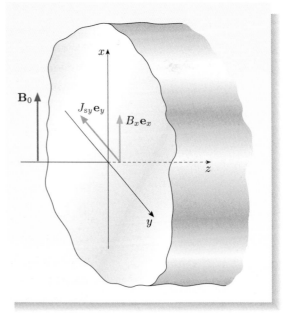

Figure 9.17 The magnetic field and current density vectors in the surface layer of a superconductor.

Exercise 9.5 The number density of free electrons in tin is $1.5 \times 10^{29}\ \mathrm{m}^{-3}$. Calculate the penetration depth predicted by the London model, assuming that all of the free electrons are superconducting, and compare the result with the value measured by Schawlow and Devlin. ∎

The numerical discrepancy between the London model prediction for the penetration depth of tin and the experimentally measured value indicates that this model has limitations. One limitation is that the model is essentially a *local* model, relating current density and magnetic field at each point. Superconductivity, though, is a non-local phenomenon, involving coherent behaviour of the superconducting electrons that are condensed into a macroscopic quantum state. The characteristic distance over which the behaviour of the superconducting electrons is linked is known as the coherence length, ξ, introduced in Section 9.1. This distance represents the distance over which the number density of the superconducting electrons changes, and is a measure of the intrinsic non-local nature of the superconducting state. The London local model is a good description if $\xi \ll \lambda$, that is, the coherence length is much shorter than the distance λ over which the fields and current density are changing. Since the penetration depth increases sharply as the temperature approaches the critical temperature (Figure 9.16), the London model becomes a good approximation in this limit. More importantly, the coherence length of superconductors decreases as the critical temperature increases and as the scattering time for normal electrons decreases. Both of these effects mean that the coherence length is short compared with the penetration depth in alloy and ceramic superconductors, so the London local model is a good approximation in these cases too, and predicted and experimental results for the penetration depth are in good agreement.

For pure elements, well below their critical temperatures, the penetration depth is generally much shorter than the coherence length, so a local model is not appropriate. In this limit, the number density of superconducting electrons does not reach the bulk value until a distance of the order of ξ, which is greater than λ, from the surface, and the reduced value of n_s accounts for the discrepancy between the predicted and experimental results for the penetration depth of tin discussed earlier.

The ratio of the penetration depth to the coherence length is an important parameter for a superconductor, and we shall return to this subject in Subsection 9.4.2.

9.4   Two types of superconductor

The two main types of superconducting materials are known as **type-I** and **type-II superconductors**, and their properties will be discussed in the remainder of this chapter. All of the pure elemental superconductors are type-I, with the exception of niobium, vanadium and technetium. The discussion of the effects of magnetic fields and currents on superconductors earlier in this chapter has been confined to thin cylinders of type-I materials like lead or tin in a *parallel* magnetic field. In Subsection 9.4.1 we shall discuss what happens when the magnetic field is *perpendicular* to cylinders made of these materials.

Superconducting alloys and high critical temperature ceramics are all type-II, and these are the materials that are used in most practical applications. In Subsection 9.4.2, we shall consider the response to a magnetic field of this type of superconductor. Such materials behave quite differently from lead and tin, and this is the reason that they are widely used.

9.4.1 Type-I superconductors

You saw in Subsection 9.2.4 that superconductivity in a tin cylinder is destroyed when an applied field with strength $B_0 > B_c$ is applied parallel to the cylinder. However, when the field is applied perpendicular to the cylinder, as shown in Figure 9.18, the field strength at points A and C is substantially greater than the strength of the applied field at a distance from the cylinder, and this is indicated by the increased concentration of the field lines shown near these points. In fact, it can be shown that the field strength at these points is a factor of two greater than the applied field strength. This means that as the applied field $\mathbf{B}_0$ is increased, the field at points A and C will reach the critical field strength B_c when $B_0 = B_c/2$.

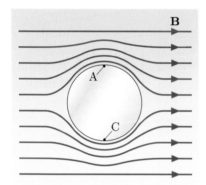

Figure 9.18 The magnetic field $\mathbf{B}$ in a plane perpendicular to the axis of a superconducting cylinder (shown in cross-section) for an applied field with $B_0 < B_c/2$.

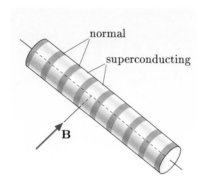

Figure 9.19 Schematic representation of the intermediate state for a cylinder of a type-I superconductor aligned perpendicular to the magnetic field.

You might think that superconductivity in the cylinder would be completely destroyed at this lower field strength. However, were this to be the case, then the material would be in the normal state with a field strength in its interior of less than B_c, which is not possible. Instead, for applied field strengths B_0 in the range $B_c/2 < B_0 < B_c$, the cylinder splits up into small slices of normal and superconducting material that run parallel to the applied field. This state in which regions of normal and superconducting material coexist in a type-I superconductor is known as the **intermediate state**, and it is shown schematically in Figure 9.19. Within the normal regions, $B = B_c$, and in the superconducting regions, B decreases rapidly and is confined to a thin layer, the width of which is determined by the penetration depth, as shown in Figure 9.20. The number density of superconducting electrons n_s increases from zero at the boundary to the bulk value over the coherence length ξ. Note that since n_s is not constant in the superconducting regions, the magnetic field strength does not fall exponentially. The proportion of the material in the normal state increases from zero for $B_0 = B_c/2$ to 100 per cent for $B_0 = B_c$.

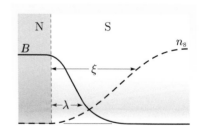

Figure 9.20 Variation of magnetic field strength and number density of superconducting electrons in the region of a boundary between normal and superconducting regions in the intermediate state of a type-I superconductor.

The lowest applied field strength at which the intermediate state appears depends on the shape of the specimen and the orientation of the field. Essentially, it is determined by the extent to which the field is deviated by the superconductor, or equivalently, by how much the field strength is enhanced at the edges of the superconductor. For the thin cylinder shown in Figure 9.21a, the field just outside is essentially the same as the applied field, so there is a direct transition from superconducting to normal state, without the intervening intermediate state. Contrast this with the thin plate oriented perpendicular to the applied field shown in Figure 9.21b, where the field strength would be greatly enhanced outside the plate's edges if it could not penetrate the plate. Samples like this enter the intermediate state when the applied field strength is a very small fraction of the critical field strength (Figure 9.21c).

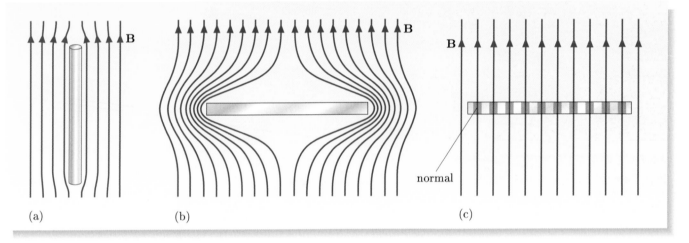

(a)   (b)   (c)

Figure 9.21   (a) A thin superconducting cylinder hardly distorts a uniform applied field. (b) Highly distorted field that would result if a magnetic field did not penetrate a thin plate. (c) Intermediate state in a thin plate.

Figure 9.22 shows the pattern of normal and superconducting regions for an aluminium plate in the intermediate state, with the field perpendicular to the surface.

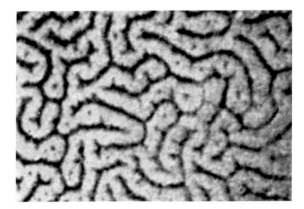

Figure 9.22   Intermediate state in an aluminium plate. Tin powder was deposited on the plate and collected in the superconducting regions — the dark areas of the image — where the magnetic field was low. The light normal regions are about 1 mm wide.

9.4.2 Type-II superconductors

For decades it was assumed that all superconductors, elements and alloys, behaved in similar ways, and that any differences could be attributed to impurities or defects in the materials. However, in 1957, Abrikosov predicted the existence of a different sort of superconductor, and Figure 9.23 shows direct evidence for the existence of what are now known as type-II superconductors. A comparison of Figures 9.23 and 9.22 indicates that the effect of an applied field on a type-II superconductor is rather different from that for type-I superconductors.

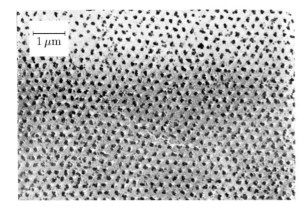

Figure 9.23 Surface of a superconducting alloy that had a magnetic field applied perpendicular to the surface. The dark regions were normal and the light regions superconducting. In this case, small ferromagnetic particles were applied to the surface, and collected where the field strength was largest. The particles remained in position when the specimen warmed up to room temperature, and the surface was then imaged with an electron microscope.

For simplicity, we shall consider first a long cylindrical specimen of type-II material, and apply a field parallel to its axis. Below a certain critical field strength, known as the **lower critical field strength** and denoted by the symbol B_{c1}, the applied magnetic field is excluded from the bulk of the material, penetrating into only a thin layer at the surface, just as for type-I materials. But above B_{c1}, the material does not make a sudden transition to the normal state. Instead, very thin cylindrical regions of normal material appear, passing through the specimen parallel to its axis. We shall refer to such a normal region as a **normal core**. The normal cores are arranged on a triangular lattice, as shown in Figure 9.23, and as the applied field is increased, more normal cores appear and they become more and more closely packed together. Eventually, a second critical field strength, the **upper critical field strength** B_{c2}, is reached, above which the material reverts to the normal state. The state that exists between the lower and upper critical field strengths, in which a type-II superconductor is threaded by normal cores, is known as the **mixed state**. As Figure 9.24 shows, both the upper and lower critical field strengths depend on temperature in a similar way to the critical field strength for a type-I material (Figure 9.11).

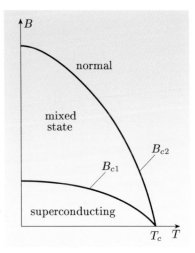

Figure 9.24 Temperature dependence of the lower critical field strength (B_{c1}) and upper critical field strength (B_{c2}) for a type-II superconductor.

The normal cores that exist in type-II superconductors in the mixed state are not sharply delineated. Figure 9.25 shows how the number density of superelectrons and the magnetic field strength vary along a line passing through the axes of three neighbouring cores. The value of n_s is zero at the centres of the cores and rises over a characteristic distance ξ, the coherence length. The magnetic field associated with each normal core is spread over a region with a diameter of 2λ, and each normal core is surrounded by a vortex of circulating current.

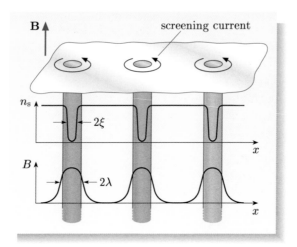

Figure 9.25   Number density of superelectrons n_s and magnetic field strength B around normal cores in a type-II superconductor.

You can see from Figure 9.25 that the coherence length ξ, the characteristic distance for changes in n_s, is shorter than the penetration depth λ, the characteristic distance for changes in the magnetic field in a superconductor. This is generally true for type-II superconductors, whereas for type-I superconductors, $\xi > \lambda$ (Figure 9.20). For a pure type-I superconductor, typical values of the characteristic lengths are $\xi \sim 1\,\mu\mathrm{m}$ and $\lambda = 50\,\mathrm{nm}$. Contrast this with the values for a widely-used type-II alloy of niobium and tin, Nb_3Sn, for which $\xi \sim 3.5\,\mathrm{nm}$ and $\lambda = 80\,\mathrm{nm}$.

The reason that the relative magnitude of the coherence length and the penetration depth is so important is that when $\xi > \lambda$, the surface energy associated with the boundary between superconducting and normal regions is positive, whereas when $\xi < \lambda$, this surface energy is negative. Justifying this statement would involve a discussion of the thermodynamics of superconductors, but for our purposes it is sufficient to just look at the consequences. For a positive surface energy, the system will prefer few boundaries and we expect relatively thick normal and superconducting regions, as observed in the intermediate state in type-I materials. Conversely, a negative surface energy favours formation of as much boundary between normal and superconducting regions as possible, and this is what happens in the mixed state in type-II materials with many narrow normal cores. The lower limit for the diameter of the cores is 2ξ, as shown in Figure 9.25, because ξ is the distance over which n_s can vary.

This energy argument does not explicitly indicate how much magnetic flux passes through each of the normal cores. However, quantum mechanical arguments show that the magnetic flux linking any superconducting loop must be quantized, and that the quantum of magnetic flux is

$$h/2e = 2.07 \times 10^{-15}\,\mathrm{T\,m^2},$$

where $h = 6.63 \times 10^{-34}\,\mathrm{J\,s}$ is Planck's constant. In fact, each of the normal cores shown in Figure 9.23 contains just one quantum of flux, since this is more favorable energetically than having two or more quanta of flux in a core.

The quantization of flux in a superconductor is of particular importance in SQUIDs, the superconducting quantum interference devices that are at the heart of the magnetometers used for measuring the magnetic fields produced by currents in the brain (see Subsection 5.3.3). A SQUID contains a small loop of superconductor with a weakly superconducting link in it, and the quantization of flux in the loop causes its electrical properties to depend on the flux applied to it, with a periodicity equal to the flux quantum. The very small magnitude of the flux quantum is responsible for the sensitivity of the device to very small magnetic fields.

A final point is worth noting about the quantum of flux: the factor of 2 in the denominator of the expression $h/2e$ is a consequence of the coupling of pairs of electrons in a superconductor and their condensation into a superconducting ground state. There is charge $-2e$ associated with each of these electron pairs.

Critical currents in type-II superconductors

The high values of the upper critical field strength B_{c2} of many type-II superconducting alloys make them very attractive for winding coils for generating high magnetic fields. For example, alloys of niobium and titanium ($NbTi_2$) and of niobium and tin (Nb_3Sn) have values of B_{c2} of about $10\,\mathrm{T}$ and $20\,\mathrm{T}$, respectively, compared with $0.08\,\mathrm{T}$ for lead, a type-I superconductor. However, for type-II materials to be usable for this purpose, they must also have high critical currents at high field strengths, and this requires some help from metallurgists to overcome a significant problem.

This problem is related to the interaction between the current flowing through a type-II superconductor in the mixed state and the 'tubes' of magnetic flux that thread through the normal cores. The electrons will experience a Lorentz force, perpendicular to both the current density and the magnetic field. We can regard this as a mutual interaction between the electrons and the flux in the normal cores, as a result of which each normal core experiences a force that is in the opposite direction to the Lorentz force on the electrons. The directions of the magnetic field, current and forces are shown in Figure 9.26.

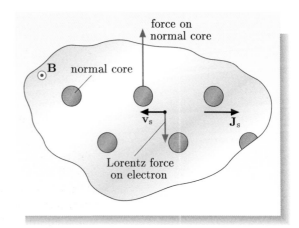

Figure 9.26   Electrons and normal cores experience forces perpendicular to the current and to the magnetic field, but in opposite directions.

This Lorentz force can cause the cores and their associated magnetic flux to move, and the flux motion will induce an emf that drives a current through the normal cores, somewhat like an eddy current. Energy is therefore dissipated in the normal cores, and this energy must come from the power supply. The energy dissipation means that the flow of electrons is impeded, and therefore there is a resistance to the flow of the current.

Flux motion is therefore undesirable in type-II superconductors, and the aim of the metallurgists who develop processes for manufacturing wire for magnets is to make flux motion as difficult as possible. This is done by introducing defects into the crystalline structure, particularly by preparing the material in such a way that it comprises many small crystalline grains with different orientations and small precipitates of different composition. These defects effectively pin the normal cores in position — they provide a potential barrier to motion of the cores, so that the force on the cores must exceed a certain value before the cores can move. The more of these flux pinning centres that are present, and the greater the potential barrier they provide, the greater will be the current required to set them in motion, i.e. the greater the critical current. So, unlike a normal conductor, for which improving the purity and reducing imperfections in the crystal structure lead to better conductivity, with type-II superconductors the inclusion of impurities and defects in the crystal structure can improve the critical current and make the material more suitable for use in electromagnets.

Undoubtedly the largest use of superconducting material for a single project is in the Large Hadron Collider at CERN, due for commissioning in 2007 (see Figure 6 of the Introduction and Figure 6.1a). The 27 km-long accelerator tunnel contains 1232 superconducting magnets that are responsible for steering the particle beams around their circular paths. Each of these magnets is 15 m long, has a mass of 35 tonnes and produces a magnetic field strength of 8.5 T. The coils in each magnet are made from about 6 km of niobium–titanium cable, with a mass of about a tonne, and will be maintained at a temperature of 1.9 K using liquid helium. To construct an accelerator with a similar specification using non-superconducting magnets would have required a 120 km tunnel and phenomenal amounts of power to operate.

Summary of Chapter 9

Section 9.1   Superconductivity was discovered in 1911, and in the century since then there have been many developments in knowledge of the properties of superconductors and the materials that become superconducting, in the theoretical understanding of superconductivity, and in the applications of superconductors.

Section 9.2   A superconductor has zero resistance to flow of electric current, and can sustain a current indefinitely. The magnetic flux remains constant in a completely superconducting circuit, since changes in the flux from the field applied to the circuit are balanced by changes to (persistent) currents induced in the circuit. For each superconductor there is a critical temperature T_c below which the material is superconducting.

Superconductors also exhibit perfect diamagnetism, with $\mathbf{B} = \mathbf{0}$ in the bulk of the material. The exclusion of magnetic field is known as the Meissner effect. An external magnetic field penetrates for a short distance into the surface of a superconducting material, and a current flows in the surface layer to screen the interior of the material from the applied field. Superconductivity is destroyed when the magnetic field strength exceeds a critical value for the material. The critical field strength falls to zero as the temperature is raised to the critical temperature. A superconducting specimen will have a critical current I_c above which the material reverts to the normal state. This critical current corresponds to the field strength exceeding the critical field strength in some region of the specimen.

Section 9.3   The two-fluid model of a superconductor regards some of the conduction electrons as behaving like normal electrons and some like superconducting electrons. For $T \ll T_c$, all of the conduction electrons are superconducting electrons, but the proportion of superconducting electrons drops to zero at the critical temperature.

For a perfect conductor (which has $R = 0$), Maxwell's equations predict that the magnetic field cannot change, except in a thin surface layer. This does not predict the Meissner effect. The London equations are relationships between current density and magnetic field that are consistent with the Meissner effect:

$$\mathrm{curl}\,\mathbf{J}_s = -\frac{n_s e^2}{m}\mathbf{B} \quad \text{and} \quad \frac{\partial \mathbf{J}_s}{\partial t} = \frac{n_s e^2}{m}\mathbf{E}.$$

When combined with Maxwell's equations, they lead to the prediction that the magnetic field strength and the surface current decrease exponentially below the surface of a superconductor, over a characteristic distance called the penetration depth λ, which is typically tens of nanometres. The London equations are local relationships and therefore are strictly valid only when $\lambda \gg \xi$, where the coherence length ξ is the characteristic distance over which n_s varies.

Section 9.4   There are two types of superconductors, type-I and type-II. For a type-I material in the form of a thin specimen parallel to the field, there is an abrupt transition to the normal state at the critical field strength B_c. When the field is inclined to the surface of a type-I material, the material exists in the intermediate state over a range of field strengths below B_c. In this state there are thin layers of normal and superconducting material, with the proportion of normal material rising to unity at field strength B_c. In type-I materials, the coherence length ξ is greater than the penetration depth λ, and the surface energy of the boundary between superconducting and normal material is positive, which favours a course subdivision into regions of normal and superconducting material.

A type-II superconductor has two critical field strengths, B_{c1} and B_{c2}, between which the material is in the mixed state. In this state the superconductor is threaded by thin cores of normal material, through which the magnetic field passes. The coherence length ξ is shorter than the penetration depth λ, and the surface energy of the boundary between superconducting and normal material is negative, which favours a fine subdivision into regions of normal and superconducting material. To take advantage of the high values of B_{c2} to produce high magnetic fields with superconducting magnets, it is essential to pin the normal cores to inhibit their motion.

Achievements from Chapter 9

After studying this chapter you should be able to do the following.

9.1   Explain the meanings of the newly defined (emboldened) terms and symbols, and use them appropriately.

9.2   Distinguish between perfect conduction and perfect diamagnetism, and give a qualitative description of the Meissner effect.

9.3 Explain how observation of a persistent current can be used to estimate an upper limit on the resistivity of a superconductor, and perform calculations related to such estimates.

9.4 Explain why the magnetic flux through a superconducting circuit remains constant, and describe applications of this effect.

9.5 Show how the London equations and Maxwell's equations lead to the prediction of the Meissner effect.

9.6 Compare and contrast the properties of type-I and type-II superconductors, particularly their response to magnetic fields.

9.7 Define the critical current, and explain how it is related to the critical field strength.

9.8 Define the penetration depth and the coherence length of superconductors, and relate them to properties of superconductivity.

9.9 Describe some of the applications of superconductivity.

Chapter 10   Special relativity and electromagnetism

At the start of the twentieth century, electromagnetism was a remarkably successful theory. In particular, Maxwell's equations predicted electromagnetic waves, explaining at one stroke the entire electromagnetic spectrum. Moreover, the measured values of ε_0 and μ_0 gave a predicted value of the speed of light, which was confirmed by experiments on electromagnetic waves. However, there were clear signals of some deep-seated problems.

A major concern was that all experiments seemed to confirm a constant speed of light (in a vacuum), irrespective of the motion of the observer or the source. This was not what most physicists of the time expected. By analogy with familiar wave phenomena, such as sound waves in air, many expected that electromagnetic waves would move at constant velocity relative to a medium that carried them. This hypothetical medium was called the *ether*, and it had to encompass the Sun and the stars in order to account for their visibility from the Earth. It seemed likely that the daily rotation of the Earth, and its annual motion around the Sun, would cause terrestrial observers to move relative to the ether, with the expected consequence that laboratory-based measurements of the speed of light would depend on the direction in which the light was travelling, and even on the time of year at which the measurements were made. However, no such effects were observed, nor have they ever been.

Of course, it was conceivable that some nearby part of the ether might be carried along by the Earth, eliminating the effects of the Earth's motion in laboratory-based experiments, but if this were so, it might equally be expected that astronomical measurements would reveal the effects of the relative motion of different parts of the ether. And even if the whole idea of an ether was wrong, one might expect the speed of light to depend on the relative motion of source and observer, yet no such effect was ever observed, nor has it been to this day. The speed of light in a vacuum, c, seems to be a constant of nature, despite any expectations to the contrary.

Another potential sign of trouble ahead concerned situations where the observed phenomena were known to depend on the *relative* motion of two bodies, yet the conventional explanation of those phenomena depended on whether or not one of those bodies could be described as being truly at rest. The prime example of this is electromagnetic induction of a current in a loop of wire (Section 7.2.1). When a magnet is moved near a stationary wire loop, the changing magnetic field is seen as creating an electric field that accounts for the current in the wire. On the other hand, when the wire is treated as moving while the magnet remains stationary, with the *relative* motion of wire and magnet exactly as it was before, there is no electric field in the wire and an induced emf due to the magnetic force on the moving electrons is responsible for the induced current. This lack of symmetry between the clearly related electromagnetic phenomena and their conventional electromagnetic explanation was certainly perplexing and, to some at least, deeply worrying.

In 1905, Albert Einstein dealt with these concerns in his paper *On the Electrodynamics of Moving Bodies*. This was the paper that introduced his celebrated theory of special relativity, which showed that there was nothing inconsistent about electromagnetism; the 'problems', such as they were, lay in assumptions that were being made about space and time. The reliability of Maxwell's equations, as interpreted by Einstein, provided the basis for a revolution in our understanding of physics.

Our aim in this chapter is to show that what you already know about electromagnetism is consistent with special relativity and to examine some of the consequences of that consistency. We start by reviewing some of the basic ideas of special relativity, and then show how, in a range of situations, the state of motion of an observer relative to an arrangement of charges and currents will influence the observed values of the charge densities and currents, and the fields they produce. We then move on to the central result of this chapter, which is that even though fields, currents and charge densities can all change under the transformations of special relativity, the form of the fundamental equations (Maxwell's equations, the equation of continuity and the Lorentz force law) remains the same.

10.1 Review of special relativity

Relativity concerns the relationships that must exist between the observations made by two or more observers in specified states of relative motion. There is no room for a complete discussion of relativity; rather, I shall assume that you already have some familiarity with the subject, and shall limit this review to those points that will be needed later when we consider charges, currents, fields, the Maxwell equations and the Lorentz force law.

10.1.1 Essentials of special relativity

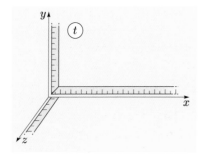

Figure 10.1   A frame of reference can be represented by a system of measuring rods and synchronized clocks that are used to assign coordinates to events.

Relativity is concerned with events. An **event** is an occurrence that takes place at a particular instant in time (typically represented by the symbol t) and at a particular point in space (typically represented by its Cartesian coordinates (x, y, z). The four quantities (t, x, y, z) that specify an event are referred to as the **coordinates** of the event. Any properly specified system for assigning time and space coordinates to an event is known as a **frame of reference** (see Figure 10.1).

Events exist irrespective of frames of reference, but it is only by using a frame of reference that an observer is able to assign coordinates to an event. In fact, it is best to think of an **observer** as an individual who is dedicated to using a particular frame of reference to describe the events that he or she observes. It is important to note that the precise location of an observer is of no significance when it comes to determining the coordinates of an event. Those coordinates will certainly depend on the observer's frame of reference, but not on the observer's location within that frame. This highlights the distinction between 'seeing' and 'observing'. What an observer 'sees' depends on when light signals from events arrive at the observer's location. What is 'observed' depends only on the events themselves and the frame of reference being used to specify them; the time assigned to an event may be thought of as that shown on an appropriately synchronized clock at the location of the event.

Special relativity is restricted to a particular class of frames of reference, known as **inertial frames**, and these are frames in which Newton's first law holds true.

Frames of reference can be in relative motion, which may be translational, rotational, or a combination of both, and the speed of the relative motion can be either uniform or non-uniform. However, any frame that moves with constant translational velocity relative to an inertial frame is also an inertial frame. The primary concern of **special relativity** is the observations made by two observers in different inertial frames, where one frame moves with constant speed in a fixed direction relative to another.

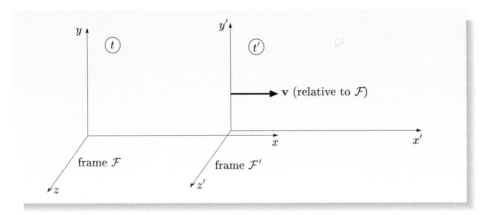

Figure 10.2   Two inertial frames in standard configuration.

In general, two inertial frames $\mathcal{F}$ and $\mathcal{F}'$ may have any relative orientation and their constant relative velocity may be in any (fixed) direction. However, as is usual in introductory discussions of special relativity, we shall restrict our attention to the situation shown in Figure 10.2 in which the corresponding axes are parallel, and the origin of $\mathcal{F}'$ moves with constant velocity $\mathbf{v} = (v, 0, 0)$ along the x-axis of frame $\mathcal{F}$. When these requirements are satisfied and, in addition, the clocks are started in such a way that the unique event defined by the coincidence of the origins of $\mathcal{F}$ and $\mathcal{F}'$ happens at time $t = 0$ in $\mathcal{F}$ and at time $t' = 0$ in $\mathcal{F}'$, the two frames are said to be in **standard configuration**. Throughout the rest of this chapter, whenever we refer to the frames $\mathcal{F}$ and $\mathcal{F}'$ you may assume that they are inertial frames in standard configuration. Restricting our discussions to frames that are in standard configuration does not imply any real limitation within special relativity; it is always possible to rotate and/or translate one of the frames if necessary, but we shall not need to do so in this chapter.

Note that the velocity component v may be positive or negative, so it would *not* be correct to describe it as the speed of $\mathcal{F}'$ as measured in $\mathcal{F}$. Also note that v is measured in frame $\mathcal{F}$, so it does not carry a prime ($'$). For convenience, we shall often refer to this single non-zero velocity component as the velocity of $\mathcal{F}'$ with respect to $\mathcal{F}$.

Now that we have dealt with matters of language and terminology, we can turn to the core of special relativity, the relationship between observations made by observers who use different inertial frames. We start with the most basic of issues — the coordinates of an event. The central question that we need to consider is as follows. If an observer in $\mathcal{F}$ assigns the coordinates (t, x, y, z) to some particular event, and an observer in $\mathcal{F}'$ assigns the coordinates (t', x', y', z') to the same event, what will be the relationship between these two sets of coordinates?

It was part of Einstein's genius to realize that the answer to this question should be based on testable scientific principles rather than traditional but untested assumptions about the nature of space and time. In his 1905 paper, Einstein based his answer to the question on two postulates, the *principle of relativity* and the *invariance of the speed of light in a vacuum*.

The **principle of relativity** asserts that no experiment can distinguish one inertial frame of reference from any other identically calibrated inertial frame or, equivalently, that the laws of physics can be written in the same form in all inertial frames. By combining this principle with the experimentally supported assertion that the speed of light in a vacuum is the same in all inertial frames, Einstein deduced the following relationships between the coordinates assigned to the same event by observers in frames $\mathcal{F}$ and $\mathcal{F}'$:

$$t' = \gamma \left(t - \frac{v}{c^2}x \right), \tag{10.1}$$

$$x' = \gamma \left(x - vt \right), \tag{10.2}$$

$$y' = y, \tag{10.3}$$

$$z' = z, \tag{10.4}$$

where

Note that $\sqrt{1 - v^2/c^2}$ should be interpreted as $\sqrt{1 - (v^2/c^2)}$, and *not* as $\sqrt{(1 - v^2)/c^2}$.

$$\gamma = \frac{1}{\sqrt{1 - v^2/c^2}}. \tag{10.5}$$

The observers clearly agree on the values of the y- and z-coordinates, but their values of the x- and t-coordinates may be quite different. The quantity γ appears very frequently in special relativity, and its dependence on the speed v is shown in Figure 10.3.

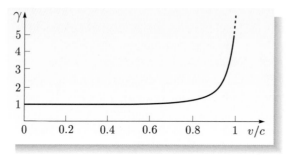

Figure 10.3   A plot of γ against v/c.

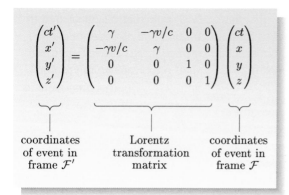

coordinates of event in frame $\mathcal{F}'$ Lorentz transformation matrix   coordinates of event in frame $\mathcal{F}$

Figure 10.4   The Lorentz transformation in matrix form. Matrix multiplication involves multiplying entries in a row of the first matrix by corresponding entries in a column of the second matrix, and adding the results. The first row gives $ct' = \gamma ct + (-\gamma v/c)x + 0 + 0$, which is equivalent to Equation 10.1.

Equations 10.1 to 10.4 are collectively known as the **Lorentz transformation**, and are a particular example of what is generally known as a *coordinate transformation*. They enable us to write the description of an event in the $\mathcal{F}'$ frame in terms of the variables of the $\mathcal{F}$ frame, and thus provide a means of expressing results obtained by one observer in terms that can be understood by another observer. (Remember, each observer is dedicated to using the coordinates of his or her own frame of reference.)

The Lorentz transformation can also be written rather elegantly using matrix notation, as shown in Figure 10.4. Here the coordinates of an event are represented by a vector with four components, (ct, x, y, z), and the Lorentz transformation operation is described by a 4×4 matrix. Note that by using ct rather than t to represent the time coordinate, we ensure that all four components have the unit of length, and we end up with a symmetric transformation matrix. A vector like (ct, x, y, z) that transforms between reference frames in the way represented in Figure 10.4 is known as a **4-vector**.

From Figure 10.2, you can see that frame $\mathcal{F}$ is travelling at velocity $\mathbf{v}' = (-v, 0, 0)$ relative to frame $\mathcal{F}'$, and this means that equations expressing the non-primed coordinates in terms of primed ones are easily obtained by replacing v with $-v$ and interchanging primed and non-primed variables. The resulting coordinate transformation is

$$t = \gamma \left(t' + \frac{v}{c^2} x' \right), \qquad (10.6)$$

$$x = \gamma \left(x' + vt' \right), \qquad (10.7)$$

$$y = y', \qquad (10.8)$$

$$z = z'. \qquad (10.9)$$

Equations 10.6 to 10.9 are sometimes known as the **inverse Lorentz transformation**; this will be of great use later. The matrix form of the inverse Lorentz transformation is shown in Figure 10.5.

$$
\begin{pmatrix} ct \\ x \\ y \\ z \end{pmatrix} = \begin{pmatrix} \gamma & \gamma v/c & 0 & 0 \\ \gamma v/c & \gamma & 0 & 0 \\ 0 & 0 & 1 & 0 \\ 0 & 0 & 0 & 1 \end{pmatrix} \begin{pmatrix} ct' \\ x' \\ y' \\ z' \end{pmatrix}
$$

coordinates of event in frame $\mathcal{F}$ — inverse Lorentz transformation matrix — coordinates of event in frame $\mathcal{F}'$

Figure 10.5 The inverse Lorentz transformation of coordinates in matrix form.

Exercise 10.1 Without using any physical argument, solve Equations 10.1 and 10.2 for t and x (i.e. express t and x in terms of t' and x'). ■

Lorentz transformations are central to the theory of special relativity and have important consequences, some of which are presented below.

10.1.2 The relativity of simultaneity and the order of events

Consider two inertial frames $\mathcal{F}$ and $\mathcal{F}'$ in standard configuration. Suppose that two events are observed to occur on the x'-axis of $\mathcal{F}'$ at the same time t' but at different positions (x_1' and x_2'). From Equation 10.6 we have

$$t_2 = \gamma \left(t' + \frac{v}{c^2} x_2' \right),$$

$$t_1 = \gamma \left(t' + \frac{v}{c^2} x_1' \right).$$

Subtracting these two equations gives

$$t_2 - t_1 = \gamma \frac{v}{c^2} (x_2' - x_1'),$$

which shows that $t_2 \neq t_1$.

According to special relativity, two events that occur simultaneously but at different positions in frame $\mathcal{F}'$ do not necessarily occur simultaneously in frame $\mathcal{F}$. In other words, two events that are simultaneous according to one inertial observer are not necessarily simultaneous according to another. An immediate, if somewhat disturbing, consequence of this is that a statement such as 'these two event are simultaneous' has no absolute (i.e. observer-independent) meaning. The statement that two events are simultaneous becomes meaningful only when it is related to some specified observer or class of observers, just as it is meaningful to say that a spacecraft is moving at some particular speed only when you know the frame of reference in which the speed is being measured. Simultaneity is a 'relative' condition, just as speed is a 'relative' quantity.

The disturbing consequences of special relativity do not stop with simultaneity. Even the order of events can depend on the frame in which they are observed. It is easy to find pairs of events that occur in one order in frame $\mathcal{F}'$ and in the opposite order in frame $\mathcal{F}$. This is not as alarming as it might sound; the notion that two completely independent events, such as two stellar explosions in different parts of the galaxy, might be observed in reverse order by one observer compared with another is hardly disturbing at all. However, it would be disturbing if one of those events might have *caused* the other; if one had been, say, the blowing up of some dynamite, and the other had been the lighting of the fuse that *caused* the dynamite to explode. In cases where one event caused, or even might have caused, the other, physicists feel that there should be some way of ensuring that all inertial observers agree about the order of the events concerned.

Fortunately, there is a way of ensuring that such causal relationships are preserved. If it is assumed that the speed of light represents the maximum speed at which material bodies can travel and at which information can be transmitted relative to an inertial observer, then it can be shown that the order of any two events that might be causally related will be the same for any other observer travelling at or below the speed of light relative to the first observer. Although there is much in the mathematics of special relativity that suggests the role of the speed of light in a vacuum as a limiting speed, it is the desire to preserve causality (the requirement that causes happen before their effects) that really leads to the special relativistic prohibition on faster-than-light travel.

10.1.3   Length contraction

Consider two inertial frames $\mathcal{F}$ and $\mathcal{F}'$ in standard configuration. Suppose that a rod is at rest along the x'-axis of $\mathcal{F}'$ and that the length of the rod, as measured in $\mathcal{F}'$, is l_0 (Figure 10.6).

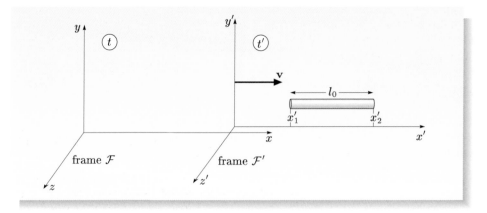

Figure 10.6   The phenomenon of length contraction.

Observed from frame $\mathcal{F}$, the rod will be moving along the x-axis with velocity $\mathbf{v}$, and the Lorentz transformation can be used to show that its length l as measured in $\mathcal{F}$ at any particular time t in that frame is given by

$$l = l_0\sqrt{1 - v^2/c^2}. \tag{10.10}$$

The length l of the moving rod is smaller than the length l_0 measured in the frame $\mathcal{F}'$ in which the rod is stationary. This phenomenon is known as **length contraction**.

Exercise 10.2 (a) Use Equation 10.2 to derive Equation 10.10.

(b) Comment on what difficulties you would encounter if instead you started from Equation 10.7. ∎

10.1.4 Time dilation

Now suppose that a clock is at rest in frame $\mathcal{F}'$ and that τ_0 is the interval between two successive ticks of the clock as measured in that frame. The inverse Lorentz transformation can be used to show that the interval τ between ticks as measured in frame $\mathcal{F}$ is given by

$$\tau = \frac{\tau_0}{\sqrt{1 - v^2/c^2}}. \tag{10.11}$$

Consequently, $\tau \geq \tau_0$, so the moving clock is observed to run slow; this phenomenon is known as **time dilation**. It means that if $v/c = 0.87$, so that $\gamma = 1/\sqrt{1 - v^2/c^2} = 2$, then the observer in frame $\mathcal{F}$ will measure a 2-second interval between ticks that are separated by only 1 second according to the observer in frame $\mathcal{F}'$. After 2 minutes have elapsed in $\mathcal{F}$, only 1 minute will have elapsed in $\mathcal{F}'$. According to the observer in $\mathcal{F}$, the moving clock in $\mathcal{F}'$ is running slow (by a factor of two).

Exercise 10.3 Use Equation 10.6 to derive Equation 10.11. ∎

10.1.5 Velocity transformation

Consider two inertial frames $\mathcal{F}$ and $\mathcal{F}'$ in standard configuration, with $\mathcal{F}'$ moving at velocity $\mathbf{v}$ in the positive x-direction with respect to $\mathcal{F}$, as in Figure 10.7. Suppose that a particle moves at a constant velocity $\mathbf{U}$ in frame $\mathcal{F}$, with components (U_x, U_y, U_z). Since both frames are inertial, the particle must also move at constant velocity in frame $\mathcal{F}'$, and it is convenient to label the velocity components in this frame by (U_x', U_y', U_z').

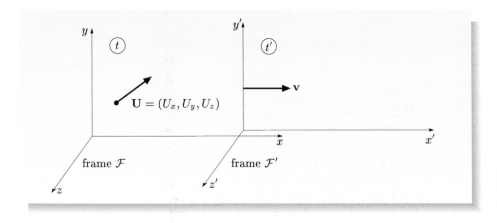

Figure 10.7 A particle travels at velocity $\mathbf{U}$ in frame $\mathcal{F}$. What is its velocity according to an observer in frame $\mathcal{F}'$?

It is worth emphasizing that velocity in the context of special relativity is defined in the same way as in Newtonian mechanics, so that the components are $(U_x, U_y, U_z) = (\mathrm{d}x/\mathrm{d}t, \mathrm{d}y/\mathrm{d}t, \mathrm{d}z/\mathrm{d}t)$ in frame $\mathcal{F}$ and

$(U'_x, U'_y, U'_z) = (\mathrm{d}x'/\mathrm{d}t', \mathrm{d}y'/\mathrm{d}t', \mathrm{d}z'/\mathrm{d}t')$ in frame $\mathcal{F}'$. With these definitions in mind, it is possible, using the Lorentz transformation, to show that the velocity of the particle as observed in frame $\mathcal{F}'$ is given by

$$U'_x = \frac{U_x - v}{1 - U_x v/c^2}, \tag{10.12}$$

$$U'_y = \frac{1}{\gamma}\frac{U_y}{1 - U_x v/c^2}, \tag{10.13}$$

$$U'_z = \frac{1}{\gamma}\frac{U_z}{1 - U_x v/c^2}. \tag{10.14}$$

Notice that the y- and z-components are different in $\mathcal{F}$ and $\mathcal{F}'$, even though the relative motion of the frames is in the x-direction.

The velocity transformation equations can be used to show that if a particle is observed to move at speed c in any direction in inertial frame $\mathcal{F}$, then it must move at speed c in any other inertial frame $\mathcal{F}'$. Let us assume that the particle's speed in frame $\mathcal{F}'$ is U'. Then

$$\left(U'\right)^2 = \left(U'_x\right)^2 + \left(U'_y\right)^2 + \left(U'_z\right)^2.$$

Squaring and adding Equations 10.12 to 10.14, we obtain

$$\left(U'\right)^2 = \frac{1}{(1 - U_x v/c^2)^2}\left[(U_x - v)^2 + \frac{1}{\gamma^2}\left(U_y^2 + U_z^2\right)\right].$$

Since the particle travels at speed c in frame $\mathcal{F}$, $U_y^2 + U_z^2 = c^2 - U_x^2$, so

$$\begin{aligned}
\left(U'\right)^2 &= \frac{1}{(1 - U_x v/c^2)^2}\left[(U_x - v)^2 + \left(1 - \frac{v^2}{c^2}\right)\left(c^2 - U_x^2\right)\right] \\
&= \frac{1}{(1 - U_x v/c^2)^2}\left[U_x^2 - 2U_x v + v^2 + c^2 - U_x^2 - v^2 + \frac{v^2 U_x^2}{c^2}\right] \\
&= \frac{c^2}{(1 - U_x v/c^2)^2}\left[1 - \frac{2U_x v}{c^2} + \frac{U_x^2 v^2}{c^4}\right] \\
&= c^2.
\end{aligned}$$

This shows that if a particle travels at speed c in one inertial frame, it will be observed to travel at the same speed in all inertial frames. Since this is an essential feature of the principle of relativity, it would have been alarming if we had not obtained this result.

10.1.6   Force transformation

Within the context of special relativity, the momentum of a particle of (rest) mass m, moving with velocity $\mathbf{U}$, is defined to be

$$\mathbf{p} = \frac{m\mathbf{U}}{\sqrt{1 - U^2/c^2}}, \tag{10.15}$$

and the force $\mathbf{F}$ on the particle is determined by the rate of change of the particle's momentum,

$$\mathbf{F} = \frac{\mathrm{d}\mathbf{p}}{\mathrm{d}t}. \tag{10.16}$$

It is useful to be able to express the components of a force observed in one inertial frame in terms of the components in another inertial frame. Once again we consider the inertial frames $\mathcal{F}$ and $\mathcal{F}'$ in standard configuration, with $\mathcal{F}'$ moving with velocity $\mathbf{v}$ in the positive x-direction with respect to $\mathcal{F}$, as in Figure 10.8.

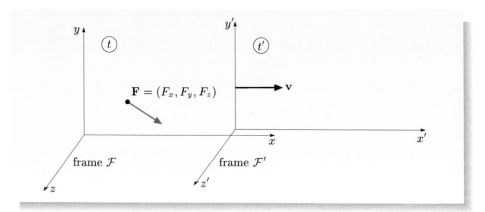

Figure 10.8 In frame $\mathcal{F}$, an observer measures a force $\mathbf{F}$ acting on a particle. What force would be measured by an observer in frame $\mathcal{F}'$?

The general result is rather complicated, so we restrict ourselves to a special case. If a particle at rest in frame $\mathcal{F}$ is subject to a force $\mathbf{F}$, then it can be shown that the components of the force in frame $\mathcal{F}'$ are related to those in $\mathcal{F}$ by

$$F'_x = F_x, \tag{10.17}$$
$$F'_y = \gamma F_y, \tag{10.18}$$
$$F'_z = \gamma F_z. \tag{10.19}$$

Notice that the x-component of the force does not change, even though the relative motion of the frames is in the x-direction.

10.2 Transforming electromagnetic quantities

In the last section we saw the central importance to special relativity of the rules for transforming the coordinates (t, x, y, z), and the consequences of these rules for transformations of velocities and forces. In this section we consider the transformation of electromagnetic quantities, such as charge, charge density and current density, and both electric and magnetic fields. An important outcome will be the recognition that, from a relativistic point of view, electric and magnetic fields are really just different aspects of a combined electromagnetic field.

10.2.1 The invariance of electric charge

It is known from many experiments that charge comes in integral multiples of e, where e is the charge on a proton and $-e$ is the charge on an electron. (The charges of quarks come in integral multiples of $e/3$, but quarks cannot exist as isolated particles except in very extreme conditions, such as those that existed in the very early Universe.) Measuring charge is essentially a counting process.

In fact, it is known to very high precision that the charge on an object does not depend on the motion of that object, and hence that the charge is independent of the frame in which it is measured. For example, experiments involving hydrogen atoms show that the charges on the proton and on the electron remain accurately equal in magnitude despite the supposed relative motion of the atom's constituents.

The fact that a charge has the same value according to all inertial observers is described by saying that electric charge is invariant under changes of inertial frame of reference. An **invariant** quantity has the same value in all inertial frames. Different inertial observers may not agree about where a charged particle is located, or about its velocity, but they will all agree about its charge.

It is important to be clear about the distinction between *invariance* (the property of being invariant under changes in the observer's frame of reference) and *conservation* (the property of being unchanged over time). For example, the momentum of an isolated system, such as a single particle, is conserved in any inertial frame, but the momentum is certainly not invariant under changes in the inertial frame.

10.2.2   Charge- and current-density transformation

Charge is invariant under changes of the observer's inertial frame of reference. However, neither the charge density ρ nor the current density $\mathbf{J}$ in a region of space are invariant.

The fact that charge density depends on the frame in which it is measured should not come as a surprise. Charge is invariant, but length is not (remember the discussion of length contraction in Subsection 10.1.3). You should therefore expect charge density to be frame dependent. As for current density, the frame dependence is even more obvious. If you imagine a uniform cylindrical cloud of charged particles at rest along the x'-axis in frame $\mathcal{F}'$, as shown in Figure 10.9, then that cylinder of charge will be moving as observed in frame $\mathcal{F}$. In frame $\mathcal{F}'$, there is a distribution of static charge, but the current density is zero. In frame $\mathcal{F}$, there are no static charges, but there is a non-zero current density. Thus current density must be a frame-dependent quantity.

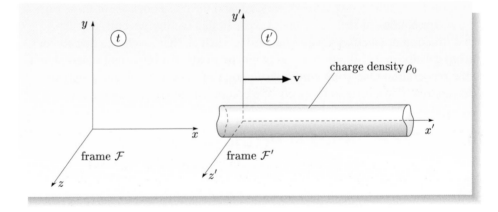

Figure 10.9   A uniform cylinder of charge at rest along the x'-axis of frame $\mathcal{F}'$. Measured in frame $\mathcal{F}'$, the charge density is ρ_0. What are the properties of such a distribution measured from frame $\mathcal{F}$?

Rather than concern ourselves with the general rules for transforming charge and current densities at this stage, let us first consider the special case shown in Figure 10.9. The uniform cylinder of charge is at rest in frame $\mathcal{F}'$, and has charge density ρ_0 in that frame. What are the corresponding charge and current densities as measured in frame $\mathcal{F}$?

The change of frame has no effect on the transverse dimensions of the cylinder, but there is a length contraction along the direction of the x-axis. Consequently, the charge will be more concentrated in frame $\mathcal{F}$. In this particular case the observed charge density in frame $\mathcal{F}$ is

$$\rho = \frac{\rho_0}{\sqrt{1 - v^2/c^2}} = \gamma \rho_0, \tag{10.20}$$

where v is the speed of frame $\mathcal{F}'$ as measured in frame $\mathcal{F}$.

Regarding the current density, imagine a small element of area δA, perpendicular to the x-axis at some fixed point on that axis. The charge δq carried through that area by the motion of $\mathcal{F}'$ in time δt measured in $\mathcal{F}$ will be the charge density in $\mathcal{F}$ (i.e. $\gamma \rho_0$) multiplied by the volume of charge carried through δA (i.e. $v\,\delta t\,\delta A$),

$$\delta q = \gamma \rho_0 v\,\delta t\,\delta A.$$

It follows that the current density J_x along the x-axis due to the cylinder, measured in $\mathcal{F}$, will be

$$J_x = \frac{\delta q}{\delta A\,\delta t} = \gamma \rho_0 v. \tag{10.21}$$

This shows quite explicitly that special relativity naturally links situations in which there is only a static charge density with those in which there is both a charge density and a current density.

Now consider a different situation, shown in Figure 10.10, in which there is a charge density ρ and a current density $\mathbf{J} = (J_x, J_y, J_z)$ in frame $\mathcal{F}$ and we want to know the observed charge and current densities in frame $\mathcal{F}'$. Note that in this case we are *not* assuming that the charge and current densities in frame $\mathcal{F}$ are due to a static distribution in frame $\mathcal{F}'$.

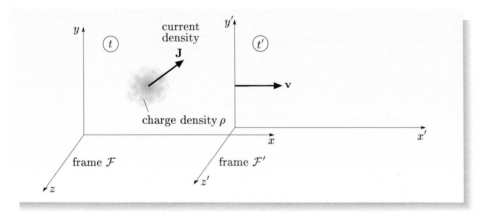

Figure 10.10   Two frames in standard configuration with a charge density ρ and a current density $\mathbf{J}$ at some point in $\mathcal{F}$. What are the corresponding densities ρ' and $\mathbf{J}'$ observed in $\mathcal{F}'$?

It actually requires much algebra to work out the transformation rule for the charge and current densities in Figure 10.10. The problem can be solved by treating the current density as being due to a uniform cylinder of charged particles, all of which move with a common velocity $\mathbf{U}$ in frame $\mathcal{F}$. It is then possible to use the Lorentz transformation for coordinates together with the velocity transformation introduced in Subsection 10.1.5 to deduce the values of the charge and current densities in frame $\mathcal{F}'$. The final result is not obvious, but it is plausible, so we shall simply quote it rather than working through the detail. The charge and current densities transform in just the same way as the time and space coordinates considered in Subsection 10.1.1. In particular:

$$\rho' = \gamma \left(\rho - \frac{v}{c^2} J_x \right), \tag{10.22}$$

$$J_x' = \gamma \left(J_x - v\rho \right), \tag{10.23}$$

$$J_y' = J_y, \tag{10.24}$$

$$J_z' = J_z. \tag{10.25}$$

If you replaced ρ by t and J_x, J_y and J_z by x, y and z in these equations, with similar changes for the primed coordinates, then you would end up with Equations 10.1–10.4.

We can represent this transformation using the matrix notation introduced in Figure 10.4. We express the charge density as $c\rho$, rather than ρ, so that it has the unit of current density, and we combine it with the components of the current density to produce a vector with four components, $(c\rho, J_x, J_y, J_z)$. The transformation rules for charge density and current density then take the form shown in Figure 10.11. Since the vector $(c\rho, J_x, J_y, J_z)$ transforms between different inertial frames of reference according to the Lorentz transformation, it is a 4-vector, and is usually referred to as the current density 4-vector.

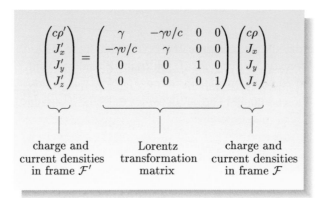

Figure 10.11 The transformation of the charge density and current density expressed in matrix form. Compare this with Figure 10.4.

Exercise 10.4   A high-energy particle is travelling at a speed of $0.95c$ relative to a cloud of charge, which has uniform charge density $\rho = 2.0 \times 10^{-12}\,\mathrm{C\,m^{-3}}$, measured in the frame in which it is stationary. What are the charge and current densities according to an observer in the frame travelling with the particle? ∎

10.2.3   Electric and magnetic field transformation

You have seen that a static charge density distribution in one inertial frame can be transformed into distributions of charge density and current density in another frame. Now, static charges create an electric field but not a magnetic field, whereas distributions of charge and current produce both an electric field and a magnetic field. If we forget about the charges and just concentrate on the observed fields, this result shows that in situations where one inertial observer detects only an electric field, another inertial observer may detect both electric *and* magnetic fields.

This is indicative of a more general result that is our concern in this section, namely that electric and magnetic fields become interwoven under changes of inertial frame, just as space and time are interwoven by the Lorentz transformation. However, the transformation of electric and magnetic fields is more complicated than that of time and space coordinates, or that of charge and current densities.

We shall not attempt any detailed derivations here. Suffice it to say that if we consider the fields produced by simple distributions of charge and current in a particular frame, then we can use the Lorentz and velocity transformations to determine the charge and current distributions that are observed in other inertial frames. It is possible to show that if frames $\mathcal{F}$ and $\mathcal{F}'$ are in standard configuration, and the electric and magnetic fields measured at some point in $\mathcal{F}$ are $\mathbf{E} = (E_x, E_y, E_z)$ and $\mathbf{B} = (B_x, B_y, B_z)$, then the fields measured at that point by an observer in frame $\mathcal{F}'$ will be

$$E'_x = E_x, \tag{10.26}$$

$$E'_y = \gamma(E_y - vB_z), \tag{10.27}$$

$$E'_z = \gamma(E_z + vB_y), \tag{10.28}$$

$$B'_x = B_x, \tag{10.29}$$

$$B'_y = \gamma\left(B_y + \frac{v}{c^2}E_z\right), \tag{10.30}$$

$$B'_z = \gamma\left(B_z - \frac{v}{c^2}E_y\right). \tag{10.31}$$

Note that in the case of $\mathbf{E}$ and $\mathbf{B}$ fields, it is the components parallel to the x-axis that are unchanged by the transformation from one frame to another. This is sometimes emphasized by presenting the field transformation in a way that stresses the different roles of field components that are parallel or perpendicular to the velocity of one frame relative to the other. To be specific, suppose that an inertial frame $\mathcal{F}'$ moves with velocity $\mathbf{v}$ as measured in an inertial frame $\mathcal{F}$, and that in $\mathcal{F}$ the electric and magnetic field components in the direction parallel to $\mathbf{v}$ are denoted by $\mathbf{E}_\parallel$ and $\mathbf{B}_\parallel$, while the components in the direction perpendicular to $\mathbf{v}$ are denoted by $\mathbf{E}_\perp$ and $\mathbf{B}_\perp$. According to an observer in frame $\mathcal{F}'$, the corresponding vector components of the transformed fields $\mathbf{E}'$ and $\mathbf{B}'$ at any particular point will be given by

$$\mathbf{E}'_\parallel = \mathbf{E}_\parallel, \tag{10.32}$$

$$\mathbf{B}'_\parallel = \mathbf{B}_\parallel, \tag{10.33}$$

$$\mathbf{E}'_\perp = \gamma(\mathbf{E}_\perp + \mathbf{v} \times \mathbf{B}_\perp), \tag{10.34}$$

$$\mathbf{B}'_\perp = \gamma\left(\mathbf{B}_\perp - \frac{\mathbf{v} \times \mathbf{E}_\perp}{c^2}\right). \tag{10.35}$$

Whichever form of the field transformation equations you choose to use, they carry an important message.

The splitting of an electromagnetic field into electric and magnetic field components is a frame-dependent activity with no absolute significance. Fundamentally, electric and magnetic fields have no independent existence; the electromagnetic field is really a single combined entity.

Essential skill

Using the field transformation equations

Worked Example 10.1

Frames $\mathcal{F}$ and $\mathcal{F}'$ are in standard configuration with $\mathcal{F}'$ travelling at velocity $\mathbf{v} = (v, 0, 0)$ relative to $\mathcal{F}$. Show that in a region where there is no magnetic field according to an observer in frame $\mathcal{F}'$, an observer in frame $\mathcal{F}$ will detect a magnetic field

$$\mathbf{B} = \frac{\mathbf{v} \times \mathbf{E}}{c^2}.$$

Solution

If $\mathbf{B}' = \mathbf{0}$ in some region of $\mathcal{F}'$, it follows from Equations 10.33 and 10.35 that an observer in frame $\mathcal{F}$ will find

$$\mathbf{B}_{\parallel} = \mathbf{0}$$

and

$$\mathbf{B}_{\perp} = \frac{\mathbf{v} \times \mathbf{E}_{\perp}}{c^2}.$$

Since $\mathbf{B}_{\parallel} = \mathbf{0}$, it follows that the resultant magnetic field detected in the relevant region by an observer in frame $\mathcal{F}$ will be

$$\mathbf{B} = \mathbf{B}_{\parallel} + \mathbf{B}_{\perp} = \frac{\mathbf{v} \times \mathbf{E}_{\perp}}{c^2}.$$

However, since the vector product of two parallel vectors (such as $\mathbf{v}$ and $\mathbf{E}_{\parallel}$) is always zero, we can write

$$\mathbf{v} \times \mathbf{E}_{\perp} = \mathbf{v} \times (\mathbf{E}_{\parallel} + \mathbf{E}_{\perp}) = \mathbf{v} \times \mathbf{E},$$

and in this way we obtain the required result,

$$\mathbf{B} = \frac{\mathbf{v} \times \mathbf{E}}{c^2}.$$

Essential skill

Using the field transformation relationships

Worked Example 10.2

Observers in different frames of reference record different electric and magnetic fields from the same charge and current sources. However, there are restrictions on the combinations of electric and magnetic fields that can be observed for a particular source distribution. Show that one restriction is that $\mathbf{E} \cdot \mathbf{B}$ is invariant for transformations between different inertial frames in standard configuration.

Solution

Let us assume that a particular source distribution produces fields $\mathbf{E}'$ and $\mathbf{B}'$ in frame $\mathcal{F}'$, which travels at velocity $\mathbf{v} = (v, 0, 0)$ relative to frame $\mathcal{F}$ and is in a standard configuration with it. We need to use the field transformation relationships, Equations 10.26–10.31, to show that $\mathbf{E}' \cdot \mathbf{B}' = \mathbf{E} \cdot \mathbf{B}$, where

E and **B** are the fields observed in another inertial frame:

$$\mathbf{E}' \cdot \mathbf{B}' = E'_x B'_x + E'_y B'_y + E'_z B'_z$$

$$= E_x B_x + \gamma^2 (E_y - v B_z) \left(B_y + \frac{v}{c^2} E_z \right)$$

$$+ \gamma^2 (E_z + v B_y) \left(B_z - \frac{v}{c^2} E_y \right)$$

$$= E_x B_x + \gamma^2 \left(1 - \frac{v^2}{c^2} \right) (E_y B_y + E_z B_z)$$

$$= E_x B_x + E_y B_y + E_z B_z$$

$$= \mathbf{E} \cdot \mathbf{B}.$$

So for a particular source distribution, $\mathbf{E} \cdot \mathbf{B}$ will have the same value in *any* inertial frames in standard configuration.

Comment: In fact, this result is true for transformation of $\mathbf{E} \cdot \mathbf{B}$ between *any* inertial frames, whether in standard configuration or not.

If we know the value of $\mathbf{E} \cdot \mathbf{B}$ in one inertial frame, then we know it in all inertial frames. So, for example, it is known that $\mathbf{E} \cdot \mathbf{B} = 0$ for an electromagnetic wave in the laboratory frame because the electric and magnetic fields are perpendicular, and since $\mathbf{E} \cdot \mathbf{B}$ is invariant, the fields associated with an electromagnetic wave must be perpendicular in all other inertial frames. It also turns out that the quantity $E^2 - c^2 B^2$ is invariant. For an electromagnetic wave, the field amplitudes are related by $E_0 = c B_0$, so again this fact remains true in all inertial frames.

Exercise 10.5   Starting from Equations 10.26 to 10.31, and using physical insight rather than lengthy algebra, write down the inverse transformation that expresses electric and magnetic field components measured in frame $\mathcal{F}$ in terms of field components measured in frame $\mathcal{F}'$.

Exercise 10.6   Show that in the case $\mathbf{v} = (v, 0, 0)$, Equations 10.32 to 10.35 are consistent with Equations 10.26 to 10.31.

Exercise 10.7   Frames $\mathcal{F}$ and $\mathcal{F}'$ are in standard configuration, with $\mathcal{F}'$ travelling at velocity $\mathbf{v} = (v, 0, 0)$ relative to $\mathcal{F}$. Show that in a region where there is no electric field according to an observer in frame $\mathcal{F}'$, an observer in frame $\mathcal{F}$ will detect an electric field

$$\mathbf{E} = -\mathbf{v} \times \mathbf{B}.$$

Exercise 10.8   A high-energy particle travels at speed $0.95c$ vertically downwards through the Earth's atmosphere in a region above the Equator where the magnetic field is 5.0×10^{-5} T in a northerly direction, and the electric field is $100 \ \mathrm{V \, m^{-1}}$ vertically downwards. What are the electric and magnetic fields in this region according to an observer in the reference frame in which the particle is at rest?   ∎

10.2.4   Partial-derivative transformation

We end this section on the transformation of electromagnetic quantities with what is little more than a technical note about partial derivatives. The basic equations of electromagnetism involve a number of partial derivatives, often appearing in expressions such as div $\mathbf{E}$ or curl $\mathbf{B}$. Rather than considering the transformation of these quantities individually, we shall concentrate our attention on an arbitrary function of t, x, y and z which we shall denote by f, and which could represent E_x, B_y, etc. We know from the Lorentz transformation that f can also be expressed as a function of t', x', y' and z'. Consequently, using the chain rule for partial derivatives we can write

$$\frac{\partial f}{\partial t'} = \frac{\partial f}{\partial t}\frac{\partial t}{\partial t'} + \frac{\partial f}{\partial x}\frac{\partial x}{\partial t'} + \frac{\partial f}{\partial y}\frac{\partial y}{\partial t'} + \frac{\partial f}{\partial z}\frac{\partial z}{\partial t'}, \tag{10.36}$$

$$\frac{\partial f}{\partial x'} = \frac{\partial f}{\partial t}\frac{\partial t}{\partial x'} + \frac{\partial f}{\partial x}\frac{\partial x}{\partial x'} + \frac{\partial f}{\partial y}\frac{\partial y}{\partial x'} + \frac{\partial f}{\partial z}\frac{\partial z}{\partial x'}, \tag{10.37}$$

$$\frac{\partial f}{\partial y'} = \frac{\partial f}{\partial t}\frac{\partial t}{\partial y'} + \frac{\partial f}{\partial x}\frac{\partial x}{\partial y'} + \frac{\partial f}{\partial y}\frac{\partial y}{\partial y'} + \frac{\partial f}{\partial z}\frac{\partial z}{\partial y'}, \tag{10.38}$$

$$\frac{\partial f}{\partial z'} = \frac{\partial f}{\partial t}\frac{\partial t}{\partial z'} + \frac{\partial f}{\partial x}\frac{\partial x}{\partial z'} + \frac{\partial f}{\partial y}\frac{\partial y}{\partial z'} + \frac{\partial f}{\partial z}\frac{\partial z}{\partial z'}. \tag{10.39}$$

Now if we restrict our attention to the case of two frames in standard configuration, the relationship between t, x, y, z and t', x', y', z' is given by Equations 10.6 to 10.9, from which we can see that

$$\frac{\partial t}{\partial t'} = \gamma, \qquad \frac{\partial x}{\partial t'} = \gamma v, \qquad \frac{\partial y}{\partial t'} = 0, \qquad \frac{\partial z}{\partial t'} = 0,$$

$$\frac{\partial t}{\partial x'} = \gamma\frac{v}{c^2}, \qquad \frac{\partial x}{\partial x'} = \gamma, \qquad \frac{\partial y}{\partial x'} = 0, \qquad \frac{\partial z}{\partial x'} = 0,$$

$$\frac{\partial t}{\partial y'} = 0, \qquad \frac{\partial x}{\partial y'} = 0, \qquad \frac{\partial y}{\partial y'} = 1, \qquad \frac{\partial z}{\partial y'} = 0,$$

$$\frac{\partial t}{\partial z'} = 0, \qquad \frac{\partial x}{\partial z'} = 0, \qquad \frac{\partial y}{\partial z'} = 0, \qquad \frac{\partial z}{\partial z'} = 1.$$

Substituting these expressions into Equations 10.36 to 10.39, we find that

$$\frac{\partial f}{\partial t'} = \gamma\frac{\partial f}{\partial t} + \gamma v\frac{\partial f}{\partial x}, \tag{10.40}$$

$$\frac{\partial f}{\partial x'} = \gamma\frac{v}{c^2}\frac{\partial f}{\partial t} + \gamma\frac{\partial f}{\partial x}, \tag{10.41}$$

$$\frac{\partial f}{\partial y'} = \frac{\partial f}{\partial y}, \tag{10.42}$$

$$\frac{\partial f}{\partial z'} = \frac{\partial f}{\partial z}. \tag{10.43}$$

We shall use these results in the next section.

You may have noticed the similarity between this transformation and the inverse Lorentz transformation given in Equations 10.6 to 10.9. This is even clearer if we write the transformation in matrix notation, as shown in Figure 10.12.

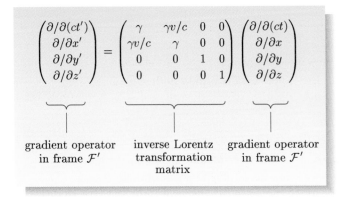

Figure 10.12 The transformation of partial derivatives expressed in matrix form.

10.3 Form invariance and electromagnetism

As noted in Subsection 10.1.1, the principle of relativity is one of the basic postulates of special relativity. One way of expressing that postulate, in the context of Einstein's theory, is to say that 'The laws of physics can be written in the same form in all inertial frames of reference'.

In other words, it should be possible to formulate laws of physics in such a way that a transformation from one inertial frame to another involves nothing more than putting primes on all the non-invariant quantities. (Invariants, such as charge or the speed of light, don't need primes because they have the same values in all inertial frames.) Laws that can be formulated in this way are said to be **form invariant**.

In the case of Newtonian mechanics, prior to the introduction of special relativity most physicists would have accepted that the key relationships for a free particle moving at velocity **U** included:

the definition of momentum,

$$\mathbf{p} = m\mathbf{U}; \tag{10.44}$$

the definition of total energy,

$$E = \tfrac{1}{2}mU^2; \tag{10.45}$$

and Newton's second law,

$$\mathbf{F} = m\mathbf{a} = m\frac{\mathrm{d}\mathbf{U}}{\mathrm{d}t}. \tag{10.46}$$

However, following the introduction of special relativity in 1905, it was clear that accepting Equations 10.44 to 10.46 as form-invariant laws had unacceptable consequences (including the non-conservation of momentum and energy). Instead, particle mechanics had to be reformulated, so that the form-invariant relationships became

$$\mathbf{p} = \frac{m\mathbf{U}}{\sqrt{1 - U^2/c^2}}, \tag{10.47}$$

$$E = \frac{mc^2}{\sqrt{1 - U^2/c^2}}, \tag{10.48}$$

$$\mathbf{F} = \frac{d\mathbf{p}}{dt}, \tag{10.49}$$

Some authors make use of a quantity called relativistic mass which varies with the speed of the particle. We make no use of this concept. In this chapter, m is always the rest mass and does not depend on the particle's speed.

where the mass m is an invariant sometimes called the *rest mass*, and the transformation rules for $\mathbf{U}$ and $\mathbf{F}$ are those given in Subsections 10.1.5 and 10.1.6. If the speed U is much less than the speed of light, then we can use the approximate relationship

$$\frac{1}{\sqrt{1 - U^2/c^2}} \simeq 1 + \frac{1}{2}\frac{U^2}{c^2}, \quad \text{for } U \ll c,$$

to simplify Equations 10.47 and 10.48, and we find

$$\mathbf{p} \simeq m\mathbf{U} \quad \text{and} \quad E \simeq mc^2 + \tfrac{1}{2}mU^2.$$

This reveals the usefulness of Equations 10.44 and 10.45 in providing 'low speed' approximations, and also reveals the need to recognize the contribution of the *mass energy*, mc^2, to the expression for the total energy of a particle.

In this section we shall consider the basic relationships of electromagnetism in the context of special relativity. First we shall ask if they are in need of the sort of modification that had to be applied to mechanics, and then we shall consider the deeper issue of form invariance in electromagnetism.

10.3.1 Are the laws of electromagnetism form invariant?

In the absence of media, the basic relationships of electromagnetism, expressed in an inertial frame $\mathcal{F}$, may be written as follows.

Maxwell's equations:

$$\operatorname{div}\mathbf{E} = \frac{\rho}{\varepsilon_0}, \tag{10.50}$$

$$\operatorname{div}\mathbf{B} = 0, \tag{10.51}$$

$$\operatorname{curl}\mathbf{E} = -\frac{\partial\mathbf{B}}{\partial t}, \tag{10.52}$$

$$\operatorname{curl}\mathbf{B} = \mu_0\mathbf{J} + \varepsilon_0\mu_0\frac{\partial\mathbf{E}}{\partial t}. \tag{10.53}$$

The equation of continuity (expressing charge conservation):

$$\frac{\partial\rho}{\partial t} + \operatorname{div}\mathbf{J} = 0. \tag{10.54}$$

The Lorentz force law:

$$\mathbf{F} = q(\mathbf{E} + \mathbf{v}\times\mathbf{B}). \tag{10.55}$$

Now, in Sections 10.1 and 10.2 we have already set out the rules for transforming the quantities $\mathbf{F}$, $\mathbf{U}$, ρ, $\mathbf{J}$, $\mathbf{E}$ and $\mathbf{B}$, together with any relevant partial derivatives (including those in the div and curl operations), from one inertial frame $\mathcal{F}$ to another inertial frame $\mathcal{F}'$, provided that those two frames are in standard configuration. We also know that charge is invariant under such changes of frame, and so is c, and ε_0 and μ_0 are also invariant. Using all this, we can directly check the form invariance of Equations 10.50 to 10.55 under transformations between $\mathcal{F}$ and $\mathcal{F}'$.

We did not provide the general rule for transforming $\mathbf{F}$, but what was given in Section 10.1 will be sufficient for our needs in this chapter.

Form invariance of the equation of continuity

If a relationship such as the equation of continuity (Equation 10.54) is form invariant, then in frame $\mathcal{F}'$ an observer should find that

$$\frac{\partial \rho'}{\partial t'} + \text{div}' \, \mathbf{J}' = 0, \tag{10.56}$$

where $\text{div}' = \left(\dfrac{\partial}{\partial x'}, \dfrac{\partial}{\partial y'}, \dfrac{\partial}{\partial z'} \right)$.

Is Equation 10.56 really the result of a transformation from frame $\mathcal{F}$ to frame $\mathcal{F}'$? Using Equations 10.22 to 10.25 (to transform ρ' and $\mathbf{J}'$) and Equations 10.40 to 10.43 (to transform the partial derivatives), we see that

$$\frac{\partial \rho'}{\partial t'} + \text{div}' \, \mathbf{J}' = \gamma^2 \left(\frac{\partial}{\partial t} + v \frac{\partial}{\partial x} \right) \left(\rho - \frac{v}{c^2} J_x \right)$$

$$+ \gamma^2 \left(\frac{v}{c^2} \frac{\partial}{\partial t} + \frac{\partial}{\partial x} \right) (J_x - v\rho) + \frac{\partial J_y}{\partial y} + \frac{\partial J_z}{\partial z}$$

$$= \gamma^2 \left(\frac{\partial \rho}{\partial t} - \frac{v}{c^2} \frac{\partial J_x}{\partial t} + v \frac{\partial \rho}{\partial x} - \frac{v^2}{c^2} \frac{\partial J_x}{\partial x} \right)$$

$$+ \gamma^2 \left(\frac{v}{c^2} \frac{\partial J_x}{\partial t} - \frac{v^2}{c^2} \frac{\partial \rho}{\partial t} + \frac{\partial J_x}{\partial x} - v \frac{\partial \rho}{\partial x} \right) + \frac{\partial J_y}{\partial y} + \frac{\partial J_z}{\partial z}$$

$$= \gamma^2 \left(1 - \frac{v^2}{c^2} \right) \frac{\partial \rho}{\partial t} + \gamma^2 \left(1 - \frac{v^2}{c^2} \right) \frac{\partial J_x}{\partial x} + \frac{\partial J_y}{\partial y} + \frac{\partial J_z}{\partial z}$$

$$= \frac{\partial \rho}{\partial t} + \text{div} \, \mathbf{J}.$$

We have shown that Equation 10.56 implies Equation 10.54 (and vice versa); the equation of continuity takes the same form in frames $\mathcal{F}$ and $\mathcal{F}'$ — it is form invariant.

This invariance can be confirmed quite neatly using the matrix formalism. In terms of matrices, we can write the equation of continuity as

$$\begin{pmatrix} \dfrac{\partial}{\partial (ct)} & \dfrac{\partial}{\partial x} & \dfrac{\partial}{\partial y} & \dfrac{\partial}{\partial z} \end{pmatrix} \begin{pmatrix} c\rho \\ J_x \\ J_y \\ J_z \end{pmatrix} = 0.$$

You have seen that the gradient operator transforms according to the inverse Lorentz transformation (Figure 10.12), and the current density 4-vector transforms according to the Lorentz transformation matrix (Figure 10.11). So transforming the equation of continuity involves the combination of an inverse

Lorentz transformation and a normal Lorentz transformation, and not surprisingly these two transformations cancel out. This again demonstrates that if the equation of continuity is true in one inertial frame, then it is true in all inertial frames.

Form invariance of the Lorentz force law

The Lorentz force law is form invariant, as you can demonstrate in the following exercise.

Exercise 10.9   Two inertial frames $\mathcal{F}$ and $\mathcal{F}'$ are in standard configuration. A charge q is at rest in frame $\mathcal{F}'$, where there are fields $\mathbf{E}'$ and $\mathbf{B}'$. Use the field transformations to show that if the Lorentz force law is valid in frame $\mathcal{F}'$, then it is also valid in frame $\mathcal{F}$.   ■

This exercise verified the form invariance of the Lorentz force law for the special case of the charge being at rest in frame $\mathcal{F}'$. Extending this to more general cases requires the full force transformation, and a lot more algebra! The exercise also shows why the $\mathbf{v} \times \mathbf{B}$ term appears in the Lorentz force law: it is essential to ensure the form invariance of this law.

In a similar fashion, Maxwell's equations (10.50 to 10.53) can also be shown to be form invariant. One subtlety is that it is necessary to consider Equations 10.50 and 10.53 together when transforming from the primed to the non-primed frames, and the same is true for the other pair of Maxwell's equations (Equations 10.51 and 10.52).

The implication of the form invariance of Equations 10.50 to 10.55 is that electromagnetism in the absence of media is fully 'relativistic'. It does not need the kind of modification that was necessary in mechanics. We shall not demonstrate the form invariance of Maxwell's equations here, because of the large amount of algebra it would involve, but we shall look more deeply into its consequences in the next subsection.

10.3.2   A single electromagnetic field

In previous chapters we have regarded electric fields and magnetic fields as two distinct entities. But as you have seen in Subsection 10.2.3, these fields are really two aspects of a unified electromagnetic field, and observers in different inertial frames will measure different values of the electric and magnetic components of this electromagnetic field. There is no unique answer to the question 'What are the electric and magnetic fields at point P?', because the answer depends on the motion of the observer relative to P.

The unified nature of the electromagnetic field can be made more explicit by the the use of matrix notation. We showed in Figure 10.4 that transformations of the coordinates of events between different inertial frames could be expressed in a simple and elegant way by using the 4-vector (ct, x, y, z) to describe an event, and using a symmetrical 4×4 matrix — the Lorentz transformation matrix — to describe the transformation process. Similarly, in Figure 10.11 we showed that the transformation of charge density and current density can be expressed as a multiplication of the Lorentz transformation matrix and the current density 4-vector $(c\rho, J_x, J_y, J_z)$. However, the electromagnetic field is more complicated than the coordinates of an event, or the charge density and current density at a point, both of which can be represented by 4-vectors, because there are six components to the electromagnetic field, $(E_x, E_y, E_z, B_x, B_y, B_z)$. The electromagnetic field cannot therefore be represented by a 4-vector.

The electromagnetic field is best represented by a 4×4 matrix (more correctly referred to as a tensor), and this has the following form:

$$\begin{pmatrix} 0 & -E_x/c & -E_y/c & -E_z/c \\ E_x/c & 0 & -B_z & B_y \\ E_y/c & B_z & 0 & -B_x \\ E_z/c & -B_y & B_x & 0 \end{pmatrix}. \tag{10.57}$$

Note that this is antisymmetric, so it has only six independent components, and these correspond to the three components of the electric field and the three components of the magnetic field. Transforming fields from one inertial frame to another involves a more complicated multiplication operation involving the field tensor and two Lorentz transformation matrices, and we shall not discuss that here. However, we shall look at how Maxwell's equations can be represented in this formalism.

Consider the matrix equation

$$\begin{pmatrix} \dfrac{\partial}{\partial(ct)} & \dfrac{\partial}{\partial x} & \dfrac{\partial}{\partial y} & \dfrac{\partial}{\partial z} \end{pmatrix} \begin{pmatrix} 0 & -E_x/c & -E_y/c & -E_z/c \\ E_x/c & 0 & -B_z & B_y \\ E_y/c & B_z & 0 & -B_x \\ E_z/c & -B_y & B_x & 0 \end{pmatrix}$$

$$= \mu_0 \begin{pmatrix} c\rho & J_x & J_y & J_z \end{pmatrix}. \tag{10.58}$$

On the left-hand side we have the product of the four components of the gradient operator (introduced in Figure 10.12) with the electromagnetic field tensor, and on the right-hand side is the current density 4-vector. This equation is just another way of writing two of Maxwell's equations in free space. The first component of this equation gives

$$\frac{1}{c}\frac{\partial E_x}{\partial x} + \frac{1}{c}\frac{\partial E_y}{\partial y} + \frac{1}{c}\frac{\partial E_z}{\partial z} = \mu_0 c\rho,$$

which reduces to Gauss's law, $\operatorname{div} \mathbf{E} = \rho/\varepsilon_0$, since $\mu_0 c^2 = 1/\varepsilon_0$. The remaining three components give the vector components of the Ampère–Maxwell law in the x-, y- and z-directions.

Now we can write a second matrix equation as follows:

$$\begin{pmatrix} \dfrac{\partial}{\partial(ct)} & \dfrac{\partial}{\partial x} & \dfrac{\partial}{\partial y} & \dfrac{\partial}{\partial z} \end{pmatrix} \begin{pmatrix} 0 & -B_x & -B_y & -B_z \\ B_x & 0 & E_z/c & -E_y/c \\ B_y & -E_z/c & 0 & E_x/c \\ B_z & E_y/c & -E_x/c & 0 \end{pmatrix}$$

$$= \begin{pmatrix} 0 & 0 & 0 & 0 \end{pmatrix}. \tag{10.59}$$

The 4×4 matrix that appears here can be derived from the matrix in Equation 10.58 by substituting $\mathbf{B}$ for $\mathbf{E}/c$ and substituting $-\mathbf{E}/c$ for $\mathbf{B}$.

This equation represents the no-monopole law and Faraday's law. So Maxwell's four equations can be written as two matrix equations. These equations are rather different in nature. Equation 10.58 contains charge and current densities on the right-hand side, and this equation describes how fields originate from their sources. Equation 10.59 contains no source terms, but describes conditions that all electric and magnetic fields must satisfy. It is interesting to note that the absence of source terms on the right-hand side of this equation is a consequence of our assumption that magnetic monopoles do not exist. If magnetic monopoles did exist, there would be source terms on the right-hand side of Equation 10.59, involving $(c\rho^{\mathrm{mag}}, J_x^{\mathrm{mag}}, J_y^{\mathrm{mag}}, J_z^{\mathrm{mag}})$, where ρ^{mag} would be the density of magnetic monopoles and J_x^{mag} would be the current density of magnetic monopoles in the x-direction, etc. This would make Maxwell's equations more symmetrical — and (even) more beautiful — but we have no evidence that monopoles do exist, and classical electromagnetism assumes that they do not.

Equations 10.58 and 10.59 are cumbersome to use, and would become even more unwieldy if expressed in terms of spherical or cylindrical coordinates, so we shall stick with the familiar vector calculus forms of Maxwell's equations for practical calculations. Nevertheless, the matrix forms of Maxwell's equations are useful from a theoretical standpoint, since they show clearly that the electric and magnetic fields are just components of a single electromagnetic field tensor. In Book 1 we discussed the electromagnetic field, but almost immediately split this field up into an electric field and a magnetic field. Now, we have succeeded in recombining the electric and magnetic fields. The basic quantity that represents the *electromagnetic* field is the tensor that appears in Equation 10.57.

The electric and magnetic fields are components of this electromagnetic field tensor in much the same way that x, y and z are components of the position vector in ordinary three-dimensional space. The components of a given position vector change if we rotate the axes of our coordinate system, but the position vector itself retains its meaning as representing a particular displacement from the origin to a given point. Similarly, the six components of the electric and magnetic fields may all change with a change of the reference frame. In one reference frame there might be an electric field and no magnetic field, whereas in another reference frame there might be both electric and magnetic fields. The components of the electromagnetic field tensor depend on the choice of reference frame, but the electromagnetic field tensor itself continues to describe the *same* electromagnetic field from different viewpoints.

Summary of Chapter 10

Section 10.1   The theory of special relativity concerns the relationships between observations made by observers who use inertial frames of reference (i.e. frames in which Newton's first law holds true) that are in uniform relative motion. For inertial frames $\mathcal{F}$ and $\mathcal{F}'$ in standard configuration, the coordinates of an event observed at (t, x, y, z) in $\mathcal{F}$ are related to the coordinates (t', x', y', z') of the same event in $\mathcal{F}'$ by the Lorentz transformation (Equations 10.1 to 10.4). The effect of such a transformation is reversed by the inverse Lorentz transformation (Equations 10.6 to 10.9). Special relativity may be used to deduce the relativity of simultaneity, the relativity of length (length contraction), and the relativity of intervals of time (time dilation). It may also be used to deduce transformation rules for the components of a velocity $\mathbf{U}$ (Equations 10.12 to 10.14) and for the components of a force $\mathbf{F}$ (Equations 10.17 to 10.19), where $\mathbf{F}$ is defined as the rate of change of momentum, and momentum is defined by the relation $\mathbf{p} = m\mathbf{U}/\sqrt{1 - U^2/c^2}$.

Section 10.2   The charge q of a particle is an invariant quantity that takes the same value in all inertial frames. Other invariants are the (rest) mass m of a particle, the speed of light in a vacuum c, and the constants ε_0 and μ_0. Under a transformation between inertial frames $\mathcal{F}$ and $\mathcal{F}'$, the charge density ρ and the current density **J**, in the combination $(c\rho, J_x, J_y, J_z)$, behave in the same way as the coordinates (ct, x, y, z). Under the same transformation, the partial derivatives $(\partial/\partial(ct), \partial/\partial x, \partial/\partial y, \partial/\partial z)$ obey the inverse Lorentz transformation, and the electric and magnetic field components become intermingled as described by Equations 10.26 to 10.31.

Section 10.3   The principle of relativity demands that laws of physics should be form invariant under a transformation from one inertial frame to another. Unlike the laws of Newtonian mechanics, the laws of electromagnetism (including Maxwell's equations, the equation of continuity and the Lorentz force law) satisfy this requirement. The form invariance of electromagnetic laws can be demonstrated using the transformation rules for **F**, **U**, ρ, **J**, **E**, **B** and the relevant partial derivatives. This involves a great deal of algebra. The unified nature of the electromagnetic field can be made explicit by expressing the electromagnetic field as a tensor that incorporates the three electric and three magnetic field components.

Achievements from Chapter 10

After studying this chapter you should be able to do the following.

10.1 Explain the meanings of the newly defined (emboldened) terms and symbols, and use them appropriately.

10.2 Recall the basic ideas and transformations of special relativity.

10.3 Explain what is meant by an invariant.

10.4 Use the transformations for **E** and **B**, and ρ and **J**, to solve simple problems involving inertial frames in standard configuration.

10.5 Explain what is meant by form invariance, and recall which equations of electromagnetism are form invariant.

10.6 Demonstrate the form invariance of the equation of continuity and the Lorentz force law, and discuss the extension of that demonstration to other laws of electromagnetism.

Chapter 11   Revision and consolidation

Books 1 and 2 have introduced all of the fundamental laws of electromagnetism, and in this brief chapter you will not meet any new laws or concepts. Instead, the aim is to ensure that you have a firm foundation upon which to base your study of the final book for the course, *Electromagnetic waves*, by reviewing, revising and consolidating material that you have studied earlier. We shall survey some important results, and in particular compare the basic results of electrostatics and magnetostatics. We shall also review the various versions of Maxwell's equations that you have met, since these will continue to play a major role in the rest of the course.

To complement your study of this chapter, you should:

- look again at parts of this book, and Book 1, which relate to topics that you are not confident that you understand;
- try any exercises that you have omitted so far;
- repeat exercises and study worked examples related to topics about which you are unsure;
- try some of the exercises from the course website.

These activities will also allow you to develop further your skills at solving electromagnetism problems.

11.1   Electrostatics and magnetostatics

In the first half of this book we concentrated on electrostatics, the study of electric fields generated by static charges, and magnetostatics, the study of magnetic fields generated by steady currents. The main results of Chapters 2–5 are summarized in Table 11.1.

We have used τ as the symbol for volume in the table, as elsewhere in this book, to avoid confusion with the potential V.

● Study Table 11.1 carefully, trying to recall the meaning of each of the equations, and comparing and contrasting the entries for electrostatics in the middle column and for magnetostatics in the right-hand column. There are obvious similarities between the two columns, but also some significant differences.

○ Some of the similarities and differences are discussed below. If you are unsure of the meaning of any of the equations, now would be an appropriate time to look again at the section(s) in Book 1 or Book 2 where they were introduced and discussed. Use the contents pages, index and glossary to locate the appropriate topics.

Table 11.1 Comparison of electrostatics and magnetostatics.

		Electrostatics	Magnetostatics
1	Force and field – on point charge q – on current element $I\,\delta\mathbf{l}$	$\mathbf{F}_{\mathrm{elec}} = q\mathbf{E}$ $\mathbf{F}_{\mathrm{elec}} = \mathbf{0}$	$\mathbf{F}_{\mathrm{mag}} = q\mathbf{v} \times \mathbf{B}$ $\mathbf{F}_{\mathrm{mag}} = I\,\delta\mathbf{l} \times \mathbf{B}$
2	Elementary law – field due to small source at $\mathbf{r}'$ – field due to distribution	Coulomb's law $\mathbf{E}(\mathbf{r}) = \dfrac{q}{4\pi\varepsilon_0} \dfrac{(\mathbf{r}-\mathbf{r}')}{\lvert\mathbf{r}-\mathbf{r}'\rvert^3}$ $\mathbf{E}(\mathbf{r}) = \dfrac{1}{4\pi\varepsilon_0} \displaystyle\int_{\tau'} \dfrac{\rho(\mathbf{r}')(\mathbf{r}-\mathbf{r}')}{\lvert\mathbf{r}-\mathbf{r}'\rvert^3}\,\mathrm{d}\tau'$	Biot–Savart law $\delta\mathbf{B}(\mathbf{r}) = \dfrac{\mu_0 I}{4\pi} \dfrac{\delta\mathbf{l} \times (\mathbf{r}-\mathbf{r}')}{\lvert\mathbf{r}-\mathbf{r}'\rvert^3}$ $\mathbf{B}(\mathbf{r}) = \dfrac{\mu_0}{4\pi} \displaystyle\int_{\tau'} \dfrac{\mathbf{J}(\mathbf{r}') \times (\mathbf{r}-\mathbf{r}')}{\lvert\mathbf{r}-\mathbf{r}'\rvert^3}\,\mathrm{d}\tau'$
3	Source law – differential version – integral version	Gauss's law $\operatorname{div}\mathbf{E} = \rho/\varepsilon_0$ $\displaystyle\int_S \mathbf{E}\cdot\mathrm{d}\mathbf{S} = \dfrac{1}{\varepsilon_0}\int_\tau \rho\,\mathrm{d}\tau = \dfrac{Q}{\varepsilon_0}$	Ampère's law $\operatorname{curl}\mathbf{B} = \mu_0\mathbf{J}$ $\displaystyle\oint_C \mathbf{B}\cdot\mathrm{d}\mathbf{l} = \mu_0 \int_S \mathbf{J}\cdot\mathrm{d}\mathbf{S} = \mu_0 I$
4	Field constraint – field–potential relationship – source–potential relationship	$\operatorname{curl}\mathbf{E} = \mathbf{0}$ (conservative) $\mathbf{E} = -\operatorname{grad}V$ $V(\mathbf{r}) = \dfrac{1}{4\pi\varepsilon_0} \displaystyle\int_{\tau'} \dfrac{\rho(\mathbf{r}')}{\lvert\mathbf{r}-\mathbf{r}'\rvert}\,\mathrm{d}\tau'$	$\operatorname{div}\mathbf{B} = 0$ (no-monopole law) $\mathbf{B} = \operatorname{curl}\mathbf{A}$ $\mathbf{A}(\mathbf{r}) = \dfrac{\mu_0}{4\pi} \displaystyle\int_{\tau'} \dfrac{\mathbf{J}(\mathbf{r}')}{\lvert\mathbf{r}-\mathbf{r}'\rvert}\,\mathrm{d}\tau'$
5	Dipole – moment – potential energy – torque in field – produces distant field	two opposite charges $\mathbf{p} = q\mathbf{d}$ $U = -\mathbf{p}\cdot\mathbf{E}$ $\boldsymbol{\Gamma} = \mathbf{p} \times \mathbf{E}$ $\mathbf{E}_{\mathrm{dip}}(\mathbf{r}) = -\dfrac{1}{4\pi\varepsilon_0}\operatorname{grad}\left(\dfrac{\mathbf{p}\cdot\mathbf{r}}{r^3}\right)$	current in loop $\mathbf{m} = \lvert I\rvert\,\Delta\mathbf{S}$ $U = -\mathbf{m}\cdot\mathbf{B}$ $\boldsymbol{\Gamma} = \mathbf{m} \times \mathbf{B}$ $\mathbf{B}_{\mathrm{dip}}(\mathbf{r}) = -\dfrac{\mu_0}{4\pi}\operatorname{grad}\left(\dfrac{\mathbf{m}\cdot\mathbf{r}}{r^3}\right)$
6	Field due to matter – charge / current density – surface charge / current density Auxiliary field – obeys source law – for LIH materials – where	$\mathbf{P} = n\langle\mathbf{p}\rangle = \chi_E\varepsilon_0\mathbf{E}$ $\rho_{\mathrm{b}} = -\operatorname{div}\mathbf{P}$ $\sigma_{\mathrm{b}} = \mathbf{P}\cdot\hat{\mathbf{n}}$ $\mathbf{D} \equiv \varepsilon_0\mathbf{E} + \mathbf{P}$ $\operatorname{div}\mathbf{D} = \rho_{\mathrm{f}}$ $\mathbf{E} = \mathbf{D}/\varepsilon\varepsilon_0$ $\varepsilon = 1 + \chi_E$	$\mathbf{M} = n\langle\mathbf{m}\rangle = \chi_B\mathbf{B}/\mu_0$ $\mathbf{J}_{\mathrm{b}} = \operatorname{curl}\mathbf{M}$ $\mathbf{i}_{\mathrm{b}} = \mathbf{M} \times \hat{\mathbf{n}}$ $\mathbf{H} \equiv \mathbf{B}/\mu_0 - \mathbf{M}$ $\operatorname{curl}\mathbf{H} = \mathbf{J}_{\mathrm{f}}$ $\mathbf{B} = \mu\mu_0\mathbf{H}$ $\mu = 1/(1 - \chi_B)$
7	Boundary conditions – flux through closed surface – line integral round loop	(no free surface charge) $\int_S \mathbf{D}\cdot\mathrm{d}\mathbf{S} = 0 \Rightarrow D_\perp$ continuous $\oint_C \mathbf{E}\cdot\mathrm{d}\mathbf{l} = 0 \Rightarrow E_\parallel$ continuous	(no free surface current) $\int_S \mathbf{B}\cdot\mathrm{d}\mathbf{S} = 0 \Rightarrow B_\perp$ continuous $\oint_C \mathbf{H}\cdot\mathrm{d}\mathbf{l} = 0 \Rightarrow H_\parallel$ continuous
8	Energy in capacitor or inductor Energy density in field – for LIH materials	$U = \frac{1}{2}Q^2/C$ $u = \frac{1}{2}\mathbf{D}\cdot\mathbf{E}$ $u = \frac{1}{2}\varepsilon\varepsilon_0 E^2$	$U = \frac{1}{2}LI^2$ $u = \frac{1}{2}\mathbf{B}\cdot\mathbf{H}$ $u = \frac{1}{2}B^2/\mu\mu_0$

The first row of Table 11.1 shows how the forces on a test charge are related to the fields. The electrostatic force $\mathbf{F}_{\text{elec}} = q\mathbf{E}$ applies whether the test charge is moving or not, whereas the magnetic force $\mathbf{F}_{\text{mag}} = q\mathbf{v} \times \mathbf{B}$ arises only if the test charge is moving in a magnetic field. These two forces comprise the Lorentz force, $\mathbf{F} = q(\mathbf{E} + \mathbf{v} \times \mathbf{B})$. Not surprisingly, the magnetic force on a *current element* $I\,\delta\mathbf{l}$ has a similar form to that on a moving charge, and this expression applies whether we are interested in the force on an electrically-neutral current-carrying wire or an electron beam. The electric force is zero for a neutral current-carrying wire, but for the current associated with an electron beam the force will be simply the sum of the electric forces on the individual electrons, as given in the first line of the table.

Row 2 quotes the elementary laws that determine the fields due to point-like sources. Coulomb's law gives the electric field due to a static point charge q. The Biot–Savart law gives the magnetic field due to an infinitesimal line element $\mathrm{d}\mathbf{l}$ carrying a steady current I. Note that the constants ε_0 and μ_0 are defined in such a way that when the factor ε_0 appears in the denominator in electrostatics, the factor μ_0 appears in the numerator in magnetostatics, and vice versa, as you can see by examining the entries in subsequent rows in the table. Of course, we are generally interested in *distributions* of charge or current, and then the field is calculated by replacing the point charge q by $\rho(\mathbf{r}')\,\mathrm{d}\tau'$, or replacing the current element $I\,\delta\mathbf{l}$ by $\mathbf{J}(\mathbf{r}')\,\mathrm{d}\tau'$, and integrating over the volume τ' containing the distributions.

Coulomb's law and the Biot–Savart law are very powerful, and in principle can be used to determine the field for any specified source distribution. However, the vector nature of the integrands in the expressions in the third line of row 2 makes them difficult to evaluate in practice. It is often more convenient to sidestep these expressions and to use the results in rows 3 and 4. The philosophy underlying these results is very different. The concept of a field is rather incidental to Coulomb's law and the Biot–Savart law, and rows 1 and 2 can easily be combined to eliminate $\mathbf{E}$ and $\mathbf{B}$ altogether. But rows 3 and 4 place a far greater emphasis on the field concept. Via the div and curl operators, they focus attention on the spatial variations of the fields and their links to sources. The field-theory approach has two main advantages. First, it is often simpler to use than the elementary laws of row 2 — that is, it leads to simpler mathematics. Second, it is more readily extended to non-static situations — when the sources are neither stationary charges nor steady currents.

In electrostatics, an electric field $\mathbf{E}$ is related to a time-independent charge density ρ via Gauss's law. This can be written either in a differential version (involving $\mathrm{div}\,\mathbf{E}$) or in an integral version (involving the integral of $\mathbf{E}$ over a closed surface). The mathematical equivalence of these two versions follows from the divergence theorem. In magnetostatics, a magnetic field $\mathbf{B}$ is related to a time-independent current density $\mathbf{J}$ via Ampère's law. This too can be written either in a differential version (involving $\mathrm{curl}\,\mathbf{B}$) or in an integral version (involving the integral of $\mathbf{B}$ round a closed loop). The mathematical equivalence of these two versions follows from the curl theorem.

Gauss's law specifies $\mathrm{div}\,\mathbf{E}$ and Ampère's law specifies $\mathrm{curl}\,\mathbf{B}$, but neither of these conditions is sufficient to completely determine $\mathbf{E}$ or $\mathbf{B}$. Row 4 lists further constraints on the electrostatic and magnetostatic fields. In electrostatics, the electric field has *zero curl*, $\mathrm{curl}\,\mathbf{E} = \mathbf{0}$, and $\mathbf{E}$ can be written as the gradient of a scalar field, $\mathbf{E} = -\operatorname{grad} V$. The electrostatic potential V is related to a volume integral of the charge density. In magnetostatics, the magnetic field has *zero divergence*, $\operatorname{div} \mathbf{B} = 0$ — the no-monopole law. As a consequence, $\mathbf{B}$ can be written as the curl of a vector field $\mathbf{A}$, the vector potential, which is related to a volume integral of the current density. For both $\mathbf{E}$ and $\mathbf{B}$, we have now specified both their divergence and their curl, and these are sufficient to determine the fields, apart from a uniform constant field. Expressions for the divergence and curl of $\mathbf{E}$ and $\mathbf{B}$ comprise, in fact, the versions of Maxwell's equations that apply when the fields and sources are independent of time:

$$\operatorname{div} \mathbf{E} = \rho/\varepsilon_0, \quad \operatorname{curl} \mathbf{E} = \mathbf{0}, \quad \operatorname{div} \mathbf{B} = 0, \quad \operatorname{curl} \mathbf{B} = \mu_0 \mathbf{J}.$$

Row 5 deals with the special case of dipole sources. There are clear similarities between the electrostatic and magnetostatic formulae. We have not explicitly introduced expressions for the torque on a magnetic dipole, or the magnetic field it produces, but they have the same form as the expressions for electric dipoles. Dipole sources are of particular interest because they are the key to understanding fields in and around dielectric and magnetic materials. In both types of material, induced dipoles are produced in atoms by an applied field, and if permanent atomic or molecular dipoles are present, they become preferentially aligned with the field.

Row 6 summarizes the effects of materials on electrostatic and magnetostatic fields. We consider only media that are homogeneous and isotropic. In addition, we generally assume that the susceptibilities χ_E and χ_B are independent of the applied field, in which case a material is said to be linear.

In electrostatics, materials become polarized in an applied electric field. The polarization vector $\mathbf{P}$ is the resultant electric dipole moment per unit volume; it is proportional to the macroscopic electric field $\mathbf{E}$ (i.e. the average electric field *including* contributions from the polarized medium). In magnetostatics, materials are magnetized by an applied magnetic field. The magnetization vector $\mathbf{M}$ is the resultant magnetic dipole moment per unit volume; it is proportional to the macroscopic magnetic field $\mathbf{B}$ (i.e. the average magnetic field *including* contributions from the magnetized medium). The electric susceptibility χ_E is always positive, so $\mathbf{P}$ always points in the same direction as $\mathbf{E}$, and values for solids and liquids are typically of the order of 1–10, so an applied electric field is modified substantially in and around a dielectric material. The magnetic susceptibility χ_B is positive for paramagnetic and ferromagnetic materials, but negative for diamagnetic materials, so $\mathbf{M}$ either points in the same direction as $\mathbf{B}$, or points in the opposite direction. However, for both paramagnetic and diamagnetic materials the magnitude of the susceptibility is generally of the order of 10^{-4}–10^{-6}, so they produce only a small perturbation of the applied field. This is not the case for ferromagnetic materials, where most of the $\mathbf{B}$ field is due to the magnetization of the material. Polarization and magnetization produce distributions of bound charge and bound current, respectively, in the volume and on the surface of material. The bound charge density is *minus* the divergence of the polarization, while the bound current density is equal to *plus* the curl of the magnetization. (This sign difference leads to several other sign differences in subsequent equations.)

We define fields **D** and **H** that obey simplified source equations, involving only the *free* charge and *free* current densities. The advantage of these fields is that they can often be found directly, without any knowledge of the polarization or magnetization of surrounding or nearby media. In practical terms, **H** is a more useful quantity than **D**. The reason is that **H** is determined by the free current density, a quantity that is readily measured on a meter. In contrast, **D** is determined by the free charge density, a quantity that is rather difficult to measure. (In electrostatics, one normally measures potential difference, which is directly related to **E**.) Within a linear, isotropic, homogeneous (LIH) medium, the macroscopic field **E** is proportional to the field **D**, and the macroscopic field **B** is proportional to the field **H**. The proportionality factors involve the relative permittivity ε and the relative permeability μ.

At the interface between different dielectric media, we must ensure that certain boundary conditions for the **E** and **D** fields are satisfied, and analogous boundary conditions for **B** and **H** apply at the interface between different magnetic materials. Assuming that there is no free charge and no free current at the interface, the conditions for the fields **D** and **B** are derived by equating their flux through a closed pillbox straddling the interface to zero, and this leads to the conditions that $D_\perp$ and $B_\perp$ are both continuous across the interface. The conditions for **E** and **H** are derived by equating the circulation around a rectangular loop straddling the interface to zero, and this leads to the conditions that $E_\parallel$ and $H_\parallel$ are both continuous across the interface. If we regard **E** and **B** as one pair of analogous fields — these are the fields that directly affect a charge q via the Lorentz force law — and **D** and **H** as another pair, we see that the boundary conditions take *opposite* forms in electrostatics and magnetostatics.

The final row of Table 11.1 compares expressions for electromagnetic energy. The energy can be related directly to the source charges and currents; for example, for a capacitor the stored energy is $\frac{1}{2}Q^2/C$, whereas for an inductor it is $\frac{1}{2}LI^2$. But the energy can equally well be related to the electric and magnetic fields generated by the sources, and the two expressions for the energy densities of these fields, $\frac{1}{2}\mathbf{D}\cdot\mathbf{E}$ and $\frac{1}{2}\mathbf{B}\cdot\mathbf{H}$ are applicable to both static and time-dependent fields, as you will see in Book 3.

11.2   Beyond static fields

In the previous section we summarized the important results for electric and magnetic fields that remain constant in time. Even with this restriction, there was plenty to marvel at and plenty to study! But when this restriction is lifted and we consider fields changing in time, a whole new world opens up. Time-varying magnetic fields have electric fields associated with them, even when there are no stationary electric charges around to act as sources, and time-varying electric fields have magnetic fields associated with them just as electric currents do. These relationships are encapsulated in the two of Maxwell's equations that were not mentioned in the previous section because they are not relevant for static fields:

$$\text{Faraday:}\ \ \operatorname{curl}\mathbf{E} = -\frac{\partial \mathbf{B}}{\partial t}; \quad \text{Ampère–Maxwell:}\ \ \operatorname{curl}\mathbf{H} = \mathbf{J}_\mathrm{f} + \frac{\partial \mathbf{D}}{\partial t}.$$

Clearly, in the absence of any time dependence, these two equations reduce to the familiar equations

$$\operatorname{curl} \mathbf{E} = \mathbf{0} \quad \text{and} \quad \operatorname{curl} \mathbf{H} = \mu_0 \mathbf{J}_{\mathrm{f}},$$

which describe the irrotational property of static electric fields and Ampère's law, respectively.

Maxwell's four equations can be written in a number of different ways, and four of these are shown inside the front cover. There are differential versions that relate derivatives of the fields (in terms of divs and curls) to charges, currents and time-derivatives of fields; these are local relationships that relate quantities measured at a point in space and time. There are also integral versions of the equations that relate surface or line integrals of fields to volume or surface integrals of charges, currents and time-derivatives of fields; these are clearly non-local relationships, and analytic solutions are generally possible only in situations where there is a high degree of symmetry. But the equations can also be separated into those that are written in terms of the fields $\mathbf{E}$ and $\mathbf{B}$ and the sources ρ and $\mathbf{J}$, which are the *total* charge density and *total* current density, and those that are written in terms of four fields, $\mathbf{E}$, $\mathbf{D}$, $\mathbf{B}$ and $\mathbf{H}$, and the *free* charge density ρ_{f} and the *free* current density $\mathbf{J}_{\mathrm{f}}$. It is important to note that these sets of equations are completely equivalent: both sets apply equally to fields in free space and fields in materials. In free space, $\rho = 0$, $\mathbf{J} = 0$, $\mathbf{D} = \varepsilon_0 \mathbf{E}$ and $\mathbf{B} = \mu_0 \mathbf{H}$, so the differential versions of both sets of equations reduce to

$$\operatorname{div} \mathbf{E} = 0, \quad \operatorname{div} \mathbf{B} = 0, \quad \operatorname{curl} \mathbf{E} = -\frac{\partial \mathbf{B}}{\partial t}, \quad \operatorname{curl} \mathbf{B} = \varepsilon_0 \mu_0 \frac{\partial \mathbf{E}}{\partial t}.$$

In materials, both sets are still valid, but the equations that involve the total charge density and total current density are not particularly useful since we usually know only the free charge and free current, and do not know the bound charge and bound current. However, the second set involves $\mathbf{D}$ and $\mathbf{H}$ as well as $\mathbf{E}$ and $\mathbf{B}$, so we need to know the relationships between these quantities to solve a problem. We generally restrict our attention to LIH materials for which $\mathbf{D} = \varepsilon \varepsilon_0 \mathbf{E}$ and $\mathbf{B} = \mu \mu_0 \mathbf{H}$.

Thus time-dependent electric fields and magnetic fields are linked via Maxwell's equations: they cannot be considered separately, but are aspects of a single phenomenon – *electromagnetism*. Time-dependent fields lead to a host of new phenomena and applications, including dynamos and alternators for generating AC electricity, magnetic braking, inductive heating, transformers, resonant AC circuits, and above all, the generation and propagation of electromagnetic waves, first predicted by Maxwell in 1867 and demonstrated by Hertz in 1887. The study of electromagnetic waves is a major part of Book 3.

However, the linking of time-dependent electric and magnetic fields revealed by Faraday's law and the Ampère–Maxwell law is only one aspect of the much deeper linking of the fields revealed by the theory of special relativity. Electric and magnetic fields are not distinct entities, but two aspects of a single entity, the electromagnetic field, and the separation of this field into electric and magnetic parts is dependent on the motion of an observer. If a line charge is stationary in my frame of reference, I will observe an electric field in the region around it but no magnetic field. If you are travelling at high speed parallel to the line charge, you will observe a magnetic field due to the moving charge as well as a (different) electric field. This also indicates that charge densities and current densities are relative concepts. In most everyday situations, although the electric and magnetic fields are linked via Faraday's law and the Ampère–Maxwell law, there is a well-defined separation of electric and magnetic fields for the frame of reference appropriate for the problem. However, even though the fields and their sources have different values according to observers in different reference frames, Maxwell's equations, the equation of continuity and the Lorentz force law all take exactly the same form in all inertial frames, which means that they qualify to be fundamental 'laws of physics'.

Solutions to exercises

Ex 1.1 (a) The total flux (or flow) of electric current out of a closed surface is equal to the rate of decrease of the total electric charge within the volume enclosed by that surface.

(b) We can use the divergence theorem to replace the term on the left-hand side of the integral version of the equation of continuity:

$$\int_S \mathbf{J} \cdot \mathrm{d}\mathbf{S} = \int_V \operatorname{div} \mathbf{J} \, \mathrm{d}V.$$

Also, on the right-hand side of the equation we can interchange the order of the differentiation with respect to time and the integration over volume:

$$-\frac{\mathrm{d}}{\mathrm{d}t} \int_V \rho \, \mathrm{d}V = -\int_V \frac{\partial \rho}{\partial t} \, \mathrm{d}V.$$

Note that we have replaced the time derivative by a partial derivative, since ρ is a function of position as well as of time. Thus

$$\int_V \operatorname{div} \mathbf{J} \, \mathrm{d}V = -\int_V \frac{\partial \rho}{\partial t} \, \mathrm{d}V,$$

and since this is true whatever the volume V over which we integrate, no matter how small, the integrands must be identical, i.e.

$$\operatorname{div} \mathbf{J} = -\frac{\partial \rho}{\partial t}.$$

Ex 1.2 A steady current flow requires that $\operatorname{div} \mathbf{J} = 0$, since otherwise there would be a build up or decrease in the charge in a region, which would affect the current flow. In this case,

$$\operatorname{div} \mathbf{J} = \frac{\partial J_x}{\partial x} + \frac{\partial J_y}{\partial y} + \frac{\partial J_z}{\partial z}$$

$$= J_0 \left[\frac{\partial(xy)}{\partial x} + \frac{\partial(2yz)}{\partial y} + \frac{\partial(x - yz - z^2)}{\partial z} \right]$$

$$= J_0 [y + 2z - y - 2z] = 0,$$

so this function could represent a steady current.

Ex 1.3 To derive the integral version of Gauss's law from the differential version, first integrate both sides of Equation 1.3 over any volume V:

$$\int_V \operatorname{div} \mathbf{E} \, \mathrm{d}V = \int_V \frac{\rho}{\varepsilon_0} \, \mathrm{d}V.$$

Then use the divergence theorem to replace the volume integral of $\operatorname{div} \mathbf{E}$ by a surface integral:

$$\int_V \operatorname{div} \mathbf{E} \, \mathrm{d}V = \int_S \mathbf{E} \cdot \mathrm{d}\mathbf{S},$$

and hence obtain the required integral version of Gauss's law:

$$\int_S \mathbf{E} \cdot \mathrm{d}\mathbf{S} = \frac{1}{\varepsilon_0} \int_V \rho \, \mathrm{d}V.$$

The differential version of Gauss's law is a local relationship. (The integral version relates the charge contained in any volume, however large, to the electric flux through the surface bounding that volume, so it certainly is not a local relationship.)

Ex 1.4 The charge density depends only on the distance r from the origin, so it has spherical symmetry. This suggests that we should use spherical coordinates (r, θ, ϕ) to solve this problem. The spherical symmetry means that the electric field must be in a radial direction at any point, since there is no reason to favour inclination of the field at any particular angle to the radial direction. Also, the magnitude of the field must be the same for all points at the same distance r from the origin.

To find the field at a distance r from the origin, we apply the integral version of Gauss's law,

$$\int_S \mathbf{E} \cdot \mathrm{d}\mathbf{S} = \frac{1}{\varepsilon_0} \int_V \rho \, \mathrm{d}V,$$

to a spherical surface of radius r centred on the origin. At all points on this surface, $\mathbf{E}(\mathbf{r}) = E_r(r)\mathbf{e}_r$, so the field is perpendicular to the surface, and therefore parallel to the vector $\mathrm{d}\mathbf{S}$ representing an element of area on this surface. The left-hand side of the equation therefore becomes

$$\int_S \mathbf{E} \cdot \mathrm{d}\mathbf{S} = \int_S E_r(r) \, \mathbf{e}_r \cdot \mathrm{d}\mathbf{S} = \int_S E_r(r) \, \mathrm{d}S.$$

Since $E_r(r)$ is constant on the spherical surface S, this integral reduces to $4\pi r^2 E_r(r)$.

The volume integral in Gauss's law can be evaluated by breaking down the spherical volume into spherical shells that have thickness δr and volume $\delta V = 4\pi r^2 \, \delta r$. Thus for a sphere of radius a, the volume integral is

$$\frac{1}{\varepsilon_0} \int_V \rho(r) \, \mathrm{d}V = \frac{1}{\varepsilon_0} \int_0^a \rho(r) \, 4\pi r^2 \, \mathrm{d}r.$$

For $a \leq R$ we have $\rho(r) = br^2$, and the integral version of Gauss's law becomes

$$4\pi a^2 E_r(a) = \frac{1}{\varepsilon_0} \int_0^a br^2\, 4\pi r^2\, dr$$

$$= \frac{4\pi b}{\varepsilon_0} \int_0^a r^4\, dr = \frac{4\pi b}{\varepsilon_0} \times \frac{a^5}{5}.$$

Thus

$$E_r(a) = ba^3/5\varepsilon_0 \quad \text{for } a \leq R.$$

For $a > R$, contributions to the volume integral come only from regions with $a \leq R$, so the upper limit of the volume integral is R. Thus

$$4\pi a^2 E_r(a) = \frac{1}{\varepsilon_0} \int_0^R br^2\, 4\pi r^2\, dr = \frac{4\pi b}{\varepsilon_0} \times \frac{R^5}{5},$$

so

$$E_r(a) = bR^5/5\varepsilon_0 a^2 \quad \text{for } a > R.$$

Ex 1.5 According to the no-monopole law, magnetic fields are always divergence-free (Equation 1.5).

(a) Using the expression for div **B** in spherical coordinates (from inside the back cover),

$$\text{div}\left(\frac{k}{r}\mathbf{e}_r\right) = \frac{1}{r^2}\frac{\partial}{\partial r}\left(r^2 \times \frac{k}{r}\right) = \frac{k}{r^2}.$$

(b) Using Cartesian coordinates,

$$\text{div}\left(k(y\mathbf{e}_x + x\mathbf{e}_y)\right) = k\left(\frac{\partial y}{\partial x} + \frac{\partial x}{\partial y}\right) = 0.$$

(c) Using cylindrical coordinates,

$$\text{div}\left[k\left(1 - \frac{r}{R}\right)\mathbf{e}_\phi\right] = \frac{1}{r}\frac{\partial}{\partial \phi}\left[k\left(1 - \frac{r}{R}\right)\right] = 0.$$

Thus fields (b) and (c) are divergence-free, so both could represent magnetic fields, whereas field (a) has non-zero divergence, so could *not* represent a magnetic field.

Ex 1.6 To derive the integral version of Faraday's law from the differential version, first integrate both sides of Equation 1.7 over any surface S that is bounded by a closed loop C:

$$\int_S (\text{curl}\,\mathbf{E}) \cdot d\mathbf{S} = -\int_S \frac{\partial \mathbf{B}}{\partial t} \cdot d\mathbf{S}.$$

According to the curl theorem, we can replace the surface integral of curl **E** on the left-hand side by a line integral of **E**:

$$\int_S (\text{curl}\,\mathbf{E}) \cdot d\mathbf{S} = \oint_C \mathbf{E} \cdot d\mathbf{l}.$$

Also, we can reverse the order of integration and differentiation on the right-hand side:

$$-\int_S \frac{\partial \mathbf{B}}{\partial t} \cdot d\mathbf{S} = -\frac{d}{dt}\int_S \mathbf{B} \cdot d\mathbf{S}.$$

Combining these two steps leads to the integral version of Faraday's law.

Comment: To obtain the differential version from the integral version, simply reverse the steps described above.

Ex 1.7 Within a solenoid, the magnetic field is uniform and parallel to the axis of the solenoid: this axial symmetry suggests that it would be appropriate to use cylindrical coordinates for this problem, with the z-axis along the axis of the solenoid. The electric field is related to the changing magnetic field by Faraday's law, $\text{curl}\,\mathbf{E} = -\partial\mathbf{B}/\partial t$. So we need to use the expression for curl in cylindrical coordinates from inside the back cover. However, since the field **B** is in the z-direction and is uniform within the solenoid, $\partial\mathbf{B}/\partial t$ can have only a component in the z-direction, so we need to consider only the z-component of curl **E**. Thus

$$\frac{1}{r}\left(\frac{\partial(rE_\phi)}{\partial r} - \frac{\partial E_r}{\partial \phi}\right) = -\frac{\partial B_z}{\partial t}.$$

By symmetry, any radial component E_r could not depend on the angle ϕ, so $\partial E_r/\partial \phi = 0$. Now since the magnetic field within the solenoid does not depend on position, the equation linking E_ϕ and B_z is straightforward to solve by integrating over r:

$$rE_\phi = -\int r\frac{\partial B_z}{\partial t}\, dr$$

$$= -\frac{\partial B_z}{\partial t}\int r\, dr$$

$$= -\frac{\partial B_z}{\partial t} \times \frac{r^2}{2} + \text{constant}.$$

So

$$E_\phi = -\frac{r}{2}\frac{\partial B_z}{\partial t},$$

where we have set the integration constant equal to zero because the azimuthal field on the axis must be zero. The electric field lines form circular loops centred on the axis of the solenoid, with the magnitude of the field proportional to the radius of the loop and to the rate of change of the magnetic field.

Ex 1.8 Faraday's law applies to *changing* magnetic fields, but if the magnetic field is constant in time, then $\partial \mathbf{B}/\partial t = \mathbf{0}$, and we obtain $\operatorname{curl} \mathbf{E} = \mathbf{0}$. This latter equation applies for *static* fields, and for electrostatic fields in simply-connected regions, $\operatorname{curl} \mathbf{E} = \mathbf{0}$ is equivalent to $\oint_C \mathbf{E} \cdot \mathrm{dl} = 0$: both are statements of the fact that electrostatic fields are conservative.

Ex 1.9 The solenoid is symmetrical under rotations about the vertical axis through its centre, so we use cylindrical coordinates with the z-axis aligned with the solenoid's axis. The symmetry indicates that the magnetic field must be independent of ϕ. Also, if the solenoid were reflected in a plane through the z-axis, the sense of the current would be unchanged, but according to the reflection rule for magnetic fields, both B_r and B_z would be reversed, which means that both of these components must be equal to zero. Thus

$$\mathbf{B} = B_\phi(r, z)\mathbf{e}_\phi.$$

To determine B_ϕ, apply Ampère's law to a circular path, radius r, centred on the z-axis and in a plane perpendicular to the axis. Since the field is constant along this path and parallel to it, $2\pi r \times B_\phi = \mu_0 N I$ (where N is the number of turns), so

$$B_\phi = \mu_0 N I / 2\pi r.$$

(Note that B_ϕ depends on r only, not on z or the shape of the cross-section of the coil.)

If we substitute the values $N = 100$, $I = 3.0\,\mathrm{A}$ and $r = 0.24\,\mathrm{m}$, then we obtain

$$\mathbf{B} = (2.5 \times 10^{-4}\,\mathrm{T})\mathbf{e}_\phi.$$

Ex 1.10 From Equation 1.13,

$$\mathbf{F} = q(E\mathbf{e}_x + v\mathbf{e}_z \times B\mathbf{e}_y) = q(E - vB)\mathbf{e}_x.$$

Ex 2.1 (a) The spherical symmetry of the charge distribution means that the electric field must be radial and depend only on r. Applying Gauss's law to a spherical surface of radius $r < R$, which must contain a fraction r^3/R^3 of the total electronic charge, we find

$$E_{\text{cloud}} \times 4\pi r^2 = (r^3/R^3)Ze/\varepsilon_0,$$

so

$$E_{\text{cloud}}(r) = (Ze/4\pi\varepsilon_0 R^3) \times r, \quad \text{for } r < R.$$

(b) The nucleus will be in equilibrium at a distance d from the centre of the electron cloud where the field attracting it to the centre of the electron cloud is equal in magnitude and opposite in direction to the applied field $\mathbf{E}_{\text{applied}}$. Thus

$$E_{\text{applied}} = E_{\text{cloud}}(d) = \left(\frac{Ze}{4\pi\varepsilon_0 R^3}\right) \times d,$$

so

$$d = \left(\frac{4\pi\varepsilon_0 R^3}{Ze}\right) \times E_{\text{applied}}.$$

This shows that $d \propto E_{\text{applied}}$, and the dipole moment is $p = Zed$, so $p \propto E_{\text{applied}}$.

Comment: Though this exercise used a rather unrealistic model for the charge density of the electron cloud, the proportionality between dipole moment and electric field derived here is also true for dipoles induced in real atoms, and it is also true for the dipole moments associated with permanent dipoles that we consider in the next subsection.

Ex 2.2 Copper is a good conductor, so the field within the copper is zero. The atoms within the block are therefore not polarized — they have no induced dipole moment because there is no local electric field to polarize the atoms.

Ex 2.3 The surface charge density is given by $\sigma_b = \mathbf{P} \cdot \hat{\mathbf{n}} = P \cos\theta$, where θ is the angle between the normal to the surface of the sphere and the direction of the polarization vector $\mathbf{P}$.

At point A, $\theta = 0°$, so $\sigma_b = P \cos 0° = P$.
At point B, $\theta = 90°$, so $\sigma_b = P \cos 90° = 0$.
At point C, $\theta = 60°$, so $\sigma_b = P \cos 60° = P/2$.
At point D, $\theta = 120°$, so $\sigma_b = P \cos 120° = -P/2$.

Ex 2.4 (a) The bound volume charge density is $\rho_b = -\operatorname{div}\mathbf{P}$, and since $P_x = a + bx$, $P_y = 0$ and $P_z = 0$,

$$\rho_b = -\left(\frac{\partial P_x}{\partial x} + \frac{\partial P_y}{\partial y} + \frac{\partial P_z}{\partial z}\right)$$

$$= -\frac{\partial}{\partial x}(a + bx) = -b.$$

So $\rho_b = -b$ is constant throughout the block.

(b) The bound surface charge density is $\sigma_b = \mathbf{P} \cdot \hat{\mathbf{n}}$. The polarization is parallel to four of the faces, so $\sigma_b = 0$ for these faces. For the face in the plane $x = 0$,

$$\sigma_b = a\mathbf{e}_x \cdot (-\mathbf{e}_x) = -a.$$

For the face in the plane $x = l$,

$$\sigma_b = (a + bl)\mathbf{e}_x \cdot \mathbf{e}_x = a + bl.$$

The surface charge densities are constant across these two faces.

(c) Volume charge $= \rho_b \times$ volume $= -bl^3$. On the plane $x = 0$ the surface charge is

$$\sigma_b \times \text{area} = -al^2,$$

and on the plane $x = l$ the surface charge is

$$(a + bl) \times l^2 = al^2 + bl^3.$$

The sum of the volume charge and the charge on the two charged faces is therefore zero.

Comment: Note that the net bound charge must always be zero, because charge is not added or removed when the material is polarized.

Ex 2.5 Since $C = \varepsilon \varepsilon_0 A/d$ (Equation 2.15),

$$A = \frac{Cd}{\varepsilon \varepsilon_0}$$

$$= \frac{30 \times 10^{-15}\,\text{F} \times 17 \times 10^{-9}\,\text{m}}{13 \times 8.85 \times 10^{-12}\,\text{C}^2\,\text{N}^{-1}\,\text{m}^{-2}}$$

$$= 4.4 \times 10^{-12}\,\text{m}^2.$$

The area A is the product of the depth of the trench and its circumference, so the circumference is

$$4.4 \times 10^{-12}\,\text{m}^2/4.4 \times 10^{-6}\,\text{m} = 1.0 \times 10^{-6}\,\text{m}.$$

Ex 2.6 (a) The cylindrical symmetry of the cable means that the fields must be radial and directed away from the axis of the cable (since the inner wire is positively charged). To determine the field $\mathbf{D}$, we apply the integral version of Gauss's law to a cylinder of length L, radius r, concentric with the axis of the cable. The field $\mathbf{D}$ is perpendicular to the cylinder's curved surface, and has a constant magnitude at this surface, and $\mathbf{D}$ is parallel to the circular end-faces of the cylinder. For $r_1 < r < r_2$, the amount of free charge enclosed by the cylinder is λL, so

$$\int \mathbf{D} \cdot \text{d}\mathbf{S} = D_r(r) \times 2\pi r L = \lambda L.$$

Thus $D_r(r) = \lambda/2\pi r$. For $r < r_1$, there is no free charge enclosed by the cylinder — it is all on the surface of the wire — so $D_r(r)$ is zero in the central conductor, as expected since both $\mathbf{E}$ and $\mathbf{P}$ are zero inside a conductor. For $r > r_2$, there is zero net charge within the cylinder — the positive charge on the inner wire is balanced by the negative charge on the outer cylindrical conductor — so $D_r(r) = 0$ outside the cable too.

The radial field $E_r(r)$ can be determined using Equation 2.14:

$$E_r(r) = \frac{D_r(r)}{\varepsilon \varepsilon_0} = \frac{\lambda}{2\pi \varepsilon \varepsilon_0 r},$$

for $r_1 < r < r_2$. The polarization is also radial:

$$P_r(r) = (\varepsilon - 1)\varepsilon_0 E_r(r) = \frac{\varepsilon - 1}{\varepsilon}\frac{\lambda}{2\pi r}.$$

Comment: The absence of fields outside coaxial cables is one reason for their widespread use. Electrical signals can be transmitted along them without the fields produced by these signals interfering with other equipment.

(b) The capacitance per unit length of the cable is the ratio of the charge per unit length on the positive conductor divided by the potential difference ΔV between the positive and negative conductors. From the definition of potential,

$$\Delta V = -\int_{r_2}^{r_1} \mathbf{E} \cdot \text{d}\mathbf{r},$$

where the upper limit corresponds to the positively-charged wire. Thus

$$\Delta V = -\int_{r_2}^{r_1} \frac{\lambda}{2\pi \varepsilon \varepsilon_0 r}\,\text{d}r = \frac{\lambda \ln(r_2/r_1)}{2\pi \varepsilon \varepsilon_0}.$$

Hence

$$\text{capacitance per unit length} = \lambda \left/ \left[\frac{\lambda \ln(r_2/r_1)}{2\pi \varepsilon \varepsilon_0}\right]\right.$$

$$= \frac{2\pi \varepsilon \varepsilon_0}{\ln(r_2/r_1)}.$$

Ex 2.7 (a) Since these are LIH materials, $\mathbf{E}$ and $\mathbf{P}$ are in the same direction as $\mathbf{D}$ in each layer. These fields have no component parallel to the boundary in the top layer, and the boundary condition $E_{1\parallel} = E_{2\parallel}$ indicates that this must also be true for the other two layers. So $\mathbf{D}$ must be perpendicular to the boundaries in all three layers, and from the condition $D_{1\perp} = D_{2\perp}$ we deduce that its magnitude D is the same in all three layers, $2.0 \times 10^{-10}\,\text{C}\,\text{m}^{-2}$.

(b) For an LIH material, $\mathbf{D} = \varepsilon \varepsilon_0 \mathbf{E}$, so in the top and bottom layers

$$E = \frac{2.0 \times 10^{-10}\,\text{C}\,\text{m}^{-2}}{2.5 \times 8.85 \times 10^{-12}\,\text{C}^2\,\text{N}^{-1}\,\text{m}^{-2}}$$

$$= 9.0\,\text{N}\,\text{C}^{-1},$$

and in the middle layer

$$E = \frac{2.0 \times 10^{-10}\,\mathrm{C\,m^{-2}}}{1.5 \times 8.85 \times 10^{-12}\,\mathrm{C^2\,N^{-1}\,m^{-2}}}$$
$$= 15.1\,\mathrm{N\,C^{-1}}.$$

These $\mathbf{E}$ fields are in the same direction as $\mathbf{D}$, i.e. perpendicular to the boundaries.

The polarization field is related to $\mathbf{D}$ by the relation $\mathbf{P} = \mathbf{D} \times (\varepsilon - 1)/\varepsilon$. So in the top and bottom layers

$$P = 2.0 \times 10^{-10}\,\mathrm{C\,m^{-2}} \times (2.5 - 1)/2.5$$
$$= 1.2 \times 10^{-10}\,\mathrm{C\,m^{-2}},$$

and in the middle layer

$$P = 2.0 \times 10^{-10}\,\mathrm{C\,m^{-2}} \times (1.5 - 1)/1.5$$
$$= 6.7 \times 10^{-11}\,\mathrm{C\,m^{-2}}.$$

(c) The density of *bound* charge at a boundary can be found by applying the integral version of Gauss's law that involves $\mathbf{E}$ and the total charge Q to a thin pillbox straddling the boundary, that is,

$$\int_S \mathbf{E} \cdot \mathrm{d}\mathbf{S} = Q/\varepsilon_0 = (Q_\mathrm{f} + Q_\mathrm{b})/\varepsilon_0.$$

The question states that there is no free charge, i.e. $Q_\mathrm{f} = 0$. Thus if the fields on either side of the boundary have magnitudes E_1 and E_2, with E_1 pointing towards the boundary and E_2 away from the boundary, then since these fields are normal to the plane surfaces of the pillbox, the Gaussian integral becomes

$$E_2 A - E_1 A = Q_\mathrm{b}/\varepsilon_0 = \sigma_\mathrm{b} A/\varepsilon_0,$$

where A is the area of the plane faces of the pillbox, and σ_b is the density of bound charge at the boundary. Thus

$$\sigma_\mathrm{b} = \varepsilon_0(E_2 - E_1).$$

For the upper boundary, the field pointing away from the boundary is $E_2 = 15.1\,\mathrm{N\,C^{-1}}$ and the field pointing towards the boundary is $E_1 = 9.0\,\mathrm{N\,C^{-1}}$, so

$$\sigma_\mathrm{b} = 8.85 \times 10^{-12}\,\mathrm{C^2\,N^{-1}\,m^{-2}}$$
$$\times (15.1 - 9.0)\,\mathrm{N\,C^{-1}}$$
$$= +5.4 \times 10^{-11}\,\mathrm{C\,m^{-2}}.$$

For the lower boundary, the magnitudes of the fields towards and away from the boundary are interchanged, so the sign of the charge density is changed, and

$$\sigma_\mathrm{b} = -5.4 \times 10^{-11}\,\mathrm{C\,m^{-2}}.$$

Ex 2.8   We assume that the fields $\mathbf{E}$ and $\mathbf{D}$ are uniform and perpendicular to the plates. There will be no *free* current in the dielectric, so $\mathrm{curl}\,\mathbf{B} = \mu_0\,\partial\mathbf{D}/\partial t$. If we use Cartesian coordinates, with the z-axis perpendicular to the plates, then

$$\mathbf{D} = \varepsilon\varepsilon_0\mathbf{E} = \varepsilon\varepsilon_0 E_z \mathbf{e}_z = \varepsilon\varepsilon_0(V_0/d)\sin\omega t\,\mathbf{e}_z,$$

since $E_z = V/d$. So

$$\mathrm{curl}\,\mathbf{B} = \mu_0\,\partial\mathbf{D}/\partial t = \varepsilon\varepsilon_0\mu_0(V_0\omega/d)\cos\omega t\,\mathbf{e}_z.$$

This shows that $\mathrm{curl}\,\mathbf{B}$ is in the z-direction, and it has the same magnitude at all points in the dielectric at any instant, but it varies sinusoidally with time.

Ex 3.1   The relevant equations are $\mathrm{div}\,\mathbf{E} = \rho/\varepsilon_0$ and $\mathrm{div}\,\mathbf{B} = 0$. The first equation (Gauss's law) shows that charge density acts as a source of electric field; that is why the electric field lines in Figure 3.4 are discontinuous, changing direction at the ends of the dielectric where polarization produces surface charges. The second equation (the no-monopole law) shows that there is no magnetic equivalent of electric charge; that is why the magnetic field lines are continuous.

Ex 3.2   The appropriate entries for the table can be deduced from Figures 3.4, 3.5 and 3.6, and are shown below.

Dielectric	Diamagnet	Paramagnet
same	opposite	same
opposite	opposite	same
same	opposite	same

Comment: I find it useful to remember that, within their own volumes, *di*electrics and *di*amagnets both oppose the applied field. Since I know that lines of $\mathbf{B}$ are continuous, while lines of $\mathbf{E}$ are not, and that paramagnets (and ferromagnets) display the opposite behaviour to diamagnets, I can work out the remaining relationships.

Ex 3.3   The spherical symmetry of the problem strongly suggests the use of spherical coordinates. In this case, $M_r = M_r(r)$, $M_\theta = 0$ and $M_\phi = 0$. Now $\mathbf{J}_\mathrm{b} = \mathrm{curl}\,\mathbf{M}$, and from the expression for $\mathrm{curl}\,\mathbf{M}$ in spherical coordinates inside the back cover, it is clear that all three components of $\mathrm{curl}\,\mathbf{M}$ involve partial derivatives of one component with respect to the other two coordinates — there are no terms involving $\partial M_r/\partial r$. So all three components of $\mathrm{curl}\,\mathbf{M}$ are zero outside the shell. Hence $\mathbf{J}_\mathrm{b} = \mathbf{0}$.

The magnetization surface current per unit length, $\mathbf{i}_b = \mathbf{M} \times \hat{\mathbf{n}}$, is also zero, because the magnetization vector is parallel to the surface normal at all points on the outer surface of the sphere, and antiparallel to the normal at the inner surface. Explicitly, if R is the radius of the sphere, then

$$\mathbf{i}_b = \mathbf{M} \times \hat{\mathbf{n}} = M_r(R)\mathbf{e}_r \times \hat{\mathbf{n}}.$$

Since $\hat{\mathbf{n}} = \mathbf{e}_r$ at the outer surface, and $\hat{\mathbf{n}} = -\mathbf{e}_r$ at the inner surface, and $\mathbf{e}_r \times \mathbf{e}_r = \mathbf{e}_r \times (-\mathbf{e}_r) = \mathbf{0}$, we conclude that there are no magnetization currents within the volume of the sphere or on its surface. No currents mean there is no $\mathbf{B}$ field externally, so the magnetization cannot be detected outside the shell.

Ex 3.4 Because the surrounding medium is homogeneous, the problem has axial symmetry, and it is safe to assume that the field is of the form $\mathbf{H} = H_\phi(r)\mathbf{e}_\phi$. So the problem is most easily solved by evaluating the line integral of $\mathbf{H}$ in Equation 3.9 around a circular path of radius $r > a$, centred on the axis of the wire. The field has a constant magnitude H along this path, and is parallel to the path elements, so

$$\oint \mathbf{H} \cdot \mathrm{dl} = H \times 2\pi r = I_f.$$

We conclude that $H = I_f/2\pi r$. The detailed nature of the surrounding medium has not entered this calculation, so the $\mathbf{H}$ field in glass would be the same as that in air (or in any other material). However, the $\mathbf{B}$ field in glass would be different to that in air, and in the next subsection we shall discuss how we can determine $\mathbf{B}$ if $\mathbf{H}$ is known.

Ex 3.5 The field $\mathbf{H}$ remains the same since it depends only on the free current — the current in the solenoid. Using Equations 3.10 and 3.11, along with values of χ_B from Table 3.2, we can see that the magnitude of $\mathbf{B}$ will

(a) decrease slightly when diamagnetic copper is inserted,

(b) increase slightly when paramagnetic aluminium is inserted, and

(c) increase greatly when ferromagnetic iron is inserted.

Comment: The effect of ferromagnetic materials on the $\mathbf{B}$ field is put to good use in electromagnets, as you will see in Section 3.6.

Ex 3.6 In order to determine the form of the graphs, we exploit the axial symmetry of this problem. We assume that the wire lies along the z-axis of cylindrical

coordinates, and first consider a circular loop of radius $r < r_0$, centred on the axis, and perpendicular to it. Since the current density is uniform, the loop is threaded by a free current $I_f \times (\pi r^2/\pi r_0^2)$. From the symmetry of the problem, we can assume that the field is of the form $\mathbf{H} = H_\phi(r)\mathbf{e}_\phi$, so Ampère's law gives

$$\oint \mathbf{H} \cdot \mathrm{dl} = 2\pi r H_\phi(r) = I_f \frac{r^2}{r_0^2}.$$

So inside the wire ($r < r_0$),

$$H_\phi = \left(\frac{I_f}{2\pi r_0^2}\right) r$$

and

$$B_\phi = \mu\mu_0 H_\phi = \left(\frac{\mu\mu_0 I_f}{2\pi r_0^2}\right) r.$$

The fields outside the wire are found in a similar way, using a loop of radius $r > r_0$, concentric with the wire and lying wholly outside it. Applying Ampère's law to this loop gives

$$\oint \mathbf{H} \cdot \mathrm{dl} = 2\pi r H_\phi(r) = I_f,$$

so outside the wire ($r > r_0$),

$$H_\phi = \left(\frac{I_f}{2\pi}\right) \frac{1}{r}.$$

In the air outside the wire, $\mu_{air} \simeq 1$, so

$$B_\phi = \mu_0 H_\phi = \left(\frac{\mu_0 I_f}{2\pi}\right) \frac{1}{r} \quad \text{for } r > r_0.$$

Figure S3.1 shows the field variations for a wire with $\mu = 2$.

Note that:

- $H \propto r$ and $B \propto r$ for $r < r_0$;

- $H \propto 1/r$ and $B \propto 1/r$ for $r > r_0$;

- H is continuous across the surface of the wire, but B drops by a factor of μ ($= 2$) at the surface of the wire.

Comment: Note that B changes discontinuously at the surface of the wire. The general conditions relating fields on either side of a boundary between different media will be discussed in the next section. Note also that the field outside the wire is independent of the material from which the wire is made — you cannot generate a larger external field using iron wire rather than copper.

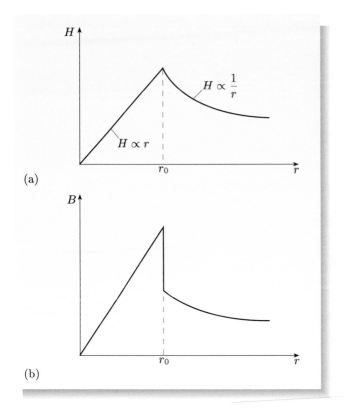

(a)

(b)

Figure S3.1 Graphs of (a) H and (b) B against distance from the centre of a current-carrying wire with relative permeability $\mu = 2$.

Ex 3.7 As indicated in Figure S3.2, the mu-metal plate effectively shields points behind it from a magnetic field $\mathbf{B}$ provided that the field lines are refracted sufficiently to emerge from the side edges of the plate rather than its bottom surface.

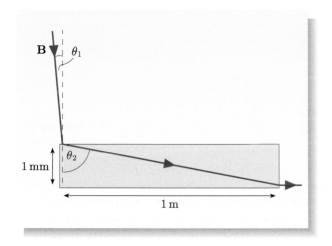

Figure S3.2 Shielding by a mu-metal plate.

Since the plate is 1 m wide and 1 mm thick, we require $\tan\theta_2 > 1000$. Using Equation 3.16 and setting $\mu_1 = 1$

for air and $\mu_2 = 50\,000$ for mu-metal, we find

$$\tan\theta_1 = \frac{\mu_1}{\mu_2}\tan\theta_2 > \frac{1}{50\,000} \times 1000 = \frac{1}{50}.$$

Thus the condition for effective shielding at all points immediately behind the plate is $\tan\theta_1 > 1/50$, which is satisfied for $\theta_1 > 1.1°$.

Ex 3.8 The fields within the cylinder will be uniform in regions not too close to the ends. The appropriate boundary condition to use is that $H_\parallel$ is continuous across any boundary. Outside the cylinder, $\mathbf{H} = \mathbf{B}_0/\mu_0$. Since this field is parallel to the sides of the cylinder, it is safe to conclude that $\mathbf{H}_c = \mathbf{B}_0/\mu_0$ inside the cylinder. The values of $\mathbf{B}_c$ and $\mathbf{M}_c$ follow from Equations 3.7 and 3.10:

$$\mathbf{B}_c = \mu_c\mu_0\mathbf{H}_c = \mu_c\mathbf{B}_0$$

and

$$\mathbf{M}_c = \frac{\mathbf{B}_c}{\mu_0} - \mathbf{H}_c = \frac{(\mu_c - 1)\mathbf{B}_0}{\mu_0}.$$

Ex 3.9 Values of μ for typical diamagnetic and paramagnetic materials differ from 1 by less than 0.0001, so the ratios μ/μ_{air} will differ from 1 by similar amounts. From Equation 3.16 it follows that $\tan\theta$ is practically the same on either side of the boundary, so the field lines are essentially undeviated.

Ex 3.10 The relative permeability of the material is given by

$$\mu = B/\mu_0 H$$

$$= \frac{1\,\text{T}}{4\pi \times 10^{-7}\,\text{T m A}^{-1} \times 1000\,\text{A m}^{-1}}$$

$$= 796.$$

Then rearranging Equation 3.18 and substituting appropriate data, we find

$$I = \frac{1\,\text{T} \times (2\pi \times 0.20\,\text{m} - 0.010\,\text{m} + 796 \times 0.010\,\text{m})}{796 \times 4\pi \times 10^{-7}\,\text{T m A}^{-1} \times 400}$$

$$= 23\,\text{A}.$$

Comment: If you used the approximation $B \simeq \mu_0 NI/w$, then the current calculated would be 20 A. In this problem, $2\pi r = 1.26\,\text{m}$ is not negligible compared with $w\mu = 7.96$.

Ex 4.1 The charge density is related to the potential by Poisson's equation, $\nabla^2 V = -\rho_f/\varepsilon\varepsilon_0$. As the electrostatic potential has spherical symmetry, we need to use the form of ∇^2 for spherical coordinates, which is given inside the back cover. However, the spherical symmetry of $V(\mathbf{r})$ means that it has no dependence on either θ or ϕ, so we require only the first term, which involves derivatives with respect to r:

$$\nabla^2 V = \frac{1}{r^2}\frac{d}{dr}\left(r^2\frac{dV}{dr}\right).$$

(Note that we use the operator d/dr for *ordinary* differentiation here because V is a function of r only, and is independent of θ and ϕ.) Now

$$\frac{dV}{dr} = \frac{d}{dr}\left(Ae^{-r/a}\right) = -\frac{A}{a}e^{-r/a}.$$

So

$$\frac{d}{dr}\left(r^2\frac{dV}{dr}\right) = \frac{d}{dr}\left(-\frac{Ar^2}{a}e^{-r/a}\right)$$
$$= -\frac{2Ar}{a}e^{-r/a} + \frac{Ar^2}{a^2}e^{-r/a}.$$

Hence

$$\nabla^2 V = \frac{1}{r^2}\frac{d}{dr}\left(r^2\frac{dV}{dr}\right) = \frac{A}{a^2}\left(1 - \frac{2a}{r}\right)e^{-r/a}.$$

Then, from Poisson's equation,

$$\rho_f = -\varepsilon\varepsilon_0\nabla^2 V = \frac{A\varepsilon\varepsilon_0}{a^2}\left(\frac{2a}{r} - 1\right)e^{-r/a}.$$

Ex 4.2 In Cartesian coordinates,

$$\mathbf{E} = -\,\mathrm{grad}\,V = -\frac{\partial V}{\partial x}\mathbf{e}_x - \frac{\partial V}{\partial y}\mathbf{e}_y - \frac{\partial V}{\partial z}\mathbf{e}_z.$$

For the parallel plate capacitor,

$$V(z) = V_0 + \left(\frac{V_d - V_0}{d}\right)z.$$

So

$$\mathbf{E} = -\frac{dV(z)}{dz}\mathbf{e}_z = -\frac{V_d - V_0}{d}\mathbf{e}_z.$$

Ex 4.3 (a) The electrostatic potential V satisfies Laplace's equation $\nabla^2 V = 0$. Because of the spherical symmetry of the situation, we shall use spherical coordinates with their origin at the geometric centre of the capacitor. Furthermore, because of the spherical symmetry, the electrostatic potential V depends only on r, i.e. $V = V(r)$. So the expression for Laplace's equation in spherical coordinates, given inside the back cover, reduces to

$$\frac{1}{r^2}\frac{d}{dr}\left(r^2\frac{dV}{dr}\right) = 0.$$

Integrating this once, we obtain

$$r^2\frac{dV}{dr} = A, \quad\text{or}\quad \frac{dV}{dr} = \frac{A}{r^2},$$

where A is a constant of integration. Integrating again, we obtain

$$V(r) = -\frac{A}{r} + B,$$

where B is a second constant.

Using the boundary condition $V(r_1) = V_1$ leads to

$$V_1 = -\frac{A}{r_1} + B,$$

and the boundary condition $V(r_2) = V_2$ leads to

$$V_2 = -\frac{A}{r_2} + B.$$

Solving these two simultaneous equations for the constants A and B gives

$$A = \frac{r_1 r_2}{r_2 - r_1}(V_2 - V_1),$$

$$B = \frac{r_2 V_2 - r_1 V_1}{r_2 - r_1}.$$

So

$$V(r) = -\frac{r_1 r_2(V_2 - V_1)}{r_2 - r_1}\frac{1}{r} + \frac{r_2 V_2 - r_1 V_1}{r_2 - r_1}.$$

(b) The electrostatic field is given by $\mathbf{E} = -\,\mathrm{grad}\,V$. Because $V = V(r)$, the expression for $\mathrm{grad}\,V$ in spherical coordinates reduces to

$$\mathbf{E} = -\frac{dV}{dr}\mathbf{e}_r.$$

Substituting the expression for $V(r)$ from part (a),

$$\mathbf{E} = -\frac{r_1 r_2(V_2 - V_1)}{r_2 - r_1}\frac{1}{r^2}\mathbf{e}_r.$$

Ex 4.4 (a) The free charge density is zero between the plates of the capacitor, so the electrostatic potential in each material satisfies Laplace's equation, i.e. $\nabla^2 V_1 = 0$ and $\nabla^2 V_2 = 0$. As the plate dimensions are large compared with their spacing, we have planar symmetry and so the electrostatic potential has no x- or y-dependence, and Laplace's equation reduces to

$$\frac{d^2 V_1}{dz^2} = 0 \quad\text{for } 0 \le z \le d,$$

$$\frac{d^2 V_2}{dz^2} = 0 \quad\text{for } d \le z \le 2d.$$

(b) The solution to Worked Example 4.2 shows that the general solutions to Laplace's equation in the two regions are

$$V_1(z) = A_1 z + B_1 \quad \text{for } 0 \le z \le d,$$

$$V_2(z) = A_2 z + B_2 \quad \text{for } d \le z \le 2d,$$

where A_1, B_1, A_2 and B_2 are constants of integration.

(c) At the plate at $z = 0$, the boundary condition is $V_1(0) = 0$, so

$$0 = (A_1 \times 0) + B_1 = B_1.$$

Similarly, at the plate at $z = 2d$ the boundary condition is $V_2(2d) = V_C$, so

$$V_C = 2A_2 d + B_2.$$

At the boundary between the two dielectrics, the potential is continuous, $V_1(d) = V_2(d)$, so

$$A_1 d + B_1 = A_2 d + B_2.$$

Finally, the boundary condition for the gradient of the potential perpendicular to the interface (Equation 4.15) at $z = d$ is

$$\varepsilon_1 \left[\frac{dV_1}{dz} \right]_{z=d} = \varepsilon_2 \left[\frac{dV_2}{dz} \right]_{z=d},$$

which leads to

$$\varepsilon_1 A_1 = \varepsilon_2 A_2.$$

Comment: These four equations for the four boundary conditions are sufficient to determine the four constants of integration. Wading through the algebra would lead to expressions for V_1 and V_2 that satisfy Laplace's equation and the boundary conditions and which must therefore be the solution to this problem. The potentials are

$$V_1 = \frac{\varepsilon_2 V_C z}{(\varepsilon_1 + \varepsilon_2)d},$$

$$V_2 = \frac{\varepsilon_1 V_C z}{(\varepsilon_1 + \varepsilon_2)d} + \frac{V_C(\varepsilon_2 - \varepsilon_1)}{\varepsilon_1 + \varepsilon_2}.$$

Ex 4.5 (a) An obvious solution is $V(\mathbf{r}) = V_0$ inside the enclosure. This satisfies Laplace's equation and it satisfies the boundary condition that the potential is V_0 at the surface of the enclosure.

(b) According to the uniqueness theorem, there is only one possible solution, so the solution in part (a) must be correct.

Comment: This means that inside any conducting enclosure, no matter what its shape, the potential is a constant and the electric field is zero. This is why sensitive electronic circuits are enclosed in metal boxes to protect them from variations in the electric field outside the enclosure.

Ex 4.6 (a) Laplace's equation is a linear differential equation, so any linear combination of solutions to the equation must also be a solution. Since we know that the expression for the potential quoted for an infinite line charge is a solution, adding two expressions with similar forms must also produce a valid solution.

(b) We require that the position of the conducting plate is an equipotential with $V = 0$. Now, at all points on this plane, $r_1 = r_2$, so $\ln(r_2/r_1) = 0$. The plane is therefore an equipotential, and we can make this potential zero by choosing the constant V_0 to be zero. We also require that the potential close to the line charge varies as $-\lambda \ln r_1 / 2\pi\varepsilon_0$, and Equation 4.17 will have this form when the distance from the original line charge is very small.

Ex 4.7 In order to ensure that the electrostatic potential is zero on the planes OX and OY, we need to introduce *three* image charges, at B, C and D as shown in Figure S4.1.

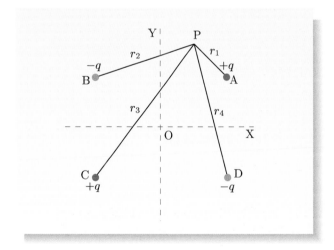

Figure S4.1 A point charge at A and its three image charges at B, C and D.

With this arrangement, for any point on plane OX, the sum of the potentials due to the charges at A and D cancel, and those due to B and C cancel. Similarly, on plane OY, the potentials due to the charges at A and B cancel, as do those due to the charges at C and D. So the four charges match the boundary conditions that

257

$V = 0$ on OX and OY, and also the condition that $V \to 0$ as $r \to \infty$. The required electrostatic potential at a point P is therefore

$$V = \frac{1}{4\pi\varepsilon_0}\frac{q}{r_1} - \frac{1}{4\pi\varepsilon_0}\frac{q}{r_2} + \frac{1}{4\pi\varepsilon_0}\frac{q}{r_3} - \frac{1}{4\pi\varepsilon_0}\frac{q}{r_4},$$

where the distances are as defined in Figure S4.1.

Ex 4.8 (a) The field is uniform for large r. Therefore

$$V_1 = A_1 r \cos\theta = -E_0 r \cos\theta,$$

so

$$A_1 = -E_0.$$

Condition (iv) means that $B_2 = 0$. We can therefore rewrite the potential functions as

$$V_1 = -E_0 r \cos\theta + \frac{B_1 \cos\theta}{r^2} \quad \text{for } r \geq R,$$

$$V_2 = A_2 r \cos\theta \quad \text{for } r \leq R.$$

(b) Using the results from part (a), condition (ii) leads to

$$-E_0 R + \frac{B_1}{R^2} = A_2 R.$$

From condition (iii), we have

$$-E_0 - \frac{2B_1}{R^3} = \varepsilon A_2.$$

Solving these two simultaneous equations, we obtain

$$A_2 = -\frac{3}{\varepsilon + 2} E_0,$$

$$B_1 = \frac{\varepsilon - 1}{\varepsilon + 2} R^3 E_0.$$

Ex 4.9 Using Equation 4.27,

$$V_A = \tfrac{1}{4}(0.5 + 0.25 + 0 + 0) = 0.1875,$$

$$V_B = \tfrac{1}{4}(1 + 0.5 + 0 + 0.25) = 0.4375,$$

$$V_C = \tfrac{1}{4}(0.5 + 0 + 0.25 + 0) = 0.1875,$$

$$V_D = \tfrac{1}{4}(1 + 0 + 0.5 + 0.25) = 0.4375.$$

Ex 5.1 The most striking feature of the field is its symmetry. The field lines are circles centred on an axis through the current element. The field strength falls off with the square of the distance $|\mathbf{r} - \mathbf{r}'|$ from the current element. For a constant distance, the field varies as the sine of the angle between the direction of $\delta\mathbf{l}'$ and the direction of $(\mathbf{r} - \mathbf{r}')$.

Ex 5.2 Using the right-hand grip rule, we deduce that the field will be in the y-direction. Its strength is given by Equation 5.8,

$$B = \frac{\mu_0 I}{4\pi d}[\sin\alpha_S - \sin\alpha_R],$$

where $d = 3.0\,\text{m}$, $\sin\alpha_S = 4.0\,\text{m}/\text{PS} = 4.0/5.0$, and $\sin\alpha_R = \sin 0° = 0$. So

$$\mathbf{B} = \frac{10^{-7}\,\text{T m A}^{-1} \times 30\,\text{A} \times 0.80}{3.0\,\text{m}}\mathbf{e}_y$$

$$= (8.0 \times 10^{-7}\,\text{T})\,\mathbf{e}_y.$$

Ex 5.3 The fields due to all four sides are perpendicular to the plane of the loop and away from you. The fields at P due to the closer two sides are equal, and the angles α from P to the end-points are $45°$ and approximately $\tan^{-1}(199) \simeq 90°$ for each side. Thus the total field strength due to these two sides is

$$B = 2 \times \frac{\mu_0 I}{4\pi d}[\sin 45° - \sin(-90°)]$$

$$= \frac{2 \times 10^{-7}\,\text{T m A}^{-1} \times 10\,\text{A}}{1.0 \times 10^{-2}\,\text{m}}[0.707 + 1]$$

$$= 3.4 \times 10^{-4}\,\text{T}.$$

Since the other two sides are 200 times further away from P, the $1/d$ factor in the expression for B means that we can ignore their contributions in this approximate calculation.

Ex 5.4 At the centre,

$$[\sin\alpha_B - \sin\alpha_A] = [\sin 45° - \sin(-45°)]$$

$$= 2/\sqrt{2} = \sqrt{2},$$

and at one end,

$$[\sin\alpha_B - \sin\alpha_A] = [2/\sqrt{5} - \sin 0°]$$

$$= 2/\sqrt{5}.$$

The ratio is therefore $2/\sqrt{5}\sqrt{2} = 2/\sqrt{10} = 0.63$.

Ex 5.5 The field will be the vector sum of the fields due to the two semicircles and the two straight lines. The straight-line segments do not produce a magnetic field at the origin, since the term $\delta\mathbf{l}' \times (\mathbf{r} - \mathbf{r}')$ in the Biot–Savart law is zero for measurement points on the axis of the current element. Each small element of the smaller semicircle produces a field perpendicular to the plane of the loop and away from you, and each element of the larger semicircle produces a field in the opposite direction. The magnitudes of these fields must be half of the fields that would be produced at the centres of circular loops of the same radii.

Using the expression $B = \mu_0 I / 2a$ for the field strength at the centre of a circular loop of radius a, the total field from the two semicircles, and therefore from the complete loop, is

$$\mathbf{B} = \tfrac{1}{2}\frac{\mu_0 I}{2a}(-\mathbf{e}_z) + \tfrac{1}{2}\frac{\mu_0 I}{4a}\,\mathbf{e}_z = -\frac{\mu_0 I}{8a}\,\mathbf{e}_z.$$

Ex 5.6   Only the tangential component of the current dipole in Figure 5.19 generates an external field that has a radial component at the surface of the scalp. By symmetry, the field will be in an azimuthal direction around the axis defined by the direction of the current dipole. Using the right-hand grip rule, the field will be out of the top of the head on the left of the dipole, and into the head on the right. Directly above the current dipole, the radial field will be zero. The field will drop away quickly at larger distances because of the inverse-square dependence on distance in the Biot–Savart law.

Ex 5.7   Using the Biot–Savart law, the field at P is along the negative z-direction. Its magnitude is given by

$$B = \frac{\mu_0 I\,\delta l'}{4\pi \times \text{SP}^2}$$
$$= \frac{10^{-7}\,\text{T m A}^{-1} \times 1.0 \times 10^{-9}\,\text{A m}}{(10^2 - 7.1^2) \times 10^{-4}\,\text{m}^2}$$
$$= 2.0 \times 10^{-14}\,\text{T},$$

where the separation between current dipole and field point has been calculated using Pythagoras's theorem. The field component in the radial direction is

$$2.0 \times 10^{-14}\,\text{T} \times \cos 135° = -1.4 \times 10^{-14}\,\text{T}.$$

Ex 5.8   At large negative x, the z-component of field, B_z, is positive but small, as the source is far away. Using similar arguments, B_z is small and negative at large positive x. For $x = 0$, B_z is zero, as the field is parallel to the conductor surface. Between the extreme values, B_z has a maximum at an intermediate negative value of x, and a minimum at an intermediate positive value of x, as shown in Figure S5.1.

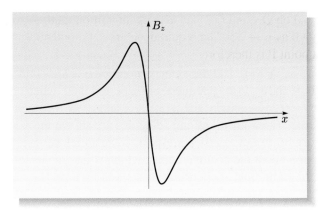

Figure S5.1   Solution to Exercise 5.8.

Ex 6.1   We shall assume that the z-axis is vertically downwards along the axis of the microscope column. The accelerating field, $-E_z\mathbf{e}_z$, causes uniform acceleration, $a_z = -e \times -E_z/m = eE_z/m$. Applying the constant acceleration equation, $v_z^2 = v_{z0}^2 + 2a_z z$, with $v_{z0} = 0$, $E_z = -3.0 \times 10^4\,\text{V m}^{-1}$ and $z = 5 \times 10^{-2}\,\text{m}$, leads to

$$v_z = \left(\frac{2eE_z z}{m}\right)^{1/2}$$
$$= [2 \times 1.60 \times 10^{-19}\,\text{C} \times 3.0 \times 10^4\,\text{V m}^{-1}$$
$$\times 5.0 \times 10^{-2}\,\text{m}/9.11 \times 10^{-31}\,\text{kg}]^{1/2}$$
$$= 2.3 \times 10^7\,\text{m s}^{-1}.$$

Comment: The same result could be obtained by equating the increase in kinetic energy, $\tfrac{1}{2}mv^2$, to the work done by the electric force, $-eE_z \times z$, or by equating the decrease in electrical potential energy, $-eV$, of an electron when it moves through a potential difference V to the increase in its kinetic energy, $\tfrac{1}{2}mv^2$, where $V = Ez$.

Ex 6.2   (a) The centripetal acceleration of the particle is directed towards the axis of the helix, so the force $q\mathbf{v} \times \mathbf{B}$ at any point on the path in Figure 6.4 must point towards this axis. If you place your outstretched right hand so that the fingers are aligned with the velocity vector at any point on the helix, and then rotate your wrist so that your fingers can bend in the direction of the field, your extended thumb will point in the direction of the vector product, $\mathbf{v} \times \mathbf{B}$, and this is towards the helix axis. So q must be positive in order that the force, $q\mathbf{v} \times \mathbf{B}$, is directed towards the axis, as required for the helical path in Figure 6.4.

(b) Since q is positive, $\omega_c = qB/m$ and $r_c = mv_\perp/qB$. Also, we are assuming $x_0 = 0$, $y_0 = 0$ and $\phi_0 = 0$, so we can write the x- and y-components of Equations 6.7 and 6.6 as $x = -r_c \cos \omega_c t$, $y = r_c \sin \omega_c t$, $v_x = v_\perp \sin \omega_c t$ and $v_y = v_\perp \cos \omega_c t$. So at $t = 0$, $x = -r_c$, $y = 0$, and the velocity components are $v_x = 0$ and $v_y = v_\perp$. A quarter of a period later, when $\omega_c t = \pi/2$, we obtain $x = 0$, $y = r_c$, and $v_x = v_\perp$ and $v_y = 0$. These positions and velocities are shown in Figure S6.1, and clearly correspond to an anticlockwise rotation about the positive z-axis, which is into the page for the right-handed coordinate system in Figure 6.4a.

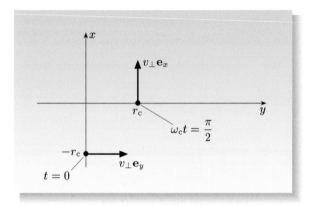

Figure S6.1 Solution to Exercise 6.2(b).

Ex 6.3 The magnetic force, $-e\mathbf{v} \times \mathbf{B}$, on the electrons must be in the $+x$-direction, and the right-hand rule indicates that the magnetic field must therefore be in the $+y$-direction.

The z-component of velocity of the electrons is unaffected by the scanning magnetic field, so the time Δt taken by the electrons to traverse the scanning field is $\Delta t = z_m/v_z$. During the time Δt that an electron is in the scanning field, it experiences a constant force of magnitude $ev_z B$ in the x-direction, and therefore has an acceleration of magnitude $ev_z B/m$ in that direction. So its x-component of velocity as it leaves the scanning field is

$$v_x = a_x t = \frac{ev_z B}{m} \Delta t = \frac{eBz_m}{m}.$$

After leaving the scanning field, the electron must travel a distance x_s in the x-direction while travelling z_s in the z-direction. So we require

$$\frac{x_s}{z_s} = \frac{v_x}{v_z} = \frac{eBz_m}{v_z m}.$$

Thus

$$\begin{aligned}
B &= \frac{mx_s v_z}{ez_s z_m} \\
&= \left(9.11 \times 10^{-31}\,\text{kg} \times 5.0 \times 10^{-6}\,\text{m}\right) \\
&\quad \times \left(2.3 \times 10^7\,\text{m s}^{-1}\right) \\
&\quad \div \left(1.60 \times 10^{-19}\,\text{C} \times 0.10\,\text{m} \times 1.0 \times 10^{-3}\,\text{m}\right) \\
&= 6.5 \times 10^{-6}\,\text{T}.
\end{aligned}$$

Ex 6.4 The cyclotron frequency is $|q|B/m$, so to match the frequency of the deuterium ions, the oscillator frequency will need to be reduced by a factor of 2, to $3.5 \times 10^7\,\text{rad s}^{-1}$. The negative deuterium ions will orbit in the opposite sense to the protons, so the direction of injection will need to be reversed, and the exit port and the direction of the extracting field will also need to be reversed.

To find the energy of the emerging ions, we note that $r_c = mv_\perp/|q|B$, and the maximum value of r_c and the values of $|q|$ and B are fixed. This means that doubling the mass must halve the maximum speed attained. But the energy is $\frac{1}{2}mv^2$, so the deuterium ions will have half of the energy of the protons, i.e. 15 MeV.

Ex 6.5 The electrons will travel in helical paths that have axes parallel to the field direction. These paths touch the axis of the beam (as shown in Figure 6.7) and have a radius equal to the cyclotron radius. For electrons with $v_\perp = \sqrt{2k_B T/m}$, the typical thermal speed in two dimensions, the cyclotron radius should be half of the required beam radius, i.e. 2.5 mm. Thus, rearranging the expression for the cyclotron radius, and substituting for $v_\perp$, we find

$$\begin{aligned}
B &= \frac{mv_\perp}{er_c} \\
&= \frac{\sqrt{2mk_B T}}{er_c} \\
&= [2 \times 9.11 \times 10^{-31}\,\text{kg} \\
&\quad \times 1.38 \times 10^{-23}\,\text{J C}^{-1} \times 10^3\,\text{K}]^{1/2} \\
&\quad \div \left(1.60 \times 10^{-19}\,\text{C} \times 2.5 \times 10^{-3}\,\text{m}\right) \\
&= 4.0 \times 10^{-4}\,\text{T}.
\end{aligned}$$

Ex 6.6 The drift velocity is calculated from Equation 6.14:

$$\mathbf{v}_d = \frac{mv_\parallel^2}{qBR_B}\,\widehat{\mathbf{R}}_B \times \widehat{\mathbf{B}}.$$

Over the Equator, $\mathbf{B}$ is directed to the north, and $\mathbf{R}_B$ is away from the Earth's centre and therefore perpendicular to **B**. So $\widehat{\mathbf{R}}_B \times \widehat{\mathbf{B}}$ has a magnitude of unity and its direction — the direction of the drift — is towards the west. Hence

$$v_{\mathrm{d}} = mv_{\parallel}^2/qBR_B$$

$$= \frac{1.67 \times 10^{-27}\,\mathrm{kg} \times (2.0 \times 10^6\,\mathrm{m\,s^{-1}})^2}{1.60 \times 10^{-19}\,\mathrm{C} \times 4.7 \times 10^{-7}\,\mathrm{T} \times 8.4 \times 10^6\,\mathrm{m}}$$

$$= 1.1 \times 10^4\,\mathrm{m\,s^{-1}}.$$

Comment: Note that $v_{\mathrm{d}} \ll v_{\parallel}$, as you might anticipate from the use of the term 'drift'. In this example, when the proton travels 2000 km in the direction of the field, it travels 11 km towards the west, which is about a quarter of its cyclotron radius.

Ex 6.7 From Equation 6.9, we have for the electrons

$$r_{\mathrm{c}} = \frac{mv_{\perp}}{|q|B}$$

$$= \frac{\sqrt{2mE_{\mathrm{kin}}}}{eB}$$

$$= \frac{(2 \times 9.11 \times 10^{-31}\,\mathrm{kg} \times 500\,\mathrm{V} \times 1.60 \times 10^{-19}\,\mathrm{C})^{1/2}}{1.60 \times 10^{-19}\,\mathrm{C} \times 1.0 \times 10^{-3}\,\mathrm{T}}$$

$$= 0.075\,\mathrm{m}.$$

A proton will have a cyclotron radius that is $\sqrt{m_{\mathrm{p}}/m_{\mathrm{e}}} = 43$ times larger, i.e. 3.2 m. So the cyclotron radii of electrons and protons are both very much smaller than the magnetic field loop structures observed.

Ex 6.8 With the field gradient superimposed, the field at A in Figure 6.17 is weaker than required to maintain the original circular orbit, and since $r_{\mathrm{c}} = mv_{\perp}/|q|B$, the cyclotron radius of the orbit at this point will be larger than for the original orbit. Conversely, the stronger field at C means that the cyclotron radius there is smaller than for the original orbit. The effect that this has is shown in Figure S6.2 — the orbit drifts in the y-direction, transverse to the direction of the field and to the direction of grad B.

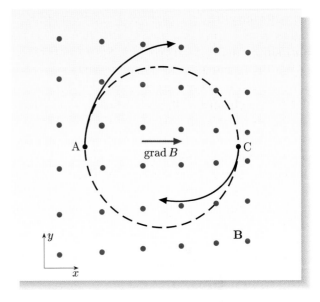

Figure S6.2 Solution to Exercise 6.8.

Comment: The field and field-strength gradient in this exercise are in the same directions as those in Figure 6.15, so, unsurprisingly, the solution to this exercise predicts the same direction for the drift of a positively-charged particle as we deduced earlier.

Ex 6.9 The drift velocity in this case is given by Equation 6.20,

$$\mathbf{v}_{\mathrm{d}} = \frac{mv_{\perp}^2}{2qB^3}\,\mathbf{B} \times \mathrm{grad}\,B.$$

Using spherical coordinates, with the $\theta = 0$ direction aligned with the magnetic dipole's axis, the field strength B depends only on r. This means we need consider only the $\mathbf{e}_r$-component of grad B (see inside back cover), since the $\mathbf{e}_\theta$- and $\mathbf{e}_\phi$-components are zero. So grad $B = (\partial B/\partial r)\mathbf{e}_r = -(3C/r^4)\mathbf{e}_r$, and at radius R this becomes grad $B = -(3B/R)\mathbf{e}_r$. Substituting this expression into the equation for $\mathbf{v}_{\mathrm{d}}$, we obtain

$$\mathbf{v}_{\mathrm{d}} = \frac{mv_{\perp}^2}{2qB^3}(-B\mathbf{e}_\theta) \times \left(-\frac{3B}{R}\mathbf{e}_r\right)$$

$$= \frac{mv_{\perp}^2}{2qB^3} \times \frac{3B^2}{R}(-\mathbf{e}_\phi),$$

where we have used the relationship between the unit vectors $\mathbf{e}_\theta \times \mathbf{e}_r = -\mathbf{e}_\phi$. Thus the drift is in the

$-\phi$-direction, i.e. from east to west. The drift speed is

$$v_d = \frac{3mv_\perp^2}{2qBR}$$

$$= \frac{3 \times 1.67 \times 10^{-27}\,\text{kg} \times (2.0 \times 10^6\,\text{m s}^{-1})^2}{2 \times 1.60 \times 10^{-19}\,\text{C} \times 4.7 \times 10^{-7}\,\text{T} \times 2.6 \times 10^7\,\text{m}}$$

$$= 5.1 \times 10^3\,\text{m s}^{-1}.$$

Comment: Note that this contribution to the drift — due to the variation in the strength of the field — is in the same direction as, and of similar magnitude to, the drift due to the curvature of the field lines, which was calculated in Exercise 6.6. The net drift velocity is the sum of the two terms.

Ex 6.10 (a) Charge q appears in the drift velocity equations (6.14 and 6.20), so particles with opposite charges must drift in opposite directions.

(b) The drift is always perpendicular to the magnetic field direction. For a field with varying strength, the drift is perpendicular to the gradient of the field strength; for a field with varying direction, the drift is perpendicular to a vector from the centre of curvature to a point on the field line.

(c) The drift speed is proportional to mv^2, and therefore proportional to the kinetic energy. This means that 1 MeV electrons and 1 MeV protons have the same drift speed (but drift in opposite directions).

Comment: Note that the drift speed is proportional to mass (Equation 6.19), so protons drift about 2000 times faster than electrons if they have the same speed.

Ex 6.11 The field strength at the centre of a current loop is $B = \mu_0 I/2r$, so the current required is

$$I = \frac{2Br}{\mu_0} = \frac{2 \times 10^{-7}\,\text{T} \times 4 \times 6 \times 10^6\,\text{m}}{4\pi \times 10^{-7}\,\text{T m A}^{-1}}$$

$$= 4 \times 10^6\,\text{A}.$$

Ex 6.12 (a) Particles with the minimum pitch angle at the centre will just be reflected at the point where the field has the maximum value, i.e. they will have $\alpha = 90°$ and $\sin\alpha = 1$ at this point. Since $(\sin^2\alpha)/B$ is constant for each particle, the minimum pitch angle, $\alpha_{\min}$, is given by

$$\frac{\sin^2\alpha_{\min}}{B_0} = \frac{\sin^2 90°}{B_{\max}},$$

so $\sin^2\alpha_{\min} = 0.05$, and $\alpha_{\min} = 13°$.

(b) A particle will escape if the magnetic force cannot reduce v_z to zero. The z-component of the magnetic force is proportional to v_ϕ. Particles with a small pitch angle have a large value of v_z that needs to be reduced to zero, and a correspondingly small value of v_ϕ, and therefore a small magnetic force to decelerate the particle's motion in the z-direction. So if the pitch angle is too small, the horizontal force is unable to reduce the z-component of velocity to zero, and the particle emerges from the end of the bottle.

Ex 7.1 We choose the z-axis parallel to the axis of the rod. Then $\mathbf{J}$ and $\mathbf{E}$ are in the z-direction, and since both are uniform throughout the conductor, $J_z = \sigma E_z$. Now $J_z = I/A$ and $E_z = V/l$, so

$$\frac{I}{A} = \sigma\frac{V}{l}, \quad \text{or} \quad V = I\left(\frac{l}{\sigma A}\right) = IR,$$

where the resistance R is given by

$$R = \frac{l}{\sigma A}.$$

Comment: For an object with non-uniform cross-section, or an object where σ depends on position, the current density will be non-uniform. However, as long as the local form of Ohm's law is valid at all points, the non-local form $V = IR$ will also be true, and we shall show some examples of this in later sections.

Ex 7.2 If we ignore the currents along the wire and sheath, this problem has cylindrical symmetry, so we use cylindrical coordinates with the z-axis along the axis of the cable. Because of the symmetry, the electric field and the current density must be radial, and their magnitudes can depend only on r:

$$\mathbf{J}(\mathbf{r}) = J_r(r)\mathbf{e}_r = \sigma E_r(r)\mathbf{e}_r.$$

In a steady state, the current I flowing across the surface of a cylinder of radius r and length l, whose axis lies along the z-axis, must be independent of r, so

$$J_r(r) = \frac{I}{2\pi r l} = \sigma E_r(r).$$

There are no changing magnetic fields, so $\mathbf{E} = -\,\text{grad}\,V$, and the potential drop from the inner wire to the outer sheath, ΔV, is therefore given by

$$\Delta V = \int_{r_1}^{r_2} E(r)\,dr$$

$$= \frac{I}{2\pi l \sigma}\int_{r_1}^{r_2}\frac{dr}{r} = \frac{I}{2\pi l \sigma}\ln(r_2/r_1).$$

Thus the resistance of a length l of the dielectric of this cable is

$$R = \frac{\Delta V}{I} = \frac{\ln(r_2/r_1)}{2\pi l \sigma}.$$

Ex 7.3 From Equation 7.6, we have $\sigma E = I/2\pi r^2$, and therefore

$$r = \sqrt{\frac{I}{2\pi\sigma E}} = \sqrt{\frac{\Delta Q}{2\pi\sigma E \Delta t}}.$$

The distance at which the field strength is $100\,\mathrm{V\,m^{-1}}$ is given by

$$r = \sqrt{\frac{20\,\mathrm{C}}{2\pi \times 10^{-2}\,\Omega^{-1}\,\mathrm{m^{-1}} \times 100\,\mathrm{V\,m^{-1}} \times 2.0 \times 10^{-3}\,\mathrm{s}}}$$
$$= 40\,\mathrm{m}.$$

At this distance, the potential is given by

$$V = -\frac{I}{2\pi\sigma r}$$
$$= -\frac{20\,\mathrm{C}}{2.0 \times 10^{-3}\,\mathrm{s} \times 2\pi \times 10^{-2}\,\Omega^{-1}\,\mathrm{m^{-1}} \times 40\,\mathrm{m}}$$
$$= -4.0 \times 10^3\,\mathrm{V}.$$

Comment: So $40\,\mathrm{m}$ from the strike, the potential is $-4\,\mathrm{kV}$, but the magnitude of the electric field is only $100\,\mathrm{V\,m^{-1}}$. With widespread legs there would be about $100\,\mathrm{V}$ between your feet. Since $E \propto r^{-2}$, the field is larger closer to the strike. The message is: 'keep your feet together, or stand on one leg!'

Ex 7.4 When the normal to the plane of the loop is at an angle α to the magnetic field direction, the flux through the coil is $\Phi = BA\cos\alpha = abB\cos\alpha$. If we set $\alpha = 0$ at $t = 0$, so that $\alpha = \omega t$, then

$$\frac{\mathrm{d}\Phi}{\mathrm{d}t} = \frac{\mathrm{d}}{\mathrm{d}t}(abB\cos\omega t) = -abB\omega\sin\omega t.$$

This has the same magnitude as obtained by integrating the magnetic force per unit charge around the loop, but has the opposite sign, as predicted by Equation 7.12.

Ex 7.5 The electrons in the disc experience a magnetic force $-e\mathbf{v} \times \mathbf{B}$ towards the centre of the disc. Since the magnetic field is independent of time, $\mathbf{E}$ is conservative and $\int_C \mathbf{E} \cdot \mathrm{d}\mathbf{l} = 0$. From Equation 7.12 we deduce that

$$V_{\mathrm{emf}} = \oint_C (\mathbf{v} \times \mathbf{B}) \cdot \mathrm{d}\mathbf{l},$$

and within the disc the path of the integral can be taken along a radial line between the contacts shown in the figure. Then $\mathbf{v} \times \mathbf{B}$ has magnitude $vB = \omega rB$, and is in the radial direction, from axle to rim, so

$$V_{\mathrm{emf}} = \int_0^a \omega Br\,\mathrm{d}r = \tfrac{1}{2}\omega Ba^2,$$

and this emf drives a current in the external circuit from the rim to the axle.

Comment: This is an induction problem that cannot be tackled by considering the rate of change of flux within the circuit, because the flux is constant.

Ex 7.6 When the switch closes, the current in the solenoid increases rapidly, and the flux through the ring increases rapidly. The changing flux induces a current in the ring, and by Lenz's law the flux produced by this current opposes the flux produced by the solenoid. The currents in solenoid and ring must therefore flow in opposite directions, and act as magnets with like poles in close proximity. Since like poles repel each other, there will be a repulsive force on the ring, which makes it jump upwards.

Ex 7.7 The mutual inductance is the flux through the rectangular loop produced by unit current in the straight wire. Current I in the wire produces an azimuthal field of magnitude $B = \mu_0 I/2\pi r$. Since the field depends on r, we divide the rectangular loop into strips of length l and width δr at r. The flux $\delta\Phi$ through a strip is given by

$$\delta\Phi = \mathbf{B} \cdot \delta\mathbf{S} = \frac{\mu_0 I}{2\pi r} l\,\delta r,$$

so the flux through the loop is

$$\Phi = \int_{r_1}^{r_2} B(r)\,l\,\mathrm{d}r = \frac{\mu_0\,lI}{2\pi} \int_{r_1}^{r_2} \frac{\mathrm{d}r}{r}$$
$$= \frac{\mu_0\,lI\,\ln(r_2/r_1)}{2\pi}.$$

Hence

$$M = \frac{\Phi}{I} = \frac{\mu_0\,l\,\ln(r_2/r_1)}{2\pi}.$$

The induced emf is then

$$V_{\mathrm{emf}} = -M\frac{\mathrm{d}I}{\mathrm{d}t}$$
$$= -\frac{\mu_0\,l\,\ln(r_2/r_1)}{2\pi} \times 2\pi f I_0\cos(2\pi ft).$$

Substituting the values given in the exercise, the amplitude of the induced emf is

$$V_{\mathrm{emf}} = 4\pi \times 10^{-7}\,\mathrm{T\,m\,A^{-1}} \times 1.5 \times 10^{-2}\,\mathrm{m}$$
$$\times \ln(10/1.0) \times 13.5 \times 10^6\,\mathrm{Hz} \times 1.0\,\mathrm{A}$$
$$= 0.59\,\mathrm{V}.$$

Ex 7.8 Because of the axial symmetry, the magnetic field lines are circular and coaxial with the inner wire, as in Figure S7.1.

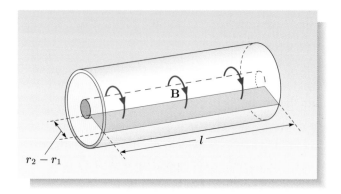

$r_2 - r_1$

Figure S7.1 For Solution 7.8.

From Ampère's law, the magnitude of the magnetic field at a radius r from the axis of the cable, for $r_1 < r < r_2$, is $B = \mu_0 I/(2\pi r)$. We need to find the magnetic flux through a length l of the cable, and this is the flux passing through a rectangular surface, of length l and width $r_2 - r_1$, lying in a plane perpendicular to the direction of **B**, shown shaded grey in Figure S7.1.

Since the field depends on r, we divide the rectangular area into strips of length l and width δr at r. The flux $\delta\Phi$ through a strip is given by

$$\delta\Phi = \mathbf{B} \cdot \delta\mathbf{S} = \frac{\mu_0 I}{2\pi r} l\, \delta r.$$

Hence the total flux through the area between the inner and outer conductors is

$$\Phi = \frac{\mu_0 Il}{2\pi} \int_{r_1}^{r_2} \frac{\mathrm{d}r}{r} = \frac{\mu_0 Il}{2\pi} \ln(r_2/r_1).$$

The inductance per unit length of the cable is therefore

$$L = \frac{\Phi}{Il} = \frac{\mu_0}{2\pi} \ln\left(\frac{r_2}{r_1}\right).$$

Ex 7.9 The solution to Exercise 7.1 showed that $R = l/\sigma A$, where l was the length of a rod in the direction of current flow, and A was the cross-sectional area perpendicular to the current flow. In this case, with a current flowing around the wall of the tube, $l \equiv 2\pi a$ and $A \equiv td$. So

$$R = 2\pi a/\sigma td.$$

The self-inductance is the flux through the tube per unit current. An azimuthal current I in the tube will produce a uniform axial field — like the field inside a long

solenoid — and the field strength can be calculated using a rectangular path like that in Figure 7.24. If the length of the rectangle is Δl, the path encloses current $I\,\Delta l/d$, so $B\,\Delta l = \mu_0 I\,\Delta l/d$, and $B = \mu_0 I/d$. The flux through the tube is $\Phi = BA = \mu_0 I\pi a^2/d$, so the self-inductance is

$$L = \Phi/I = \mu_0 \pi a^2/d.$$

Ex 8.1 From Equation 8.4 we have

$$U = \tfrac{1}{2} \sum_{i=1}^{3} q_i V_i = \tfrac{1}{2}\left(q_1 V_1 + q_2 V_2 + q_3 V_3\right),$$

where

$$V_1 = \frac{1}{4\pi\varepsilon_0}\left[\frac{q_2}{r_{12}} + \frac{q_3}{r_{13}}\right],$$

$$V_2 = \frac{1}{4\pi\varepsilon_0}\left[\frac{q_1}{r_{21}} + \frac{q_3}{r_{23}}\right],$$

$$V_3 = \frac{1}{4\pi\varepsilon_0}\left[\frac{q_1}{r_{31}} + \frac{q_2}{r_{32}}\right].$$

Hence

$$U = \frac{1}{8\pi\varepsilon_0}\left\{ q_1\left[\frac{q_2}{r_{12}} + \frac{q_3}{r_{13}}\right] + q_2\left[\frac{q_1}{r_{21}} + \frac{q_3}{r_{23}}\right] \right.$$
$$\left. + q_3\left[\frac{q_1}{r_{31}} + \frac{q_2}{r_{32}}\right] \right\}$$
$$= \frac{1}{4\pi\varepsilon_0}\left\{ \frac{q_1 q_2}{r_{12}} + \frac{q_1 q_3}{r_{13}} + \frac{q_2 q_3}{r_{23}} \right\},$$

since $r_{ij} = r_{ji}$, and this agrees with Equation 8.2.

Comment: Notice how the factor $\tfrac{1}{2}$ compensates for the double counting in the summations in Equation 8.4.

Ex 8.2 The strategy is to use Gauss's law to determine the field at radius r, then determine the potential at the surface of the sphere from $V(R) = -\int_\infty^R E_r(r)\,\mathrm{d}r$, and then make use of Equation 8.5.

The spherical symmetry of the charge distribution means that $\mathbf{E}(\mathbf{r}) = E_r(r)\mathbf{e}_r$, so we can determine $E_r(r)$ by applying the integral version of Gauss's law to a spherical Gaussian surface, radius r, concentric with the conducting sphere. This leads to

$$\varepsilon_0 E_r(r)4\pi r^2 = \sigma \times 4\pi R^2, \quad \text{so} \quad E_r(r) = \frac{\sigma R^2}{\varepsilon_0 r^2}.$$

The potential at the surface of the sphere is therefore

$$V(R) = -\int_\infty^R \frac{\sigma R^2}{\varepsilon_0 r^2}\,\mathrm{d}r = \frac{\sigma R}{\varepsilon_0}.$$

Then, using Equation 8.5, the potential energy is

$$U = \tfrac{1}{2} \int_{\text{sphere}} \sigma \times \frac{\sigma R}{\varepsilon_0}\, dS$$

$$= \frac{\sigma^2 R}{2\varepsilon_0} \times 4\pi R^2 = \frac{2\pi\sigma^2 R^3}{\varepsilon_0}.$$

Comment: There are short-cuts to obtaining this result. As we showed in Book 1, the potential outside a spherical charge distribution is identical to that for the same total charge located at the centre of the sphere, i.e. $V(R) = Q/4\pi\varepsilon_0 R$. The potential energy is therefore $U = \tfrac{1}{2}Q \times (Q/4\pi\varepsilon_0 R) = Q^2/8\pi\varepsilon_0 R$, and since $Q = 4\pi R^2 \sigma$, this is equivalent to the result derived above, $U = 2\pi\sigma^2 R^3/\varepsilon_0$.

Ex 8.3 The energy stored is

$$U = \tfrac{1}{2}CV^2 = \tfrac{1}{2} \times 16 \times 10^{-6}\,\text{F} \times (240\,\text{V})^2$$
$$= 0.46\,\text{J}.$$

The kinetic energy, $\tfrac{1}{2}mv^2$, of a 1 kg mass moving at $1\,\text{m s}^{-1}$ is 0.5 J. The gravitational energy increase is

$$mg\,\Delta h = 1\,\text{kg} \times 10\,\text{m s}^{-2} \times 5 \times 10^{-2}\,\text{m} = 0.5\,\text{J}.$$

So these examples of kinetic and gravitational energy are of similar magnitude to the energy stored in the $16\,\mu\text{F}$ capacitor when the potential difference across it is 240 V.

Ex 8.4 The spherical symmetry of the charge distribution makes it appropriate to use spherical coordinates with the origin at the centre of the spheres. Then the electric field must have the form $\mathbf{E} = E_r(r)\mathbf{e}_r$. Applying the integral version of Gauss's law to a Gaussian surface that is a sphere of radius r with its centre at the origin, and taking $\varepsilon = 1$ for air, we find

$$E = \begin{cases} 0, & \text{for } r < r_1, \\ Q/4\pi\varepsilon_0 r^2, & \text{for } r_1 \le r < r_2, \\ 0, & \text{for } r \ge r_2. \end{cases}$$

The energy stored is given by

$$U = \tfrac{1}{2}\int_\tau \mathbf{D}\cdot\mathbf{E}\,d\tau = \tfrac{1}{2}\varepsilon_0 \int_\tau E^2\,d\tau,$$

where the volume of integration is the region between the two shells, $r_1 < r \le r_2$, since $E = 0$ elsewhere. The field is spherically symmetric, so we take a volume element $\delta\tau$ that is a spherical shell of radius r and

thickness δr, i.e. $\delta\tau = 4\pi r^2\,\delta r$. Hence

$$U = \tfrac{1}{2}\varepsilon_0 \int_{r_1}^{r_2} \left(\frac{Q}{4\pi\varepsilon_0 r^2}\right)^2 4\pi r^2\,dr$$

$$= \frac{Q^2}{8\pi\varepsilon_0} \int_{r_1}^{r_2} \frac{dr}{r^2}$$

$$= \frac{Q^2}{8\pi\varepsilon_0} \left(-\frac{1}{r_2} + \frac{1}{r_1}\right)$$

$$= \frac{Q^2}{8\pi\varepsilon_0} \left(\frac{r_2 - r_1}{r_1 r_2}\right).$$

Ex 8.5 The energy corresponding to a mass m is $U = mc^2$, so we have

$$mc^2 = \frac{e^2}{8\pi\varepsilon_0 R}, \quad \text{or} \quad R = \frac{e^2}{8\pi\varepsilon_0 mc^2}.$$

Thus the radius R is

$$\frac{(1.60 \times 10^{-19})^2}{8\pi \times 8.85 \times 10^{-12} \times 9.11 \times 10^{-31} \times (3.00 \times 10^8)^2}\,\text{m}$$

which is equal to 1.4×10^{-15} m.

Ex 8.6 The energy dissipated in the resistor when the capacitor discharges is

$$U_R = \int_0^\infty IV_R\,dt$$

$$= \int_0^\infty \frac{V_0}{R}\exp\left(-\frac{t}{RC}\right) \times V_0\exp\left(-\frac{t}{RC}\right)dt$$

$$= \frac{V_0^2}{R}\int_0^\infty \exp\left(-\frac{2t}{RC}\right)dt$$

$$= \frac{V_0^2}{R}\left(\frac{-RC}{2}\right)\left[\exp\left(-\frac{2t}{RC}\right)\right]_0^\infty$$

$$= \tfrac{1}{2}CV_0^2.$$

This is equal to the energy stored in the capacitor before the switch was closed.

Ex 8.7 (a) The charge on the capacitor is $Q = CV_C$, and it eventually reaches a maximum value of CV_s. Using Equation 8.19, the charge can be rewritten as

$$Q = CV_s\left[1 - \exp\left(-\frac{t}{R_s C}\right)\right].$$

The time T required to reach 99 per cent of the maximum charge is given by

$$\frac{Q}{CV_s} = \frac{99}{100} = 1 - \exp\left(-\frac{T}{R_s C}\right),$$

which leads to

$$T = R_s C \ln 100$$
$$= 100\,\Omega \times 32 \times 10^{-6}\,\text{F} \times \ln 100$$
$$= 1.5 \times 10^{-2}\,\text{s}.$$

(b) The maximum current occurs at the start of the discharge, and is

$$\frac{V_s}{R_{chest}} = \frac{5.0 \times 10^3\,\text{V}}{75\,\Omega} = 67\,\text{A}.$$

(c) The discharge current is given by

$$I = I_0 \exp\left(-\frac{t}{R_{chest}C}\right),$$

so setting $I/I_0 = 1/10$, the time T' required is given by

$$T' = R_{chest}C \ln 10$$
$$= 75\,\Omega \times 32 \times 10^{-6}\,\text{F} \times \ln 10$$
$$= 5.5\,\text{ms}.$$

(d) The energy stored in the capacitor, U_C, and hence the energy delivered to the patient, is given by

$$U_C = \tfrac{1}{2}CV_s^2$$
$$= \frac{32 \times 10^{-6}\,\text{F} \times (5 \times 10^3\,\text{V})^2}{2}$$
$$= 400\,\text{J}.$$

Comment: This energy is only sufficient to heat a kilogram of the patient by about $0.1\,°\text{C}$. It is the current that is important, rather than the energy supplied.

Ex 8.8   The maximum energy that can be stored is

$$U_{max} = \tfrac{1}{2}CV_{max}^2$$
$$= \tfrac{1}{2} \times 1.0 \times 10^{-3}\,\text{F} \times (63\,\text{V})^2$$
$$= 2.0\,\text{J}.$$

The volume of the capacitor is

$$\pi \times (8.0 \times 10^{-3}\,\text{m})^2 \times 40 \times 10^{-3}\,\text{m}$$
$$= 8.0 \times 10^{-6}\,\text{m}^3,$$

and therefore the maximum energy density is

$$u_{max} = \frac{2.0\,\text{J}}{8.0 \times 10^{-6}\,\text{m}^3} = 0.25\,\text{MJ}\,\text{m}^{-3}.$$

Ex 8.9   (a) Replacing the emf V_s by a short-circuit is equivalent to setting $V_s = 0$ in Equation 8.22, so the current I now obeys the differential equation

$$IR + L\frac{\mathrm{d}I}{\mathrm{d}t} = 0, \quad \text{or} \quad \frac{\mathrm{d}I}{\mathrm{d}t} = -\frac{R}{L}I.$$

The solution to this equation can be obtained by the separation of variables, as used to obtain Equation 8.23, or by recognizing that the standard solution to the equation is

$$I = I_0 \exp\left(-\frac{Rt}{L}\right),$$

where I_0 is the current at $t = 0$.

Comment: As you might have anticipated, the time constant for the decay of the current is L/R, the same as the time constant when the current was being established (Subsection 8.2.1).

(b) The total energy dissipated in the resistor is

$$U_R = \int_0^\infty I^2 R\,\mathrm{d}t$$
$$= I_0^2 R \int_0^\infty \exp\left(-\frac{2Rt}{L}\right)\,\mathrm{d}t$$
$$= I_0^2 R \left[-\frac{L}{2R}\exp\left(-\frac{2Rt}{L}\right)\right]_0^\infty = \tfrac{1}{2}LI_0^2.$$

Comment: This is equal to the energy transferred to the inductor when the current was established. The fact that this energy is recovered when the current decays justifies us thinking of $\tfrac{1}{2}LI^2$ as stored potential energy.

Ex 8.10   Because of the axial and translational symmetry, the magnetic field lines are concentric circles, centred on the axis of the cylinders, so $\mathbf{H} = H_\phi(r)\,\mathbf{e}_\phi$. Applying Ampère's law, $\int_C \mathbf{H} \cdot \mathrm{d}\mathbf{l} = I$, to a circular path of radius r that follows one such field line between the cylinders gives

$$H = \frac{I}{2\pi r}.$$

Note that the field outside the cable is zero, since a circular path with $r > r_2$ encloses no net current, and the field inside the inner tube is also zero, for the same reason. The energy density of the magnetic field is $u = \tfrac{1}{2}\mathbf{B} \cdot \mathbf{H}$, and $\mathbf{B} = \mu\mu_0\mathbf{H}$, so

$$u = \tfrac{1}{2}\mu\mu_0 H^2 = \frac{\mu\mu_0 I^2}{8\pi^2 r^2}.$$

The total energy U is given by $U = \int u\,\mathrm{d}\tau$, where the integral is taken over the volume between the two tubes since the magnetic field is zero elsewhere. The symmetry leads us to choose $\delta\tau$ to be a cylindrical shell centred on the axis of the tubes and with radius r, thickness δr and length l, so that $\delta \tau = 2\pi r l \, \delta r$. Hence

$$U = \int_{r_1}^{r_2} \frac{\mu \mu_0 I^2}{8\pi^2 r^2} 2\pi r l \, dr$$

$$= \frac{\mu \mu_0 I^2 l}{4\pi} \int_{r_1}^{r_2} \frac{dr}{r}$$

$$= \frac{\mu \mu_0 I^2 l}{4\pi} \left[\ln r \right]_{r_1}^{r_2}$$

$$= \frac{\mu \mu_0 I^2 l}{4\pi} \ln \left(\frac{r_2}{r_1} \right).$$

Ex 8.11 We assume that we can neglect the field outside the specified region, and that the field is uniform within the region. Then the energy is

$$U = \frac{B^2}{2\mu_0} \times \text{volume}$$

$$= \frac{(20\,\text{T})^2}{2 \times 4\pi \times 10^{-7}\,\text{N A}^{-2}} \times \frac{\pi}{4}(0.05\,\text{m})^2 \times 0.2\,\text{m}$$

$$\simeq 60\,\text{kJ}.$$

Ex 8.12 The natural angular frequency is

$$\omega_n = 1/\sqrt{LC}$$

$$= 1/\sqrt{5.0\,\text{mH} \times 2.0\,\text{pF}} = 10^7\,\text{rad s}^{-1},$$

and the natural frequency f_n is

$$10^7\,\text{rad s}^{-1}/2\pi\,\text{rad} = 1.6\,\text{MHz}.$$

The maximum energy stored in the capacitor is equal to the maximum energy stored in the inductor, which is

$$U_C = U_L = LI_0^2/2$$

$$= 0.5 \times 5.0\,\text{mH} \times (2.5\,\text{mA})^2$$

$$= 1.6 \times 10^{-8}\,\text{J}.$$

Ex 9.1 (a) You saw in Exercise 8.9 that the current in an RL circuit (with no source of emf) decays exponentially with time:

$$I(t) = I_0 \exp(-Rt/L).$$

Comment: The time constant for the decay is L/R, so the smaller the resistance, the longer will be the time constant. Zero resistance means an infinite time constant — the current does not decay, but persists indefinitely (or as long as the material remains superconducting).

(b) The maximum possible resistance, $R_{\max}$, of the tube corresponds to the minimum possible current, which is $I(T) = 0.98 I_0$. Thus

$$0.98 = \exp(-R_{\max} T/L),$$

which can be rearranged to give

$$R_{\max} = -(L/T) \ln 0.98.$$

Now $T = 7\,\text{hours} = 7 \times 3600\,\text{s} = 2.5 \times 10^4\,\text{s}$, and $L = 1.4 \times 10^{-13}\,\text{H}$, so $R_{\max} = 1.1 \times 10^{-19}\,\Omega$.

(c) For the tube, the length of the current path, l_I, is essentially twice the width of the silicon oxide layer, and the cross-sectional area perpendicular to current flow, A_I, is the length of the tube times the thickness of the lead films. Since

$$R = \rho \times (\text{length})/(\text{area}) = \rho l_I/A_I,$$

the maximum resistivity is

$$\rho_{\max} = R_{\max} A_I/l_I$$

$$= 1.1 \times 10^{-19}\,\Omega \frac{17 \times 10^{-3}\,\text{m} \times 1.2 \times 10^{-6}\,\text{m}}{2 \times 3.2 \times 10^{-3}\,\text{m}}$$

$$\simeq 4 \times 10^{-25}\,\Omega\,\text{m}.$$

The value of the conductivity of lead at $0\,^\circ\text{C}$ is $5.2 \times 10^6\,\Omega^{-1}\,\text{m}^{-1}$, so the resistivity is

$$(5.2 \times 10^6\,\Omega^{-1}\,\text{m}^{-1})^{-1} = 1.9 \times 10^{-7}\,\Omega\,\text{m}.$$

The estimate for the maximum resistivity for superconducting lead obtained from the data in this exercise is almost 18 orders of magnitude smaller than this room temperature value.

Ex 9.2 From Table 9.1, for lead $T_c = 7.2\,\text{K}$ and $B_c(0) = 0.080\,\text{T}$. From Equation 9.1,

$$B_c(T) = B_c(0)\left[1 - \left(\frac{T}{T_c}\right)^2\right]$$

$$= 0.080\,\text{T}\left[1 - \left(\frac{4.2\,\text{K}}{7.2\,\text{K}}\right)^2\right]$$

$$= 0.053\,\text{T}.$$

Ex 9.3 From Ampère's law, the field strength B at the surface of a wire of radius R carrying a current I is $B = \mu_0 I/2\pi R$. From Equation 9.1, we also have that

$$B_c(2\,\text{K}) = 31 \times 10^{-3}\,\text{T}\left[1 - \left(\frac{2.0}{3.7}\right)^2\right]$$

$$= 21.9 \times 10^{-3}\,\text{T},$$

so the radius R required is

$$R \geq \frac{\mu_0 I}{2\pi B_c} = \frac{4\pi \times 10^{-7}\,\mathrm{N\,A^{-2}} \times 200\,\mathrm{A}}{2\pi \times 21.9 \times 10^{-3}\,\mathrm{T}}$$

$$= 1.8\,\mathrm{mm}.$$

Ex 9.4 Taking the curl of both sides of Equation 9.9 and using Ampère's law, $\mathrm{curl}\,\mathbf{B} = \mu_0 \mathbf{J}_s$, to eliminate $\mathbf{B}$, we find that

$$\mathrm{curl}(\mathrm{curl}\,\mathbf{J}_s) = -\frac{n_s e^2}{m}\,\mathrm{curl}\,\mathbf{B}$$

$$= -\frac{\mu_0 n_s e^2}{m}\mathbf{J}_s$$

$$= -\frac{1}{\lambda^2}\mathbf{J}_s.$$

We now use a standard vector identity (given inside the back cover) to rewrite the $\mathrm{curl}(\mathrm{curl}\,\mathbf{J}_s)$ term:

$$\mathrm{curl}(\mathrm{curl}\,\mathbf{J}_s) = \mathrm{grad}(\mathrm{div}\,\mathbf{J}_s) - \nabla^2 \mathbf{J}_s = -\frac{1}{\lambda^2}\mathbf{J}_s.$$

For our steady-state situation, where $\partial\rho_s/\partial t = 0$, the equation of continuity, $\partial\rho_s/\partial t + \mathrm{div}\,\mathbf{J}_s = 0$, reduces to $\mathrm{div}\,\mathbf{J}_s = 0$, so

$$\nabla^2 \mathbf{J}_s = \frac{1}{\lambda^2}\mathbf{J}_s.$$

Ex 9.5 From Equation 9.10, the penetration depth is given by $\lambda = (m/\mu_0 n_s e^2)^{1/2}$, so (in metres)

$$\lambda = \left(\frac{9.11 \times 10^{-31}}{4\pi \times 10^{-7} \times 1.5 \times 10^{29} \times (1.6 \times 10^{-19})^2}\right)^{1/2}$$

or $\lambda = 14\,\mathrm{nm}$.

This value, predicted by the London model, is about a quarter of the measured value.

Ex 10.1 Multiplying Equation 10.2 by v/c^2 and adding the result to Equation 10.1, we obtain

$$t' + \frac{v}{c^2}x' = \gamma\left(t - \frac{v^2}{c^2}t\right).$$

Using the definition of γ (Equation 10.5), this can be written as

$$t' + \frac{v}{c^2}x' = \frac{\gamma}{\gamma^2}t,$$

hence

$$t = \gamma\left(t' + \frac{v}{c^2}x'\right),$$

which is Equation 10.6.

Multiplying Equation 10.1 by v and adding Equation 10.2, we obtain

$$x' + vt' = \gamma\left(x - \frac{v^2}{c^2}x\right).$$

Using the definition of γ, this can be written as

$$x' + vt' = \frac{\gamma}{\gamma^2}x,$$

hence

$$x = \gamma\left(x' + vt'\right),$$

which is Equation 10.7.

Comment: Notice how the method used in the text is much quicker than that used in this exercise. As is often the case, it is better to invoke a physical argument rather than simply performing algebra.

Ex 10.2 (a) Suppose that the two frames are in standard configuration, and that the rod is at rest in frame $\mathcal{F}'$ and lies parallel to the x'-axis. An observer in frame $\mathcal{F}$ measures the ends of the rod to be at x_1 and x_2 at the same time t. The positions of the ends according to an observer in frame $\mathcal{F}'$ are given by

$$x_1' = \gamma\left(x_1 - vt\right),$$
$$x_2' = \gamma\left(x_2 - vt\right).$$

Hence

$$x_2' - x_1' = \gamma\left(x_2 - x_1\right).$$

However, $x_2' - x_1'$ is the length l_0 of the rod in frame $\mathcal{F}'$, where the rod is at rest, and $x_2 - x_1$ is the length l in frame $\mathcal{F}$, so

$$l = l_0\sqrt{1 - v^2/c^2}.$$

(b) If we start from Equation 10.7 instead of 10.2, we obtain

$$x_1 = \gamma\left(x_1' + vt_1'\right),$$
$$x_2 = \gamma\left(x_2' + vt_2'\right).$$

Since the rod is at rest in frame $\mathcal{F}'$, it would seem that we could choose $t_1' = t_2'$, which would lead to the incorrect result $l_0 = l\sqrt{1 - v^2/c^2}$. The fallacy in this argument is that events that are simultaneous in $\mathcal{F}'$ are not simultaneous in $\mathcal{F}$. Consequently, an observer in $\mathcal{F}$ would be recording the positions of the ends of the rod at different times, which would not lead directly to a measurement of the rod's length.

Comment: This problem does not arise with the method used in part (a), because the rod is at rest in frame $\mathcal{F}'$ so the positions of its ends, x'_1 and x'_2, are independent of the time of measurement.

Ex 10.3 Suppose that a clock is at rest in frame $\mathcal{F}'$, and an observer records ticks at times t'_1 and t'_2. Using Equation 10.6, we can relate these times to those observed in frame $\mathcal{F}$ by

$$t_1 = \gamma \left(t'_1 + \frac{v}{c^2} x'_1 \right),$$
$$t_2 = \gamma \left(t'_2 + \frac{v}{c^2} x'_2 \right).$$

However, since the clock is stationary in $\mathcal{F}'$, we know that $x'_1 = x'_2$, and therefore

$$t_2 - t_1 = \gamma \left(t'_2 - t'_1 \right),$$

or

$$\tau = \frac{\tau_0}{\sqrt{1 - v^2/c^2}}.$$

Comment: Notice that in this case it *is* easier to use the inverse Lorentz transformation. We could use Equation 10.1, but since the clock is moving in frame $\mathcal{F}$, this would mean that x_1 and x_2 would not be equal. We would therefore have to use the length contraction formula (Equation 10.10) to eliminate $x_2 - x_1$.

Ex 10.4 In the frame where the charge cloud is stationary, $\rho = 2.0 \times 10^{-12}\,\text{C m}^{-3}$ and $\mathbf{J} = \mathbf{0}$. We use Equations 10.22–10.25 to determine the charge and current densities in the frame of the high-energy particle:

$$\rho' = \gamma \left(\rho - \frac{v}{c^2} J_x \right) = \gamma\rho,$$
$$J'_x = \gamma \left(J_x - v\rho \right) = -\gamma v\rho,$$
$$J'_y = J_y = 0,$$
$$J'_z = J_z = 0.$$

Now, $\gamma = 1/\sqrt{1 - v^2/c^2} = 1/\sqrt{1 - 0.95^2} = 3.20$, so

$$\rho' = 3.20 \times 2.0 \times 10^{-12}\,\text{C m}^{-3}$$
$$= 6.4 \times 10^{-12}\,\text{C m}^{-3}$$

and

$$J'_x = -\gamma v\rho$$
$$= -0.95\gamma c\rho$$
$$= -0.95 \times 3.2 \times 3.0 \times 10^8\,\text{m s}^{-1}$$
$$\quad \times 2.0 \times 10^{-12}\,\text{C m}^{-3}$$
$$= 1.8\,\text{mA m}^{-2}.$$

Ex 10.5 As in Subsection 10.1.1, to an observer in frame $\mathcal{F}'$, the frame $\mathcal{F}$ is moving parallel to the x'-axis with velocity $\mathbf{v}' = (-v, 0, 0)$. Consequently, the required inverse transformation may be obtained from Equations 10.26 to 10.31 by interchanging primed and unprimed components, and replacing v with $-v$. Noting that $\gamma(-v/c) = \gamma(v/c)$, we may write the result as follows:

$$E_x = E'_x,$$
$$E_y = \gamma \left(E'_y + vB'_z \right),$$
$$E_z = \gamma \left(E'_z - vB'_y \right),$$
$$B_x = B'_x,$$
$$B_y = \gamma \left(B'_y - \frac{v}{c^2} E'_z \right),$$
$$B_z = \gamma \left(B'_z + \frac{v}{c^2} E'_y \right).$$

Ex 10.6 Since $\mathbf{v} = (v, 0, 0)$, the direction parallel to $\mathbf{v}$ is the x-direction, so $\mathbf{E}_\parallel = (E_x, 0, 0)$ and $\mathbf{B}_\parallel = (B_x, 0, 0)$. In addition, the fields $\mathbf{E}_\perp$ and $\mathbf{B}_\perp$ may be written as $\mathbf{E}_\perp = (0, E_y, E_z)$ and $\mathbf{B}_\perp = (0, B_y, B_z)$. Substituting these vector expressions into Equations 10.32 to 10.35 and evaluating the vector products gives

$$\mathbf{E}'_\parallel = (E_x, 0, 0),$$
$$\mathbf{B}'_\parallel = (B_x, 0, 0),$$
$$\mathbf{E}'_\perp = \gamma[(0, E_y, E_z) + (0, -vB_z, vB_y)],$$
$$\mathbf{B}'_\perp = \gamma \left[(0, B_y, B_z) - \frac{1}{c^2}(0, -vE_z, vE_y) \right].$$

Retaining only non-zero components, we can rewrite these relationships as

$$E'_x = E_x,$$
$$B'_x = B_x,$$
$$E'_y = \gamma(E_y - vB_z),$$
$$E'_z = \gamma(E_z + vB_y),$$
$$B'_y = \gamma \left(B_y + \frac{v}{c^2} E_z \right),$$
$$B'_z = \gamma \left(B_z - \frac{v}{c^2} E_y \right).$$

Apart from the order in which they are written, these equations are identical to Equations 10.26 to 10.31. Hence the two sets of equations, 10.26–10.31 and 10.32–10.35, are consistent in the case $\mathbf{v} = (v, 0, 0)$.

Ex 10.7 In a region where $\mathbf{E}' = \mathbf{0}$ in frame $\mathcal{F}'$, an observer in $\mathcal{F}$ will find (according to Equations 10.32 and 10.34)

$$\mathbf{E}_{\parallel} = \mathbf{0}$$

and

$$\mathbf{E}_{\perp} = -\mathbf{v} \times \mathbf{B}_{\perp}.$$

Since $\mathbf{E}_{\parallel} = \mathbf{0}$, we can write $\mathbf{E} = \mathbf{E}_{\perp}$ and use the fact that

$$\mathbf{v} \times \mathbf{B}_{\perp} = \mathbf{v} \times (\mathbf{B}_{\parallel} + \mathbf{B}_{\perp}) = \mathbf{v} \times \mathbf{B}$$

to obtain the required result,

$$\mathbf{E} = -\mathbf{v} \times \mathbf{B}.$$

Ex 10.8 We choose a reference frame $\mathcal{F}$ for the Earth with the x-direction vertically down, the y-direction towards the north and the z-direction towards the east, as shown in Figure S10.1.

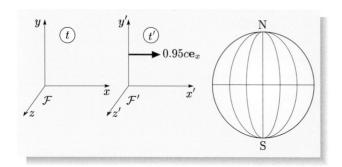

Figure S10.1 The Earth frame and the particle frame for Exercise 10.8.

The particle frame, $\mathcal{F}'$, is in standard configuration with this, travelling at speed $0.95c$ in the x-direction. Thus

$$E_x = 100\,\text{V m}^{-1},$$
$$E_y = E_z = 0,$$
$$B_y = 5.0 \times 10^{-5}\,\text{T},$$
$$B_x = B_z = 0.$$

Using the field transformation equations (10.26–10.31), with $\gamma = 1/\sqrt{1 - 0.95^2} = 3.20$, the field components

in the particle's frame are

$$E'_x = E_x = 100\,\text{V m}^{-1},$$
$$E'_y = \gamma[E_y - vB_z] = 0,$$
$$E'_z = \gamma[E_z + vB_y]$$
$$= 3.20 \times (0.95 \times 3.0 \times 10^8\,\text{m s}^{-1})$$
$$\times 5.0 \times 10^{-5}\,\text{T}$$
$$= 4.6 \times 10^4\,\text{V m}^{-1},$$
$$B'_x = B_x = 0,$$
$$B'_y = \gamma \left[B_y + \frac{v}{c^2}E_z\right]$$
$$= 3.20 \times 5.0 \times 10^{-5}\,\text{T} = 1.6 \times 10^{-4}\,\text{T},$$
$$B'_z = \gamma \left[B_z - \frac{v}{c^2}E_y\right] = 0.$$

Comment: Clearly, both the electric and magnetic field in the particle's frame are very different from those in the Earth's frame. However, for macroscopic objects in free fall in the Earth's atmosphere, with $v \sim 100\,\text{m s}^{-1}$, say, the fields would be essentially unchanged from those in the Earth's frame.

Ex 10.9 Since the charge is at rest in frame $\mathcal{F}'$, the Lorentz force equation reduces to $\mathbf{F}' = q\mathbf{E}'$. We need to find an expression for the force $\mathbf{F}$ in frame $\mathcal{F}$ in terms of the fields $\mathbf{E}$ and $\mathbf{B}$ measured in that frame. We assume that frame $\mathcal{F}'$ travels with velocity $\mathbf{v} = (v, 0, 0)$ relative to frame $\mathcal{F}$, so the velocity of the charge in frame $\mathcal{F}$ is $\mathbf{v} = (v, 0, 0)$.

We consider each of the components of the force in turn. For the x'-component, $F'_x = qE'_x$. From Equation 10.17, $F'_x = F_x$, and from Equation 10.26, $E'_x = E_x$, so

$$F_x = qE_x.$$

For the y'-component, $F'_y = qE'_y$. From Equation 10.18, $F'_y = \gamma F_y$, and from Equation 10.27, $E'_y = \gamma[E_y - vB_z]$, so

$$\gamma F_y = q\gamma[E_y - vB_z], \quad \text{or} \quad F_y = q[E_y - vB_z].$$

Similarly, for the z'-component, $F'_z = qE'_z$. From Equation 10.19, $F'_z = \gamma F_z$, and from Equation 10.28, $E'_z = \gamma[E_z + vB_y]$, so

$$\gamma F_z = q\gamma[E_z + vB_y], \quad \text{or} \quad F_z = q[E_z + vB_y].$$

Hence

$$\mathbf{F} = q\mathbf{E} + qv(-B_z\mathbf{e}_y + B_y\mathbf{e}_z).$$

But $\mathbf{v} = v\mathbf{e}_x$, so $\mathbf{v} \times \mathbf{B} = v(-B_z\mathbf{e}_y + B_y\mathbf{e}_z)$, and therefore

$$\mathbf{F} = q(\mathbf{E} + \mathbf{v} \times \mathbf{B}).$$

Acknowledgements

Grateful acknowledgement is made to the following sources:

Figure 2: Alex Bartel/Science Photo Library; *Figure 3a:* M.Serraillier/Science Photo Library; *Figure 3b:* Steve Gschmeissner/Science Photo Library; *Figure 4:* NASA/Science Photo Library; *Figure 5a:* Geoff Tompkinson /Science Photo Library; *Figure 5b:* Simon Fraser/Newcastle Hospitals NHS Trust/Science Photo Library; *Figure 6:* © Copyright CERN Geneva;

Figure 2.2: David Scharf/Science Photo Library; *Figure 3.1a:* Sheila Terry/Science Photo Library; *Figure 3.1b:* Courtesy of Prasenjit Guptasarma, University of Wisconsin-Milwaukee; *Figure 3.18:* Vacuumschmelze GmbH & Co. KG; *Figure 3.19:* © Copyright CERN Geneva; *Figure 3.21:* TopFoto.co.uk; *Figure 4.1a:* Philips Electronics UK Ltd; *Figure 4.1b:* Robert Brook/Science Photo Library; *Figure 5.3a:* © Copyright CERN Geneva; *Figure 5.22:* Vacuumschmelze GmbH & Co. KG; *Figure 6.1a:* © The Johns Hopkins University Applied Physics Laboratory; *Figure 6.1b:* Max-Planck-Institute For Radio Astronomy/Science Photo Library; *Figure 6.1c:* © Copyright CERN Geneva; *Figure 6.6b:* CC Studio/Science Photo Library; *Figure 6.13:* NASA/Science Photo Library; *Figure 7.5a:* Keith Kent/Science Photo Library; *Figure 7.8:* Environmental Geophysics Unit, National University of Ireland, Maynooth; *Figure 8.1a:* Martin Bond/Science Photo Library; *Figure 8.1b:* ISE Corporation; *Figure 8.2:* Courtesy of ACCEL Instruments GmbH; *Figure 8.10:* Andrew Lambert Photography/Science Photo Library; *Figure 8.11:* Dresden High Magnetic Field Laboratory; *Figure 8.12a:* Adam Hart-Davis/Science Photo Library; *Figure 9.1:* Science Photo Library; *Figure 9.8a:* This photograph has been provided by Railway Technical Research Institute in Japan; *Figure 9.22:* Proceedings of the Royal Society A248 464. The Royal Society; *Figure 9.23:* V Essmann and H Trauble, Max Planck Institut für Metallforschung.

Every effort has been made to contact copyright holders. If any have been inadvertently overlooked the publishers will be pleased to make the necessary arrangements at the first opportunity.

Index

Items that appear in the Glossary have page numbers in **bold type**. Ordinary index items have page numbers in Roman type.

Theorems

Gradient theorem:
$$\int_{\mathbf{r_1}}^{\mathbf{r_2}} \operatorname{grad} f \cdot \mathrm{d}\mathbf{l} = f(\mathbf{r_2}) - f(\mathbf{r_1})$$

Divergence theorem:
$$\int_V \operatorname{div} \mathbf{F} \, \mathrm{d}V = \int_S \mathbf{F} \cdot \mathrm{d}\mathbf{S}$$

Curl theorem:
$$\int_S \operatorname{curl} \mathbf{F} \cdot \mathrm{d}\mathbf{S} = \oint_C \mathbf{F} \cdot \mathrm{d}\mathbf{l}$$

Vector and vector calculus identities

$$\mathbf{a} \times (\mathbf{b} \times \mathbf{c}) = (\mathbf{a} \cdot \mathbf{c})\mathbf{b} - (\mathbf{a} \cdot \mathbf{b})\mathbf{c}$$
$$\mathbf{a} \cdot (\mathbf{b} \times \mathbf{c}) = (\mathbf{a} \times \mathbf{b}) \cdot \mathbf{c}$$
$$\operatorname{div}(f\mathbf{F}) = f \operatorname{div} \mathbf{F} + \mathbf{F} \cdot \operatorname{grad} f$$
$$\operatorname{div}(\operatorname{grad} f) = \nabla^2 f$$
$$\operatorname{div}(\operatorname{curl} \mathbf{F}) = 0$$
$$\operatorname{curl}(\operatorname{grad} f) = \mathbf{0}$$
$$\operatorname{curl}(\operatorname{curl} \mathbf{F}) = \operatorname{grad}(\operatorname{div} \mathbf{F}) - \nabla^2 \mathbf{F}$$
$$\operatorname{div}(\mathbf{F} \times \mathbf{G}) = (\operatorname{curl} \mathbf{F}) \cdot \mathbf{G} - \mathbf{F} \cdot (\operatorname{curl} \mathbf{G})$$

Various integrals

$$\int x\,\mathrm{e}^{-ax}\,\mathrm{d}x = -\frac{1}{a^2}(1 + ax)\,\mathrm{e}^{-ax}$$

$$\int x^2\,\mathrm{e}^{-ax}\,\mathrm{d}x = -\frac{1}{a^3}(2 + 2ax + a^2x^2)\,\mathrm{e}^{-ax}$$

$$\int \frac{1}{(a^2 + x^2)^{1/2}}\,\mathrm{d}x = \ln((a^2 + x^2)^{1/2} + x)$$

$$\int \frac{1}{(a^2 + x^2)^{3/2}}\,\mathrm{d}x = \frac{x}{a^2\sqrt{a^2 + x^2}}$$

$$\int_{-\infty}^{\infty} \frac{1}{(1 + x^2)^{3/2}}\,\mathrm{d}x = 2$$

$$\int_0^{2\pi} \sin^2\theta\,\mathrm{d}\theta = \int_0^{2\pi} \cos^2\theta\,\mathrm{d}\theta = \pi$$

$$\langle \sin^2\theta \rangle \equiv \frac{1}{2\pi}\int_0^{2\pi} \sin^2\theta\,\mathrm{d}\theta = \frac{1}{2}$$

$$\langle \cos^2\theta \rangle \equiv \frac{1}{2\pi}\int_0^{2\pi} \cos^2\theta\,\mathrm{d}\theta = \frac{1}{2}$$

$$\int \cos^n\theta \sin\theta\,\mathrm{d}\theta = -\frac{\cos^{n+1}(\theta)}{n + 1}$$

$$\int_0^{2\pi} \cos\theta \sin\theta\,\mathrm{d}\theta = 0$$